S0-AWT-168

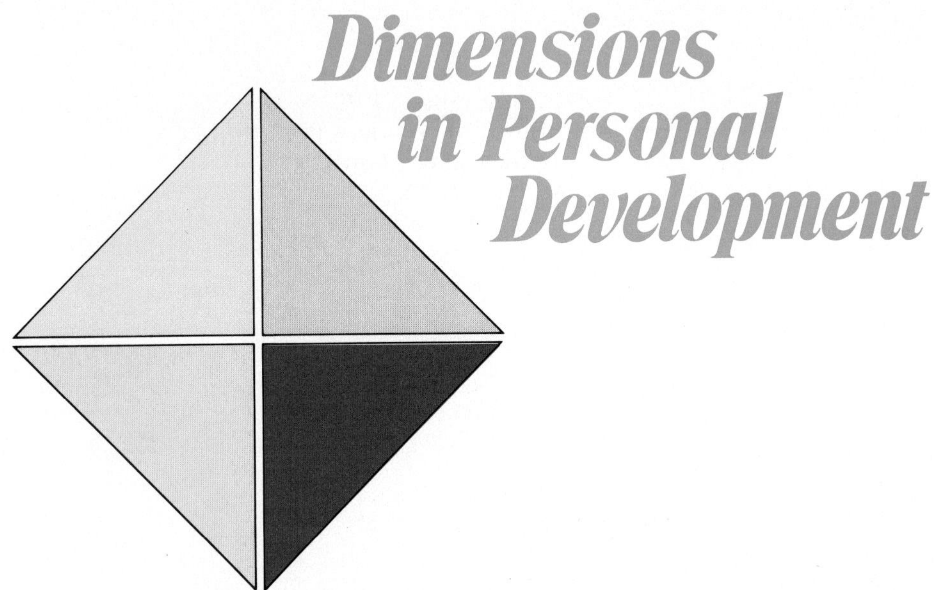

Dimensions in Personal Development

Caroline Reynolds

Texas Christian University
Fort Worth, Texas

Published by

K03 **SOUTH-WESTERN PUBLISHING CO.**

CINCINNATI WEST CHICAGO, ILL. DALLAS PELHAM MANOR, N.Y.
PALO ALTO, CALIF. BRIGHTON, ENGLAND

ISBN: 0-538-11030-9
Library of Congress Catalog Card Number: 76-11956

1 2 3 4 5 6 7 8 9 D 4 3 2 1 0 9 8 7
Printed in the United States of America

Preface

Congratulations on having the courage to say "I can improve myself." Recognizing that you have room for improvement is the first step toward "furnishing" that room. It has not been difficult in other subjects of study to identify and acknowledge your deficiencies — a typing rate that is too low, a lack of knowledge of grammar, chemistry formulas that are elusive — but because it threatens your self-image, it is very difficult to look at your personal development in order to identify and acknowledge the deficiencies.

Protecting the self-image is nothing at which to scoff. A person's self-image is the most important item influencing that person's quality of life. By daring to examine yourself and embarking upon an improvement program, you are taking a giant step toward improving the quality of your life and your future.

Typically, you've had very little help in making the most of yourself. Formal education concentrates almost solely on skills and knowledges outside the student's personal development. You've been left to provide for your self-development with haphazard methods and information.

At the same time that your society provides you with training concentrated on other areas, it abides by a system that bases rewards largely on the personal characteristics of a person. You are trained with job-related skills, but you are hired for a job based on the impression you make during a personal interview. Your resumé states very well what you have accomplished in areas outside yourself, and it often is important to your desirability as an employee. Your personal interview, however, shows what you have accomplished in terms of making yourself someone others want to be around; and the interview is where the decision is made to hire you.

DIMENSIONS IN PERSONAL DEVELOPMENT is designed to provide a systematic approach to improving your personal development. The goal of this kind of study is to make you like yourself better and to make you more desirable as a colleague, friend, and citizen.

Many people have contributed to DIMENSIONS IN PERSONAL DEVELOPMENT. Each shared that which the person had personally developed and without which this book could not be so effective. My deepest gratitude goes to the people who helped me make your program of personal development one that truly will change your life.

Two talented artists shared cheerfully their respective expertise. Travis Johnson, the world-famous hairdresser, gave not only of his talent but of his influence and inspiration to make illustrations you can understand and appreciate. Terry Webb photographed many of the illustrations. His patience and the fruit of his beautiful talent added greatly to DIMENSIONS.

Those who so generously gave of their time to pose for photographs are: Jan Bowerman, Clarence Hope, Judy Knight, Rebecca Martinez, Judy Nelson, Vicki Noblitt, Janis Oppie, Cheri Taylor, and Melba Todd. The contribution of each of these important people makes your program of personal development more interesting and easy to understand.

Many businesses contributed illustrations for use in DIMENSIONS IN PERSONAL DEVELOPMENT. They are credited with the illustrations they shared. In addition, I express my appreciation for their interest in providing materials for helping you, the student, improve yourself. Especially I thank Claire McDaniel, Marianne Mischo, J. Lance Clarke, and Victoria Meekins who made special efforts to help.

To you, the student, I give my best wishes for a productive and interesting study of ways to add those very important dimensions in personal development.

Caroline Reynolds

Contents

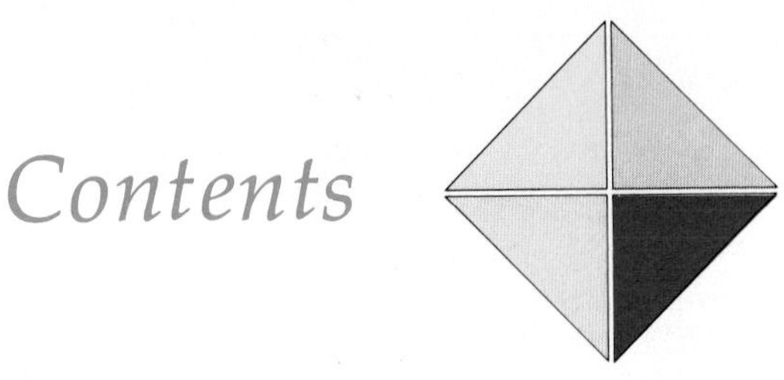

First Dimension Your Form

Part 1

The first dimension of personal development begins with analyzing your body and shaping a program that improves your form. You are a creature of habit; and your habits, good or bad, determine largely whether you are fat or slim, energetic or lazy, and often whether you are happy or sad.

Your nutritional habits are the most important determinants of the shape of your body. To get your personal development program under way, you will learn to select food that satisfies the nutritional needs of your body and helps you maintain your ideal weight.

Activity, recreational and routine, parallels your nutrition in giving you the energy and form you want. Spasmodic or occasional activity is not the answer. A life-style that incorporates a habit of activity which conditions and exercises your body is the key.

Because the most beautifully balanced form loses its effect when its movement is awkward, the graceful presentation of your form in walking, sitting, and standing is vital to your personal development. You will enjoy the satisfaction of knowing that you present yourself with grace, style, and poise.

Nurturing, conditioning, exercising, and presenting yourself – all fit into that first dimension: Your Form.

Chapter 1

Introduction — A More Successful Life

Investment of time and effort in your personal development can make more difference in your personal and professional success than any other single area of study in your education.

People are always attracted to and influenced by those who show confidence in the way they conduct themselves. Employers report that people who have spent time learning to develop themselves and their effectiveness in relationships with others are those who are most successful on the job. Conversely, they say that more people lose their jobs because of inability to get along with others than for any other reason.

Studies have been made and articles have been written on the effect of personal appearance on a person's ability to obtain employment. Well-groomed, smartly dressed people are preferred over those with less attractive appearances.

Poor health, including overweight and lack of energy, is frequently cited as a reason people cannot attain or maintain employment. Psychologists know that appearance frequently reflects how a person feels about herself and indicates somewhat her interest in the world in which she lives. Those who feel good about themselves — who have confidence, poise, serenity — usually show their acceptance of themselves and interest in life by making themselves look as good on the outside as they feel on the inside. Employers know that people who take pride in developing themselves are likely to take pride in what they do.

Your personal happiness with yourself and your professional success in your job depend upon your determination to become the most effective person you can be in terms of personal development. After all, you will be living within your body, functioning with the knowledges and skills you acquire for the rest of your life. That life can be made much more satisfying if you know you are all you want to be.

Think of some other worthwhile projects you've undertaken — ones that required real effort from you. Relive the satisfaction you experienced from a job well done. Developing and improving yourself will bring the same feelings of satisfaction. Striving to become all you can be is the most important project you will ever undertake because it will influence and often control all the remaining experiences of your life. Your capacity to enjoy life itself will largely be determined by how you feel about your own development. When you have such an important stake in the results, great amounts of time and effort are justified.

Your Future

Visualize what you want your future to be. Do you see yourself poised, self-confident — one who successfully manages a career? A home? Both with apparent ease? More specifically, do you want to be a well-groomed, tastefully dressed professional person — perhaps an office worker, a secretary, a manager, or an administrator, fitting well into a satisfying job?

Do you see yourself handling difficult situations with tact and diplomacy, moving gracefully from obstacle to obstacle in new situations? Do you envision yourself living creatively because your energies are freed from the distractions and confusion about what to wear, what to eat, what to say, and what to do? Do you see yourself valued as a friend because of the orderliness and harmony you bring to others' lives? Will you be appreciated by those around you because you are understanding and organized? If your expectations are realistic and you are willing to work at it, your future can include whatever you envision.

You can choose to become a woman with all the graces that make you effective and appealing. You can attain a svelte figure, an abundant energy level, queenly carriage, and graceful posture. You can accomplish the simple procedures of caring for your body — emphasizing your best skin, facial, and hair features, and concealing your poor ones. You can dress well yet economically for any occasion. You can converse entertainingly and clearly and maintain good relationships with others.

How do you visualize your own future?

Hairstyle by Travis Johnson — Photography by Terry Webb

More importantly, though, you can learn to care more for yourself, strengthening your self-confidence and recognizing the attributes you have. In developing your physical appearance and relationships you can correspondingly realize that your intelligence, ambition, aggressiveness, and drive can be developed in an appealing manner, gaining acceptance and getting you ahead rather than antagonizing people.

Because you've made progress in personal achievement, you will be given more opportunities to progress in other ways — in your career, in your social life, in your community. Once you are recognized as poised and self-confident, you will be encouraged and invited to participate in new areas. More opportunities to utilize all your abilities will be offered to you.

You will find that your poise and self-confidence grow as you learn to care for yourself. You will have more courage to try new things and to talk with new people. Others around you will be more comfortable as you seem more sure of yourself.

Routine activities can be simplified. Such things as automatically reaching for foods that are good for you come with knowledge and practice in good nutrition. Quickly but expertly applying makeup and arranging your hair become easy and routine with just a minimum of effort. Selecting clothing, suitable not only for your daily activities but flattering to your physical structure, becomes a pleasure easily accomplished rather than a hit-or-miss chore. The real energy of your body is reserved for your work, leisure activities, and for developing warm human relationships.

YOUR FORM

A study of good nutrition principles will open the doors to good health related to eating habits. Correcting your weight and energy levels will bring rewards in acceptance and accomplishment. Developing an exercise program that keeps your cardiovascular system working well, along with reproportioning your figure, gives you double benefits. Including such care of your health and appearance daily will make your other activities easier because of your increased alertness and energy. Your physique also will gain the benefit of better fitting clothing and graceful, floating posture. Others will recognize your poise and grace in posture and carriage, assuming that they reflect a confident young woman, knowledgeable and concerned about herself and the world around her.

YOUR RADIANCE

Procedures for grooming your body by protecting and enhancing the quality of your skin for lifetime beauty can be easily learned and adapted to a daily routine. Good hygiene aids in keeping a fresh and lovely skin. You can give a polished, finished look to your complexion. No matter what natural endowments you may have been blessed with or deprived of, a brighter happier looking face is yours with just a little effort and knowledge.

Frame that smart looking face and top that svelte, healthy body with hair that is naturally flattering and well-arranged all day. If your hair is too dry, too oily, or too anything, you can achieve an attractive style and learn the techniques of caring for it with ease.

A small "touch" here and there to complete the polished, radiant look is easily attained with knowledge about techniques for handling your nails and fragrances. Much grace can be added to your appearance with well-groomed hands and feet. The whole aura of your presence is enhanced with a subtle but pleasant fragrance.

Good habits in nutrition and exercise result in better fitting clothing and graceful, floating posture.

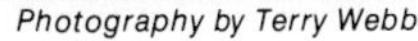

Photography by Terry Webb

Hairstyle by Travis Johnson *Photography by Terry Webb*

A brighter, happier face is yours with good grooming habits.

YOUR WARDROBE

Smart-looking clothes that complement your figure, complexion, and activities are little more than lines, colors, and your putting the two together with appropriate accents. The lines of all clothing follow some general trends that can be adapted or altered to accent your best figure features. Color can be used to accent, conceal, set a mood, and make a certain impression. You can plan your wardrobe from a few basic principles that equip you for any occasion. Even your budget will stretch farther when you know about wardrobe planning and purchasing techniques that fit your own figure, style, and activities.

Wardrobe planning and knowledge result in smart looking clothes for all occasions.

Vogue Pattern Service

YOUR RELATIONSHIPS

All personal development has its value in the way it makes you feel about yourself. The happier you are with the way you look and the way your life is going, the better your relationships with others will be. You can develop a good understanding of what makes people act and react. Knowing what motivates them to spend their time the way they do will lead you to a good understanding of how to relate and work more effectively with them.

Your communication abilities and social acumen will further enhance your effectiveness in relationships. The etiquette of office procedures and social situations makes it easier for you to enjoy both your work and your leisure time. Those about you are more comfortable because of your poise and confidence in all situations.

Vogue Pattern Service

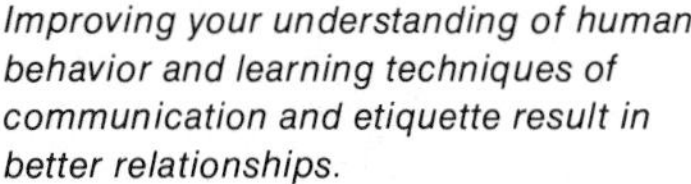

Improving your understanding of human behavior and learning techniques of communication and etiquette result in better relationships.

Your Present

The best place to start development and improvement is wherever you are now. The beginning of personal development is recognizing and identifying the areas on which you need to work. Honesty with yourself is the most essential element of this analysis. This is the time to look at yourself critically in a mirror. Recall occasions when your actions were not what you wanted them to be. Remember when you said the wrong thing because you didn't know the right thing to say. Bring brutally to the forefront of your mind the underdeveloped areas of you that you want to improve.

The following questions should help you analyze yourself. Read each one thoughtfully; and as closely as you can, answer either "yes" or "no" or estimate the percentage of time, as appropriate. If your answer is "no" 20 percent of the time or less, give yourself a zero on the question. If it is "yes" 21 to 40 percent of the time, give yourself one point; "yes" 41 to 60 percent — two points; "yes" 61 to 80 percent — three points; "yes" 81 to 90 percent — four points; "yes" 91 to 100 percent — five points. Record your rating in the "until today" column. Total your score when you have finished.

Question	Until Today	My Commitment
(1) Do you have energy enough for your day's work with some to spare for recreation?	_____	_____________________
(2) Do you weigh what you want to?	_____	_____________________
(3) Do you eat nutritiously?	_____	_____________________
(4) Do you participate regularly in a recreative activity you really like?	_____	_____________________
(5) Are you satisfied with the amount of sleep you get?	_____	_____________________
(6) Are you rested when you wake up?	_____	_____________________
(7) Is your weight distributed as you want it?	_____	_____________________
(8) Do you regularly exercise to keep your muscles firm and your body supple?	_____	_____________________
(9) Are you pleased with your posture?	_____	_____________________
(10) Do you move gracefully?	_____	_____________________
(11) Does your complexion radiate health?	_____	_____________________
(12) Are your hygiene practices effective in eliminating body odor?	_____	_____________________
(13) Can you control oiliness or dryness of your complexion?	_____	_____________________

Questions	Until Today	My Commitment
(14) Are your grooming habits such that you look your best with a minimum of effort?	_____	_____________________
(15) Are you happy with the cosmetics with which you have to make up?	_____	_____________________
(16) Do you balance or camouflage irregularities in your facial features?	_____	_____________________
(17) Are you happy with the way your hair looks?	_____	_____________________
(18) Can you change and control your hair texture, bulk, oilness, and curliness if you want to?	_____	_____________________
(19) Can you use hairpieces with skill?	_____	_____________________
(20) Do you think your hairstyle is well suited to your face shape?	_____	_____________________
(21) Are your nails well groomed?	_____	_____________________
(22) Can you correct problems with your nails?	_____	_____________________
(23) Can you prevent corns and calluses on your feet?	_____	_____________________
(24) Do you think your perfume is appropriate for you?	_____	_____________________
(25) Is clothes shopping easy for you because you know your colors and lines well?	_____	_____________________
(26) Do you always have something appropriate to wear for your regular activities?	_____	_____________________
(27) Do you think your clothes suit the occasions for which you select them?	_____	_____________________
(28) Do you think that your clothes emphasize your best features and camouflage your irregular ones?	_____	_____________________

Question	Until Today	My Commitment
(29) Do you feel that you get your money's worth from your wardrobe dollar?	_____	____________________
(30) Are you happy with the versatility of your jewelry and scarves?	_____	____________________
(31) Do your handbags and shoes fit well into your wardrobe?	_____	____________________
(32) Do you like yourself?	_____	____________________
(33) Do you understand why you feel the way you do about yourself?	_____	____________________
(34) Are you pleased with the way you spend your time?	_____	____________________
(35) Are you effective in your dealings with others?	_____	____________________
(36) Do you understand why others act as they do?	_____	____________________
(37) Do you feel you are able to get your ideas across to others?	_____	____________________
(38) Do you say whatever is appropriate for the time and occasion?	_____	____________________
(39) Can you relax and enjoy social occasions?	_____	____________________
(40) Can you make people around you feel comfortable?	_____	____________________

Set yourself some goals, and make some commitments now as to what you want your personal development program to accomplish for you. Check back through the list and the "Commitment" column. Set a realistic percentage goal and a date by which you plan to accomplish the specific goal. The maximum score is 200. Try to maintain yours between 150 and 200. Examples of goals might be: I will lose ten pounds of excess weight; I will learn to use makeup to enhance my best facial features; I will find a hairstyle that looks good on me and stays groomed all day; I will be organized about the way I spend my time.

Your Plan

To guarantee that you stick to your commitments, you will need a plan to follow that will keep you on schedule. Personal development will take some of your time and energy every day — well spent time — since all your other achievements will be influenced by your successes in this time. Design yourself a time schedule allowing, for example, for the following items:

Exercise. Decide which ten minutes of your day you will devote to figure control exercise: five minutes morning and night or ten minutes morning or ten minutes night or at midday.

Recreation. Decide on approximately three hours per week, preferably 30 to 60 minutes a day three to five times a week, in which you can participate in recreative exercise.

Weight Control. Decide what you should weigh and, figuring two pounds per week loss or gain, what you will weigh by controlling your diet each week until you reach your goal.

Posture. Decide on four times per day that you will check on your posture mentally and/or visually (if a mirror is available).

Complexion. Set two times per day for complete face cleansing, morning and night. Set a bath/shower hygiene routine time. Decide what time of day you will set aside fifteen minutes for face makeup, eyebrow shaping, etc. Designate thirty minutes per week to groom your nails.

Hair. Designate fifteen minutes each morning, ten minutes each evening and one and one-half hours per week for shampoo and set; or alter these times to fit your particular hair-care routine if your routine is substantially different.

Wardrobe. Designate ten minutes in the morning for dressing and ten minutes in the evening for selecting and readying the next day's clothes.

Relationships. Getting all the grooming areas organized will allow you time to concentrate on improving relationships. Each day resolve to smile at someone who seems to need it. Remind yourself each day of one "blessing" that you enjoy. Resolve to contribute to the good of all mankind in some way everyday. Set a time each evening when you review your day and note whether or not you accomplished improvements in your relationships.

A sample time schedule might be:

7:00– 7:10 a.m.	Figure control exercises.
7:10– 7:45 a.m.	Shower, face cleansing, makeup, hair.
7:45– 8:00 a.m.	Breakfast. I will diet until I weigh 120 pounds. My weekly goals are: 128 by September 10, 126 by September 17, 124 by September 24, 122 by October 1, 120 by October 8.
8:00– 8:10 a.m.	Dress.
8:10 a.m.	Check posture before leaving home.
10:10 a.m.	Check posture at break.
12:10 p.m.	Check posture at lunch.
7:00– 7:40 p.m.	Five times per week participate in recreative exercise such as tennis, bicycling, walking, etc.
8:00 p.m.	Check posture.
8:00– 9:30 p.m.	Once a week shampoo hair and set it (more often if needed).
9:00– 9:30 p.m.	Once a week manicure nails.
9:30– 9:40 p.m.	Prepare clothes for next day.
9:40– 9:50 p.m.	Cleanse face carefully.
9:50–10:00 p.m.	Prepare hair for next day.
10:10–10:20 p.m.	Reflect on day's relationships: I cheered someone? My "blessing" for today? My contribution?

You may prefer to shower and/or exercise in the evening rather than morning. Make your own time schedule to fit your preferences, but make it one you can and will stick to.

Becoming You

The single most important factor in your success is your belief in yourself. If you are convinced that you can accomplish your goals, very few things can prevent you. The information and directions that you need follow in the remaining pages of this book. Your success, though, will depend on you — your dedication to improvement, your effort expended, and your belief that you can do it.

Becoming all you can be is worth the time and effort. The reward is an enriched life. Now is the time — you can begin today!

Chapter 2

Nutrition

The state of your nutrition depends upon your knowledge and your habits. You will spend a great amount of your time throughout your life eating, and often it will be mainly a social experience rather than a biological one. The effects of consuming food are the same regardless of your reasons. To make nutritious choices, you need to understand your personal needs for nutrients; but eating is more than making choices. It is an activity governed by a habit.

Besides knowing which foods to eat, you must form habits of selecting them and consuming an appropriate amount. You will not find this difficult provided the eating habits you have already acquired are good. However, if your present habits are less than adequate for good nutrition, you must be very determined as well as knowledgeable to correct them.

Analyzing Nutrition

A nutritious diet is readily available today, but the problem is that frequently you don't eat to nurture your body; you eat for a number of other reasons. The guides for good nutrition are easy to understand and to follow. If they conflict with your eating habits, though, your body shows it. It shows in your weight, your energy, and often in your attitude. Since these areas form the basis of your personal development in many ways, analyzing your nutrition is a good place to begin your program of personal development.

YOUR WEIGHT

The most obvious and most easily seen indicator of your eating habits is your weight. It reflects whether you eat too much, too little, or a proper amount. Maintaining your weight within the recommended range is vital to your health as well as to your appearance.

Weight is, of course, related to the relative structure, height, and condition of your body. A chart showing desirable weights related to height (Illustration 2-1) will help you find the proper range of weight for yourself. The relative size of your frame will probably be medium unless you are very much larger or smaller than the majority of people. The height-weight chart is designed so that your height is without shoes, and your weight is what you weigh in the morning nude before you have eaten breakfast.

Your weight is directly related to how much you eat. In very simple terms, for every 3,500 calories consumed (be it from carrots, meat, or candy), one pound of fat is stored unless the calories are burned as energy. Burning the 3,500 calories requires a great deal of activity — walking approximately 36 miles, playing tennis approximately 7½ hours, or playing golf 10½ hours. While activity has an important place in your life, it will not bear the burden of overeating — your shape will!

Find your ideal weight range on the height-weight chart. If you are not in good condition; that is, if most of the padding is fatty tissue rather than muscle tissue, aim for the lower figure of the weight range. A pound of fatty tissue is several times larger than a pound of muscle tissue. Also, fatty tissue rarely deposits itself in an attractive array on your body, whereas, muscle tissue develops in a systematic pattern which improves your form. Without an extensive conditioning program designed for muscle building, you are not likely to develop excessive muscle tissue. However, with only occasional overeating, you can accumulate excessive fatty tissue — in the most unattractive places.

If you are in doubt as to whether you are padded with fat or muscle, take a good look at yourself nude in a full-length mirror. Using your thumb and forefinger, take the skin-fold test by pinching up a fold of skin and subcutaneous tissue just below your navel. You are too fat if the distance between your thumb and forefinger is 1½ inches or more.

If you pass the skin-fold test and are not too fat, you are ahead of many of your friends; but you should be knowledgeable and vigilant about controlling your weight. A critical period of weight control for young people is at about 22 years of age. Full growth is reached, and

DESIRABLE WEIGHTS FOR MEN AND WOMEN AGED TWENTY-FIVE YEARS AND OVER*#

(NUDE WEIGHT IN POUNDS)

Feet	Inches	Small frame	Medium frame	Large frame
		MEN		
5	1	104-112	110-121	118-133
5	2	107-115	113-125	121-136
5	3	110-118	116-128	124-140
5	4	113-121	119-131	127-144
5	5	116-125	122-135	130-148
5	6	120-129	126-139	134-153
5	7	124-133	130-144	139-158
5	8	128-137	134-148	143-162
5	9	132-142	138-152	147-166
5	10	136-146	142-157	151-171
5	11	140-150	146-162	156-176
6	0	144-154	150-167	160-181
6	1	148-159	154-172	165-186
6	2	152-163	159-177	170-191
6	3	156-167	164-182	174-196
		WOMEN		
4	8	87-93	91-102	99-114
4	9	89-96	93-105	101-117
4	10	91-99	96-108	104-120
4	11	94-102	99-111	107-123
5	0	97-105	102-114	110-126
5	1	100-108	105-117	113-129
5	2	103-111	108-121	116-133
5	3	106-114	111-125	120-137
5	4	109-118	113-130	124-141
5	5	113-122	119-134	128-145
5	6	117-126	123-138	132-149
5	7	121-130	127-142	136-153
5	8	125-133	131-146	140-158
5	9	129-139	135-150	144-163
5	10	133-143	139-154	148-168

*Between the ages of 18 and 25, subtract 1 pound for each year under 25.

#Modified from figures published by the Metropolitan Life Insurance Company. Their figures included shoes and indoor clothing. Figures in this table have been calculated by subtracting 1 inch from men's height and 2 inches from women's height; it was assumed that men's indoor clothing weighs 8 pounds and that women's indoor clothing weighs 5 pounds.

ILLUS. 2-1 Desirable Weights for Men and Women

there is usually a decrease in activity at that time. Unfortunately, the young person doesn't realize that her body no longer uses part of her food for growth and that she is less active in her job than she was in school until she is ten pounds heavier than she should be. This curtailment of growth as well as the inactivity obviously must be offset and accompanied by a decreased caloric intake if weight is to be controlled. Decreasing calories consumed takes a great deal of self-control and willpower because eating habits acquired over the past 20 or so years have to be broken and/or altered. This is a difficult task.

THE NUTRIENTS

Before altering your eating habits, decide why you eat at all. You eat to live, not live to eat! In order to survive, your body needs a balance of nutrients: protein, carbohydrate, fat, vitamins, and minerals. In general terms, protein is needed to repair body tissue; fat is needed for energy, insulation, and certain body functions such as elimination; carbohydrates are needed for energy. Any of these three nutrients can be changed by your body to energy. If the energy is not used, it will be stored as fat.

Photography by Terry Webb

ILLUS. 2-2 *Select snacks that contain nutrients your body needs for good health.*

Various vitamins and minerals are also necessary to your health. Some of the effects you can see and measure yourself. Vitamin A provides for night vision and skin development; C and D, for bones and teeth; and K, for digestion. The B vitamins affect your digestion, mental state, nerves, and skin. The effects of minerals are not easily seen but are dramatic. They control such areas as muscle contractions (heart rhythm) and the chemical balances necessary for absorbing and using the other nutrients. The recommended daily dietary allowances in Illustration 2-3 show the approximate amount of food nutrients your body requires.

RECOMMENDED DAILY DIETARY ALLOWANCES (ABRIDGED)[1]

[Designed for the maintenance of good nutrition of practically all healthy persons in the U.S.A.]

Persons				Food energy	Protein	Calcium	Iron	Vitamin A	Thiamin	Ribo-flavin	Niacin equiva-lent[2]	Ascorbic acid
	Age in years[3] From, up to	Weight in pounds	Height in inches	Calories	Grams	Grams	Milli-grams	Interna-tional units	Milli-grams	Milli-grams	Milli-grams	Milli-grams
Boys	10–12	77	55	2,500	45	1.2	10	4,500	1.3	1.3	17	40
	12–14	95	59	2,700	50	1.4	18	5,000	1.4	1.4	18	45
	14–18	130	67	3,000	60	1.4	18	5,000	1.5	1.5	20	55
Men	18–22	147	69	2,800	60	0.8	10	5,000	1.4	1.6	18	60
	22–35	154	69	2,800	65	0.8	10	5,000	1.4	1.7	18	60
	35–55	154	68	2,600	65	0.8	10	5,000	1.3	1.7	17	60
	55–75+	154	67	2,400	65	0.8	10	5,000	1.2	1.7	14	60
Girls	10–12	77	56	2,250	50	1.2	18	4,500	1.1	1.3	15	40
	12–14	97	61	2,300	50	1.3	18	5,000	1.2	1.4	15	45
	14–16	114	62	2,400	55	1.3	18	5,000	1.2	1.4	16	50
	16–18	119	63	2,300	55	1.3	18	5,000	1.2	1.5	15	50
Women	18–22	128	64	2,000	55	0.8	18	5,000	1.0	1.5	13	55
	22–35	128	64	2,000	55	0.8	18	5,000	1.0	1.5	13	55
	35–55	128	63	1,850	55	0.8	18	5,000	1.0	1.5	13	55
	55–75+	128	62	1,700	55	0.8	10	5,000	1.0	1.5	13	55
Pregnant				+200	65	+0.4	18	6,000	+0.1	1.8	15	60
Lactating				+1,000	75	+0.5	18	8,000	+0.5	2.0	20	60

[1]*Source: "Nutritive Value of Foods," Home and Garden Bulletin No. 72, published by U.S. Department of Agriculture.*
[2]*Niacin equivalents include dietary sources of the vitamin itself plus 1 milligram equivalent for each 60 milligrams of dietary tryptophan.*
[3]*Entries for age range 22 to 35 years represent the reference man and woman at age 22. All other entries represent allowances for the midpoint of the specified age group.*

ILLUS. 2-3 Recommended Daily Dietary Allowances

Find your category by sex and age. Follow the line across; and you will see how many calories, grams of protein, minerals, and vitamins you need on the average per day.

EMPTY CALORIES

You've known for years that candy bars and colas weren't "good" for you, but you may not have known why. They are "empty" calories, meaning that they have few if any nutrients. The calories you consume in these foods are converted to energy by your body, and your hunger is satisfied. You have energy for increased activity; but you have no protein for body repair and growth; no vitamins for radiant skin, beautiful teeth, and chemical changes for digestion of foods; no bulk for elimination; and no minerals for other body functions. All you get is energy, which, by the way, if it isn't used, is stored as *fat*. Because these "empty" calories satisfy your hunger, you are not inclined to eat the foods that do provide the nutrients your body needs.

NUTRITIOUS FOOD

The foods that do contain the nutrients you need for good health and good looks fall into various categories: milk, vegetables (groups A and B), fruit, bread, meat, and fat (Illustration 2-4). These categories form the basis of the exchange system of dietary control and are somewhat different from the "Basic 4" or "Basic 7" you may have read about. They were developed by a joint committee representing the American Diabetes Association, the American Dietetic Association, and the U.S. Public Health Service because they simplify the establishing of soundly nutritional eating habits.

One serving of any food in a category contributes approximately the same nutrients as a serving of any other food in the same category, making them interchangeable (called an exchange) in your diet.

The categories and food value for one exchange in each group are summarized in Illustration 2-5, page 20. The nutrients in Group A vegetables are not shown because they are negligible. These vegetables do belong in your diet, though, because they add bulk and variety. The miscellaneous foods, although they contribute negligible amounts of nutrients, will add variety to your diet but should not be relied upon for nutrition.

You will find the exchange system easy to learn and use to build your own eating habits throughout your life, whether you are gaining, losing, or maintaining your weight.

EXCHANGE LISTS

MILK EXCHANGES

Milk, whole	1 cup
Milk, skim*	1 cup
Milk, evaporated	½ cup
Milk, powdered whole	3–5 tbsp.#
Milk, nonfat dry*	3–5 tbsp.#
Buttermilk (from whole)	1 cup
Buttermilk (from skim)	1 cup

*Add 2 fat exchanges to diet.
#Use pkg. directions for 1 cup.

VEGETABLE EXCHANGES

Group A — 1 cup is 1 exchange

Asparagus	Eggplant	Mushrooms
Beans, string	Greens+	Okra
Broccoli+	beet greens	Peppers+
Brussels sprouts	chard, Swiss	Radish
Cabbage	dandelion	Sauerkraut
Cauliflower	kale	Squash,
Celery	mustard	summer
Chicory+	spinach	Tomatoes+
Cucumbers	turnip greens	Watercress+
Escarole+	Lettuce	

Group B — ½ cup is 1 exchange

Beets	Peas, green	Squash,
Carrots+	Pumpkin+	winter+
Onion	Rutabaga	Turnip

+High Vitamin A. Include at least 1 exchange per day.

FAT EXCHANGES

Butter or margarine	1 tsp.
Bacon, crisp	1 slice
Cream, Light 20 percent	2 tbsp.
Cream, Heavy 35–40 percent	1 tbsp.
Cream Cheese	1 tbsp.
French dressing	1 tbsp.
Mayonnaise	1 tsp.
Nuts	6 small
Oil or cooking fat	1 tsp.
Olives	5 small
Avocado	⅛, 4″ diam.

MISCELLANEOUS

Coffee	Saccharin
Tea	Spices
Clear broth	Vinegar
Bouillon (fat free)	Cranberries, unsweetened
Herbs	Lemon
Gelatin, unsweetened	Mustard, dry
Rennet tablets	Pickle, dill
	Rhubarb

MEAT EXCHANGES

Meat, poultry, med fat	1 ounce
Cold cuts	1 slice 4½″ sq. ⅛″ thick
Frankfurt (9 per lb.)	1
Fish	
cod, haddock, halibut	1 ounce
crab, lobster, tuna	¼ cup
clams, oysters, shrimp	5 small
sardines	3 med.
Cheese, cheddar	1 ounce
cottage	¼ cup
Egg	1
Peanut butter	2 tbsp.¢

¢Limit to 1 exchange per day.

BREAD EXCHANGES

Bread	1 slice
biscuit, roll 2″ diam.	1
muffin	1 med.
cornbread	1½″ cube
Cereal, cooked	½ cup
Cereal, dry	¾ cup
Crackers,	
graham	2
oyster	20 (½ cup)
saltines 2″ sq.	5
soda 2½″ sq.	3
round, thin 1½″ sq.	6–8
Flour	2½ tbsp.
Grits	½ cup cooked
Ice cream, vanilla (omit 2 fat exch.)	½ cup
Macaroni	½ cup cooked
Matzoth	½ (6½″ sq.)
Noodles	½ cup cooked
Rice	½ cup cooked
Spaghetti	½ cup cooked
Sponge cake, plain	1½″ cube
Vegetables	
beans, baked, no pork	¼ cup
beans and peas, dried	½ cup
corn, popped	1 cup
corn, fresh	⅓ cup, ½ ear
parsnips	⅔ cup
potatoes, white	1 sm. (2″ diam.)
mashed	½ cup
sweet or yam	¼ cup

FRUIT EXCHANGES

Apple	1 sm. (2″ diam.)
Applesauce	½ cup
Apricots, dried	4 halves
fresh	2 med.
Banana	½ small
Blackberries	1 cup
Blueberries	⅔ cup
Cantaloupe%	¼, 6″ diam.
Cherries	10 large
Dates	2
Figs, dried	1 small
fresh	2 large
Grapefruit%	½ small
juice	½ cup
Grape juice	¼ cup
Grapes	12
Honeydew melon	⅛, 7″ diam.
Mango	½ small
Nectarines	1 med.
Orange%	1 small
juice%	½ cup
Papaya	⅓ med.
Peach	1 med.
Pear	1 small
Pineapple	½ cup cubed
juice	⅓ cup
Plums	2 med.
Prunes	2 med.
Raisins	2 tbsp.
Raspberries	1 cup
Strawberries%	1 cup
Tangerine	1 large
Watermelon	1 cup diced

%Rich in ascorbic acid.
Include at least 1 exchange per day.

ILLUS. 2-4 Exchange Lists

EXCHANGE NUTRIENTS

Food Exchange	Weight gm	Carbo-hydrate gm	Protein gm	Fat gm	Calories
Milk*	240	12	8	10	170
Vegetables — A	—	—	—	—	—
Vegetables — B	100	7	2		35
Fruit	varies	10			40
Bread	varies	15	2		70
Meat	30		7	5	75
Fat	5			5	45

Source: Caso, E. K., *"Calculation of Diabetic Diets,"* Journal of the American Dietetic Association, *26:565,1950.*

**Skim milk has no fat and only 80 calories. Other nutrients are the same.*

ILLUS. 2-5 Exchange Nutrients

Forming Habits

If you don't like what your eating habits have done to your weight, energy, and attitude, you can do something about it. To find exactly where you are going wrong, analyze your present habits by keeping a chart for a few days of what you eat and the time of day you eat it. An analysis of what you are eating can be made by using a chart showing nutritive values of food (Appendix, pages 408–441) and comparing what you eat with your recommended daily dietary allowances (Illustration 2-3, page 17).

You can further analyze your eating habits by observing the time of day you are eating. Some patterns to observe are: Do I frequently snack shortly before meals? Do I snack as a result of advertising or suggestion of food on television or in a magazine? Do I eat when I am bored? Do I eat to delay doing things I don't like to do?

If your weight and eating habits are not what they should be, resolve this minute (not tomorrow or next Monday) to begin correcting them. Maintaining your ideal weight brings such rewards as a longer life expectancy, confidence in your self discipline, and a reflection in the mirror you can be proud of. It takes consistent and determined effort to form good eating habits, but the rewards are worth it.

MAINTAINING YOUR WEIGHT

If your weight is within the desirable limits, but an analysis of what you eat shows that your nutrition is poor, follow the exchange lists (Illustration 2-4, page 19), and try eating daily:

2 Milk exchanges
1 cup (at least) Vegetable A
1 Vegetable B exchange
3 Fruit exchanges
5 Bread exchanges
8 Meat exchanges
2 Fat exchanges

Photography by Terry Webb

ILLUS. 2-6 *Two glasses of milk per day are part of a nutritious diet. The only nutritional difference between whole and skim milk is the amount of fat in each one.*

ILLUS. 2-7 *Vegetable A exchanges provide many vitamins and much bulk in your diet.*

Photography by Terry Webb

ILLUS. 2-8 *Vegetable B exchanges provide some carbohydrate and protein. Their contribution of vitamins is necessary to a balanced diet.*

Photography by Terry Webb

ILLUS. 2-9 *Fruits provide mainly carbohydrate to your diet, but they are important, too, for the vitamins and minerals they contribute.*

Photography by Terry Webb

ILLUS. 2-10 *Most of the carbohydrates in your diet come from bread exchanges. Unless you expend the carbohydrate calories you consume, they turn to fat on your body.*

Photography by Terry Webb

ILLUS. 2-11 *Meat exchanges and milk are your major sources of protein.*

Photography by Terry Webb

Photography by Terry Webb

ILLUS. 2-12 *It is easy to consume too many fat exchanges for your needs. Only a small amount of fat each day is needed for good health.*

This will supply approximately 1,500 of your calories, and you will be sure of good nutrition. Limit your intake of foods not on the list such as cola, desserts, and candy (if you *must* indulge in "empty" calories) to the difference between the recommended number of calories you should eat and 1,500. Never let the "empty" calorie foods substitute for the nutritious ones.

LOSING WEIGHT

If you are overweight, analyze your poor eating habits and begin correcting them today. Excess weight contributes to a number of health problems and often affects your personal outlook as well as the way people respond to you. Resolve now to form habits that will enable you to live the rest of your life at your ideal weight.

In order to lose weight, you must, in addition to forming new habits, consume fewer calories daily than you use. Your recommended daily dietary allowance (Illustration 2-3) assures you of good health and normal energy. Before you undertake to routinely consume less than that which is normal for your age and height, you should consult a physician.

To lose one pound of fat, you must cut your food intake by 3,500 calories. Obviously this isn't done in a day. The speed with which weight can be lost depends upon how many calories you cut out daily. If your recommended daily allowance is 2,200 calories, you can lose approximately 2 pounds per week on 1,200 calories per day. The calculations are:

7 days @ 2,200 calories per day	=	15,400 calories per week
7 days @ 1,200 calories per day	=	8,400 calories per week
The difference	=	7,000 calories (2 pounds)

If your recomended daily allowance is 2,000 calories, you will need to cut to 1,000 per day to lose 2 pounds per week. Two pounds per week is considered safe for most people.

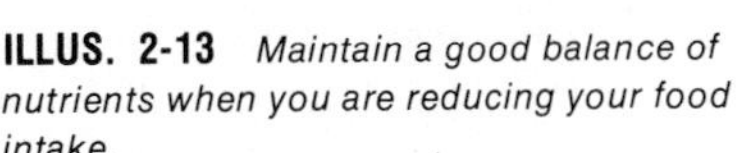

ILLUS. 2-13 *Maintain a good balance of nutrients when you are reducing your food intake.*

Florida Citrus

Using the exchange system of dietary control is an excellent way to reform your eating habits because you begin immediately to eat the foods you should eat for the rest of your life. While you are losing weight, you eat less, of course, than you will after you reach your desired weight. The foods will be the same; the amounts will be different.

The number of exchanges in each category that you should have to maintain the required number of calories in your reducing diet is shown in Illustration 2-14 . The lower portion shows sample menus. The distribution of exchanges is not rigid, but they should be fairly equally distributed throughout your day.

EXCHANGE ALLOWANCES AND SAMPLE MENUS FOR LOW-CALORIE DIETS

Food for the Day	1000 Calories	1200 Calories	1500 Calories	1500 Calories for Teenager
Milk, skim	2	2		
whole			2	3
Vegetable, group A	1	1	1	1
group B	1	1	1	1
Fruit, unsweetened	4	3	3	3
Bread	2	3	5	3
Fat	0	2	2	2
Meat	7	8	8	8
Nutritive Value				
Protein	71 gm	80 gm	84 gm	88 gm
Fat	35 gm	50 gm	70 gm	80 gm
Carbohydrate	101 gm	106 gm	136 gm	118 gm
Total Calories	1003	1194	1510	1544

1200 Calorie Sample Menu	1500 Calorie Sample Menu For Teenager
Breakfast: Orange slices Soft-cooked egg Toast — 1 slice Butter — 1 teaspoon Coffee	Breakfast: Orange juice — ½ cup Poached egg Toast — 1 slice Butter — 1 tsp. Milk — 1 cup whole
Lunch: Green salad with cheese, ham French dressing — 1 tbsp. Apple Skim Milk — 1 cup	Lunch: Sandwich — Bread — 2 slices Mayonnaise — 1 tsp. Lettuce Cheese — 1 exchange Cold cuts — 1 exchange Celery sticks Pear Milk — 1 cup whole After School: Milk, 1 cup whole
Dinner: Chicken — 2 exchanges Broccoli Carrots Dinner roll Cantaloupe — ¼ of 6-inch melon Skim milk — 1 cup	Dinner: Meatloaf — 4 exchanges Green Beans Carrots Sliced tomatoes on lettuce Hot tea with lemon
Evening Snack: Cheese — 1 ounce Saltines — 2	Evening Snack: Cheese — 1 ounce, Apple

ILLUS. 2-14 Exchange Allowances and Sample Menus for Low-Calorie Diets

OTHER MEANS OF LOSING WEIGHT

Fad Diets. Because changing life-long eating habits is very difficult, it is tempting to resort to a temporary solution, such as a fad diet, to adjust your weight. It is possible to lose weight on a fad diet, of course; but if the eating habits that made you too fat in the first place are resumed when you reach your desired weight, you will begin gaining weight as soon as you get off the fad diet. Allowing your weight to fluctuate up and down is considered detrimental to your overall health.

Many fad diets are based on consuming large amounts of water or eggs or grapefruit or all-in-one liquids or a special combination of foods. Although you can lose weight temporarily either by chemical changes or because you are taking in fewer calories, you are not correcting the real problem — your eating habits that made you fat in the first place. Once you resume those old eating habits, you will regain your lost weight.

Dietetic Foods. Beware of dietetic candy and desserts. They have little food value, and they frequently contain many calories. If you use them as a substitute for regular candy and desserts as a regular part of your diet, you are admitting that you cannot afford to consume the calories in candy and desserts; but you are not changing your eating habits. As a matter of habit, you will continue to include these kinds of foods in your diet and thus delay adopting the sorely needed new eating habits.

Activity. Like a fad diet, another ploy to delay changing your eating habits is to increase activity to burn up the excessive calories you consume. Regular exercise is good for your body, but it can't compensate for poor eating habits. Illustration 2-15 shows the time in various activities you would need to burn up calories taken in. You can see that burning an extra 1,000 calories per day for your 2-pound-per-week recommended weight loss would require a taxing amount of vigorous activity.

CALORIC CONSUMPTION IN MINUTES (ACCURATE WITHIN ONE MINUTE)

Caloric Value	Bowling	Bicycling 13 mph	Golf	Running 7.5 mph	Intermediate Down-hill Skiing	Swimming 45 yd/min	Tennis	Walking 2.5 mph
20	5	2	4	1	2	2	3	4
30	7	3	6	2	3	3	4	6
40	9	4	8	3	4	4	6	8
50	11	5	10	3	5	4	7	10
60	13	5	12	4	6	5	9	12
70	15	6	14	5	7	6	10	14
80	18	7	16	5	8	7	12	16
90	20	8	18	6	9	8	13	18
100	22	9	20	7	10	9	14	20

Higher caloric values can be obtained by adding, e.g., 120 calories expended in bowling would require 27 minutes (22 + 5).

Source: Adapted from figures in Leonard A. Larson and Herbert Michelman, International Guide to Fitness and Health, *A World Survey of Experiments in Science and Medicine Applied to Daily Living, Sponsored by The International Committee on the Standardization of Physical Fitness Assessments with the Assistance of the People-to-People Sports Committee, Inc., Crown Publishers, Inc., New York, 1973.*

ILLUS. 2-15 Caloric Consumption in Minutes

GAINING WEIGHT

If you are underweight, it will be necessary for you to consume 3,500 calories more than you use for each pound you wish to gain. Your habits, though, are what you must correct if you are to maintain normal weight. Be guided by the foods in the exchange lists (Illustration 2-4) for basic life-long nutrition. In addition, you can add a liquid supplement or some very high-calorie foods to your daily diet while you are gaining weight. Check the nutritive value of the food chart (Appendix, pages 408–441), and select foods you like that are high in calories. In addition, eat regularly; chew your food well; and get plenty of rest while you are trying to gain weight. You can be consoled by the fact that as you grow older, fewer and fewer calories are needed to maintain ideal weight.

SUMMARY

Fad diets, "dietetic" foods, exercise — none of these will compensate over the long term for poor eating habits. Your goal is to establish eating habits that will take you through life in good health at your ideal weight. Eating reasonable amounts of food from the categories listed earlier is your key to carefree living. Get started today!

Understanding Nutrition

1. What does your weight show about your nutrition?
2. Explain the critical weight control period for young people.
3. Why is it hard to change eating habits?
4. What are the recommended daily dietary allowances for you?
5. What is an "empty" calorie? How can it hurt you?
6. What is an exchange? Give an example of two fruit exchanges.
7. What is wrong with being overweight?
8. How can you determine the number of pounds per week you could lose at 1200 calories per day?
9. What is wrong with a fad diet? Dietetic candy and desserts?
10. To gain weight you should consume more calories than you use. What else can you do?

Chapter 3

Recreation and Rest

To be a truly well-developed person, you need several areas of activity in your life. Attendance at your job or school probably takes the bulk of your daylight time if you include the hour you spend getting ready to go in the morning, the seven-to-eight hours you actually spend there, the time spent in going to and from work or school, and your lunch hour. That accounts for ten or eleven hours of your time. After your household and personal care duties are fitted into your schedule, the remainder of your day is normally referred to as your leisure time. In order to be a well-rounded person with a healthy mind and body, you need to spend part of your leisure time for two very important activities: rest and recreation.

Recreation

Recreation includes not only time for relaxing in a quiet place with a good book or a favorite television show, but it also means physical activity designed to provide variety for your body from its everyday routine at work or school. If you are in a sedentary job (sitting most of the day or in activities requiring little strength), your body is suffering atrophy. Very simply, you will lose the ability to do much of anything else. It is important, then, to conscientiously plan part of your recreation time to develop power in your body to do something more than routine work. The nature of your body is such that if muscles are not used or are used only to a limited extent, they lose their capacity to be used. Unfortunately, that description applies to your heart, lungs, and vascular system also. Leisure time, then, becomes very important in terms of keeping your body physically fit.

RECREATIVE EXERCISE

There are two approaches to take in saving your body from atrophy. One is to use your recreation time for active sports that condition your vascular and pulmonary systems while you are relaxing. The other way is to look for opportunities in your day to add regular physical activity to your routine. Some of the very pleasant ways to condition your body are with active sports like hiking, bicycling, tennis, swimming, badminton, fast dancing, fencing, rowing, skating, skiing, and volleyball. However, unless you have been utilizing your heart-lung capacity beyond routine sedentary requirements, you will not be able at first to enjoy these activities regularly. You will need a plan to work up to them.

In addition to using part of your leisure time for activity that builds physical fitness for your body, it is helpful if you look for opportunities during your day to involve yourself in activity that contributes to conditioning your body. Such activity as stair climbing several times a day, a brisk walk from a bus stop to your office building every morning and night, and a quick walk in a park before eating lunch each day are good ways to work physical conditioning into your regular schedule.

RECREATIVE EXERCISE BENEFITS

Before you decide whether or not to obligate part of your leisure time to conditioning activity, consider whether or not the benefits outweigh what they cost in terms of your leisure time.

Basic Fitness. The fitness of a human body is measured according to its development in three areas: endurance, strength, flexibility. The levels of each of these areas are the result of the activity in which a person engages. Various kinds of activity can be specifically designed to achieve in one area, but each activity contributes somewhat to the level of development of the other areas.

Endurance is achieved by exercising to condition the cardiovascular and pulmonary systems. Basically, endurance depends upon how efficiently your body uses the oxygen you breathe every day in fueling the food you eat so that it can be used as energy. Cardiovascular endurance is not built by short periods of exercise, by calisthenics, or isometrics. It can only be developed by exercise that requires you to breathe more deeply and rapidly and requires your heat to pump more rapidly than it normally would in everyday routine activity. Such endurance is built by exercise programs that include jogging, brisk walking, swimming, cycling, stair climbing, and other active sports.

The theory of developing endurance by conditioning your cardiovascular system is that if you don't use your heart muscle, it atrophies. You lose that capacity which you do not use. If you call upon your heart to supply just enough power to get you through the routine activity of your day, that is all it is able to do after a period of time. If, however, you participate in an exercise program designed to expand the efficiency of your heart so that it has power to supply you with oxygen for fueling your body beyond your daily routine requirements, you become able to live beyond your routine activities.

Some of the basic benefits you can enjoy are:

(1) Your heart will operate more efficiently, beating stronger and slower but delivering more oxygen to the cells of your body to convert more of your food to energy, even during periods of routine activity.
(2) Your vascular system actually will increase in the number of blood vessels available to transport blood from your heart to your cells, opening more opportunities for converting your food into energy.
(3) Your blood will be circulating more often because of the stronger heartbeat and additional vessels, making the supply of oxygen to your cells richer.
(4) The muscles of your chest will become stronger, as will the muscles of the heart and the blood vessels themselves, in response to the increased requirement placed on them during your conditioning exercise.

Endurance is necessary to maintain good health. Since the basic truth is that the less a muscle is used, the less capacity it has for use, then the less you require of your heart and lungs, the less capacity they will have to perform. You should examine your daily routine. If all you do daily is ride to work, sit at work, ride home, and sit in front of television in the evening, you are not requiring much of your heart and lungs. Should you ever require more from them, for example, to swim, play tennis, go shopping, or walk a mile when you run out of gasoline, you might overtax them, resulting in abnormal fatigue because their capacity and efficiency have been allowed to deteriorate. Should you become ill, the normal production of your heart and lungs may not be sufficient to bring the natural defense into action efficiently if there is no reserve power. Recovery will take you longer, and your fatigue will be so great that you will not feel well as soon as you would had you been in good physical condition with reserve endurance.

Photography by Terry Webb

ILLUS. 3-1 *Keeping in shape means you have energy for activities other than those required by your work and home responsibilities.*

To distinguish exercise that conditions your cardiovascular system from that which conditions your surface muscles, cardiovascular exercise is termed recreative exercise; the other, calisthenics and isometric exercise. Many recreative sports and activities serve to fulfill your need for recreative exercise. They may also provide some calisthenic and isometric benefit.

Basically, endurance exercise or recreative exercise conditions muscles and tissue inside your body, such as your heart and lung muscles. Isometrics and calisthenic exercise condition muscles surrounding your bones. Both kinds of conditioning are necessary to a well-developed, healthy body. Isometric and calisthenic conditioning, by contributing to the strength and flexibility of your body, aids you in keeping your balance, giving your body symmetry and grace. Muscles on the surface of your body, like the muscles of your cardiovascular system, become incapable of functioning if they do not function for long periods of time. The tissue around them turns mainly to fat, which is rarely shaped to suit your aesthetic tastes. Using muscles on the surface of your body by isometric and calisthenic exercising brings muscles into action that increase the blood flow and oxygen input to those muscles, and stored fat tissue is replaced with muscle tissue.

The increased strength of well-developed muscles gives you better control of your body movement. You have the strength in your legs to walk and raise and lower yourself from a chair with more control. You are able to carry a grocery sack into your house without strain on your arms when the muscles are as strong as they should be.

Not only is strength increased with calisthenics, but flexibility and suppleness are increased. When muscles are not used, they may simply stretch or shrink. They become inflexible. Exercising them by flexing and contracting the muscles gives you more suppleness. You are able to move not only with more control but also with more grace. Although the basic benefit is to the cardiovascular and pulmonary systems, there is some benefit to surface muscles from recreative exercise.

By-Products of Recreative Exercise. Besides benefit to your cardiovascular and pulmonary systems and some conditioning to the muscles surrounding the bones near the surface of your body, recreative exercise also provides other benefits. These are the extras that occur and are really side benefits or fringe benefits of your exercise.

Recreative exercise improves your appearance. An active person looks more alert than an inactive person, and the body assumes a more pleasing shape. If you were asked to describe a person who was very successful, what would you say? Would the person be thin, fat, underdeveloped, muscular, rested, tired, alert, distracted, healthy, unhealthy? You probably would picture a successful person as one who looks the part — in good physical condition, mentally alert, with good posture and a healthy, fully developed body and mind. That is a good picture and a good goal for one who wants to feel and be successful. (Illustration 3-2, next page).

Because recreative exercise requires your cardiovascular system to perform efficiently, pumping blood through the body rapidly, vital oxygen is carried to the cells and waste is carried away. With well-fed body cells you can't help but have a better appearance. The flush of pink on a face that has been exposed briefly to cold weather is the result of efficient activity of the blood in order to keep the body warm when it is exposed to cold. The deep breathing that takes place during recreative exercise rids your body of carbon dioxide that has done its job and feeds your body with fresh oxygen for rejuvenating all processes. Deep breathing also causes you to lift your diaphragm off your stomach so that you can fill your lungs with air. The result is improved posture.

Recreative exercise aids your body by utilizing muscles other than those of the heart and lungs. If you have chosen to walk or to jog, you will be exercising and toning muscles in the lower part of your body. If you have chosen tennis, you will tone muscles both in the lower and upper parts of your body. The natural use of your arms and legs in the activity you have chosen will incidentally tone the muscles in them. The more side benefits you can attain from these activities, the less isometric

Photograph Courtesy of Cotton Incorporated

ILLUS. 3-2 *An active person looks alert and her body assumes a more pleasing shape.*

and calisthenic exercises you will need for body contouring. Your recreation may do that work for you if it is well chosen.

Another important by-product of recreative exercise is the feeling of success you get. The self-image of a person who practices good recreative exercise and rest habits is enhanced as much by the intense feeling of being alive as by the increased symmetry, muscle toning, and overall conditioning effect on the body. Conversely, one who does not exercise frequently suffers more than increased risk of occurrence of heart attack, high blood pressure, flabby muscles, and poor body condition. She suffers a poor self-image simply because she is not feeling the rewards of success from developing all that she has.

Frequently the idea of getting up out of a bed or a comfortable chair to begin a period of vigorous recreative exercise is not easy. However, with the first few deep breaths and strong heartbeats that spur the refreshing exchange of oxygen for carbon dioxide in your body, you begin to feel the reward of having made the effort. There is an exhilarating stimulation that sets this kind of exercise apart from any other. You truly develop the good "glow of health." Because you feel better when you exercise regularly in a recreative way, you will reflect this well-being in your appearance. People who feel good — really good — look good!

Recreative exercise provides for social contacts and the development of friendships in many ways. Just the fact that you are exercising for good health makes you desirable as a friend because of the good influ-

ILLUS. 3-3 *Recreative exercise provides exhilarating stimulation that reflects in your appearance.*

Revlon, Inc. *Photography by Gordon Munro*

ence you will have. Since you are doing something that all would like to do but for various reasons (usually lack of discipline) do not, people will want to know you to find out how you do it. They will be attracted to your dedication and your zest-for-living attitude.

Participating in a recreative sport for exercise provides for social contacts by bringing you around persons who are concerned with the same problems that you are. They are interested in doing more than the minimum — in living to the fullest of their capabilities in addition to benefitting their bodies. Right away you have a common bond and ground on which to start a conversation.

People who are in recreative exercise are anxious to find others who like the same kind of activity, and generally you will find them receptive to your offer of friendship. An activity that no one requires of you and that you don't have to do to earn a living is easier to stick to if you have friends who participate. The camaradarie among the participants in recreative exercise is hard to achieve in many other areas of life.

Your recreative exercise is always a good topic for conversation even with those who do not participate. It gives you a little charisma that they do not have. There is something special about your character that is attractive because you do something for which there is no scheduled payday and for which you get no special recognition from the community. You do it because it makes you healthy, invigorated, and a more attractive person. It takes some tenacity, a strong character, and real insight to work daily at a plan that requires not only time but energy, with no financial reward or recognition. Those are desirable traits for people engaging in any endeavor, especially making friends.

Recreative exercise is really so easy to take part in that the lack of difficulty may lead you to believe that anything that easy cannot be good for you. Not true! What is true is that your body is uniquely constructed to be active — your muscles, joints, and bones were designed to move — and that makes exercise easy. Walking, running, bending, swinging a racket or club, and many more activities are easy simply because your body was designed to be active. It is inactivity that destroys the body, making it stiff, achy, misshapen, and increasing its vulnerability to disease.

What conditioning and physical fitness really amounts to is having more energy to enjoy life. If you only have enough energy to get by with the necessary activity required by your job, personal care, and household chores, you have none left for recreation. That can make for a life without variety — perhaps even dull. It takes energy beyond the minimum to enjoy life, and you can develop it with a good recreative exercise program.

RECREATIVE EXERCISE PROGRAMS

There are various levels of conditioning that can be attained. A program can be designed to provide for whatever level you wish to attain. Any level above atrophy that you choose is better than what you will achieve without a program. One of the well-known programs that brings a person to a level of fitness that lowers chances of heart attack and other cardiovascular problems is the Aerobics program, as outlined in books by Doctor Kenneth Cooper and Mildred Cooper. Theirs is probably the most scientifically designed program that provides for top conditioning for physical fitness. A person who attains the level of fitness described in Aerobics truly has the capacity to enjoy all that life has to offer. The level that you choose, however, depends upon what you want for yourself.

The Aerobics Program. The uniqueness of the Aerobics program is that exercise of varying conditioning value is rated according to its conditioning value by assigning it a point value. The rating system makes it easy to compare the relative conditioning value of several activities in which you may be interested.

The plan of Aerobics follows two steps. The first is to bring you to the levels of fitness slowly so that you can safely attain each level. After you attain your ultimate goal, the second step encourages you to include a variety of activities; and point values are provided for these.

All exercise programs should start slowly so that the cardiovascular and pulmonary systems are not overtaxed. The programs illustrated (Illustration 3-4, page 36) show good ways to work up to an optimum level of fitness based on earning 24 points per week. If you feel you cannot maintain fitness requiring activity totaling 24 points a week, level off at a lower total. Any regularly maintained level of conditioning is better than none.

After you've reached the level at which you feel you can function as you desire, you can begin to vary your recreative activity. The other activities that are rated according to their point values in the Aerobic plan are provided (Illustration 3-5, page 37) so that you can maintain your selected level of fitness while you enjoy your recreation time.

Common-Sense Considerations. There are some common-sense cautions and precautions to consider. It is a good idea to have a check-up by your doctor before starting any exercise routine. The doctor will tell you if there should be any restriction on your planned activities.

It is wise not to try to build up faster than the beginning programs suggest. A sedentary heart, although grateful, will suffer shock enough with the suggested speed of progress. The programs given are for women under 30 years of age. If you are older, take them even more slowly than suggested.

All exercises should be preceded by a warming-up period (five minutes) of stretching and flexing muscles slowly to prepare the muscles to respond to the movement of the exercise. Equally important is the cooling-down period that consists of mild exercise, such as walking slowly and swinging your arms so that your heart will not be overtaxed. Because the movement of your arms and legs during exercise aids your heart in pumping blood to your body, if you stop your movement suddenly, your heart bears the entire burden in pumping extra blood until your body cools and your breathing rate slows. Since your digestive system needs the services of your cardiovascular system for digestion after you eat, don't plan to exercise within two hours after a meal. Your digestion will suffer if you direct the blood and oxygen to other parts of the body by exercising vigorously too quickly after a meal.

The most vital common-sense rule is that your exercise must be regular. To exercise spasmodically is dangerous for your heart. While you are building to the level of fitness you desire, you must exercise to earn the same number of points each day, five days out of each seven. After you reach your desired level of fitness, you may vary the amount of activity each of the five days, but they must total to your desired goal each week.

ILLUS. 3-4 EXERCISE PROGRAMS

STAIR CLIMBING EXERCISE PROGRAM

Week No.	Round Trips (average no. per minute)	Duration (minutes)	Frequency Per Week	Points Per Wk.
1	5	2:00	5	—
2	5	4:00	5	—
3	6	6:30	5	7½
4	6	7:30	5	8¾
5	6	9:45	5	11
6	7	9:00	5	15
7	7	10:30	5	17½
8	7	12:00	5	20
9	8	10:00	5	22
10	8	11:00	5	25

NOTE Applies to 10 steps, 6"–7" in height, 25°–30° incline. Use of bannister is encouraged.

STATIONARY CYCLING EXERCISE PROGRAM

Week No.	Cycling Speed mph	Duration (minutes)	Frequency Per Week	Points Per Wk.
1	12	5:00	5	5
2	12	7:30	5	5
3	12	10:00	5	5
4	15	12:30	5	7½
5	15	16:00	5	10
6	15	18:00	5	11¼
7	17½	21:00	5	15
8	20	21:00	5	20
9	20	24:00	5	22½
10	20	27:00	5	25

NOTE Add enough resistance that the pulse rate counted for 10 seconds immediately after exercise and multiplied by 6, equals the number specified. If it is higher, lower the resistance before cycling again; if it is lower, increase resistance.

Week No.	Pulse Rate
1–2	130
3–6	140
7–10	150

SWIMMING EXERCISE PROGRAM

Week No.	Distance (yards)	Time Goal (minutes)	Frequency Per Week	Points Per Wk.
1	100	3:00	5	—
2	150	3:45	5	—
3	200	5:00	5	7½
4	200	4:30	5	7½
5	250	5:30	5	10
6	300	7:00	5	12½
7	400	8:30	5	17½
8	500	11:00	5	20
9	550	12:00	5	22½
10	600	13:00	5	25

RUNNING EXERCISE PROGRAM

Week No.	Distance (miles)	Time Goal (minutes)	Frequency Per Week	Points Per Wk.
1	1	17:00	5	5
2	1	15:00	5	5
3	1½	23:00	5	7½
4	1½	21:00	5	15
5	1	10:30	5	15
6	1½	19:00	5	15
7	1½	18:00	5	15
8	2	24:00	5	20
9	1½	14:30	4	24
10	1½	13:30	4	24

NOTE First 4 weeks are walking only.

CYCLING EXERCISE PROGRAM

Week No.	Distance (miles)	Time Goal (minutes)	Frequency Per Week	Points Per Wk.
1	2.0	12:30	5	—
2	2.0	11:00	5	5
3	2.0	9:45	5	5
4	3.0	16:00	5	7½
5	3.0	14:30	5	7½
6	4.0	20:00	5	10
7	5.0	25:00	5	12½
8	6.0	30:00	5	15
9	7.0	35:00	4	22
10	8.0	40:00	4	26

WALKING EXERCISE PROGRAM

Week No.	Distance (miles)	Time Goal (minutes)	Frequency Per Week	Points Per Wk.
1	1	18:00	5	5
2	1	16:00	5	5
3	1½	25:00	5	7½
4	1½	23:00	5	7½
5	1	13:45	5	10
6	2	29:30	5	10
7	1½	21:30	5	15
8	2	28:30	5	20
9	2	27:30	5	20
10	2½	35:00	5	25

ROPE SKIPPING EXERCISE PROGRAM

Week No.	Duration (minutes)	Frequency Per Week	Points Per Wk.
1	2:30	5	—
2	5:00	5	7½
3	5:00	5	7½
4	7:30	5	11¼
5	7:30	5	11¼
6	10:00	5	15
7	12:30	5	18¾
8	14:00	5	21⅔
9	15:00	5	22½
10	16:00	5	26¼

NOTE Skip with both feet together or step over the rope, alternating feet, skipping at a frequency of 70–80 steps per minute.

ILLUS. 3-5 ADDITIONAL EXERCISES

Exercise	Duration	Points	Comments
Badminton	1 game	1½	Singles; players of equal ability; length of game, 20 minutes.
	2 games	3	
Dancing*			
Square	30 min.	2½	Count only the time you are actually dancing.
Polka	30 min.	2½	
Waltz	30 min.	1½	
Watusi, Jerk, etc.	30 min.	2	
Fencing	10 min.	1	
	20 min.	2	
Golf	9 holes	1½	No motorized carts.
	18 holes	3	
Lacrosse, Soccer	20 min.	3	Count only the time in which you are actively participating.
	40 min.	6	
Rowing	6 min.	1	2 oars, 20 strokes a minute.
	18 min.	3	
Skating	15 min.	1	Either ice or roller skating. For speed skating triple the point value.
	30 min.	2	
	60 min.	3	
Skiing	30 min.	3	Water or snow skiing, For cross-country snow skiing triple the point value.
	60 min.	6	
	90 min.	9	
Tennis	1 set	1½	Singles; players of equal ability; length of set, 20 minutes.
	2 sets	3	
Volleyball	15 min.	1	
	30 min.	2	
Walking	½ mi. (10:00)	1	Containing a 15 pound to 30 pound child.
Pushing a stroller	1 mi. (20:00)	2	
or baby carriage	1½ mi. (30:00)	3	

**Point values estimated.*

POINT VALUE FOR STATIONARY RUNNING

Steps Per Minute	Duration	Points
60–70	2:30 min.	—
60–70	5:00 min.	1¼
70–80	2:30 min.	¾
70–80	5:00 min.	1½
80–90	2:30 min.	1
80–90	5:00 min.	2
90–100	2:30 min.	1¼
90–100	5:00 min.	2½
100–110	2:30 min.	1½
100–110	5:00 min.	3

From AEROBICS FOR WOMEN by Mildred Cooper and Kenneth H. Cooper, M. D., Copyright © 1972 by Mildred Cooper and Kenneth H. Cooper, M. D., Reprinted by permission of the publishers, M. Evans and Company, New York, New York 10017.

Usually it is a good idea if you can make recreative exercise an integral part of your day, as a well-known congressman did. He jogged to work at Capitol Hill in Washington, D. C., every morning to keep himself in good condition. If you cannot jog to work, consider parking a mile away or getting off your bus or subway a mile from your place of work and getting in a brisk morning and afternoon walk. This is an excellent way to schedule exercise. It occurs regularly, it is timed, and it serves the purpose of getting to and from work. The regularity of the exercise will become habit; and with such a sensible plan, you may be able to enlist the participation of fellow workers and develop some new friends along the way.

If it is not practical to schedule your recreative exercise in such a way as to serve as a substitute for a regular part of your day, or if you choose to vary your recreative exercise, be sure that you plan for regularity, such as five times per week. It is always good to have an alternate indoor plan for your recreative exercise in the event of inclement weather. If you cannot jog, walk, or play tennis outdoors because of extreme weather, you may want to run in place indoors or use a stationary bicycle. These alternatives also serve to add variety to your exercise.

ILLUS. 3-6 *Make your recreative exercise one that you will do regularly.*

Photography by Terry Webb

Often a person who has chosen well will not like to vary her routine of recreative exercise. She is protective of her time because of the vitalized way that regular exercise makes her feel. She unfailingly avoids any activity that may infringe upon her schedule for performing it. Joggers and walkers frequently are people who jealously guard their schedule of exercise because they enjoy it so much.

REGULAR RECREATIVE EXERCISE

Since the regularity of your participation in recreative exercise is the most important part of your physical conditioning program, consider some ways to make it more appealing and easier for you to take part in regularly. Timing is of prime importance. The availability of facilities, the climate, and the environment in which you exercise are other vital considerations. On the personal side, you want to suit your exercise to your innate preferences, your age, and your size. You may want to recruit a buddy for morale purposes.

Time Schedule. Take stock of your time and how you spend it. Conditioning your body will take some of your day approximately five times a week at first. Think about how much time you are willing to invest regularly in getting your body into condition. Most programs begin with as little as thirty minutes a day. Jogging, walking, rope skipping, cycling, swimming, and stair climbing all require about 30 minutes per day. After you reach the level of fitness you desire, you may want to alternate long exercise periods with an exercise that does not take as much time. For example, if tennis is your sport, you can play tennis perhaps only two or three times a week and alternate with a 30-minute walk or cycling interval.

You are more likely to participate regularly if you set aside a certain time of day for your exercise. You will not plan other things during that time, and your family and friends will become accustomed to allowing you that time for yourself.

When you schedule your recreative exercise program, take advantage of your "built-in body time clock." If you are an early riser who is wide awake at six a.m., plan your exercise for early in the morning. If you are a "night owl," plan to run in place during the evening news. If you have an hour for lunch, take advantage of your lunch schedule by planning to use the first 30 minutes for your recreative exercise and the last 30 minutes for eating your lunch.

Some people find it beneficial to get up a little earlier in the morning to get in the recreative exercise before other events of the day begin. The advantages of this time of day are that few things are going on to distract or interfere with your exercise and that once you do it, you do not have to plan around it again during the day. Also, you get the benefit of that increased blood flow and oxygen intake all day long. A person who participates during this time of day rarely has a day of the "blahs." Her body is too vital and alive to be "blah." Morning exercise, though, should be taken before breakfast since you should not have vigorous exertion within two hours after a meal.

Often, part of the noon hour can be utilized for exercise. A nutritious lunch can be brought from home and eaten in the park after you walk or jog. It really gives you a break from your work, and this is time that usually is wasted. A side benefit is that such a plan keeps you from shopping during lunchtime — probably saving you money.

Stair climbing can be done as you arrive at work, if you work on an upper floor. An advantage of this kind of recreative exercise plan, which fits into your work schedule, is that it frees your leisure time for other activities.

If you haven't gotten your exercise in before late afternoon, set aside a certain time to complete it. Although the late afternoon is a beautiful time of day for outdoor exercise, you may have to guard against the fatigue of the work day discouraging you from your exercise program. If you wait until after dinner, or if you live in a section of the country where it becomes dark early, outdoor activity may have to be done after dark. Be sure that it is safe for you to participate at that time outdoors so that you won't be discouraged.

The time is there for you to condition your body if you want to. Look carefully at your schedule, your preferences, and at what will work for you. Then make a plan that is easy to keep, so that you can be physically fit with energy to spare.

Facilities. Carefully select a recreative exercise program that does not require facilities that may not be available regularly. The easier it is to take part in the activity, the more regularly you will want to do it.

Of the beginning programs, one requires no personal equipment at all — only stairs to climb. Running and walking require only good, supportive tennis shoes; rope skipping, only a jump rope. The other three, of course, require a swimming pool, a bicycle, or a stationary bicycle. Be sure that you can afford the costs of whatever program you select. If facilities or equipment are required, they must be available to you five times per week.

If you are using part of your workday for walking or jogging, take your extra shoes in a shoe bag each day. Arrange to measure your route with a car odometer, or ask your bus driver to measure the distance between the two points on your planned route. You can, of course, use an odometer that straps to your body or one attached to a bicycle to measure your distances.

ILLUS. 3-7 *Be sure you have regular access to the facilities needed for your exercise program.*

Photography by Terry Webb

Climate and Environment. Your climate makes a difference in whether you should choose an indoor or outdoor exercise activity. Cold weather, unless it is below freezing for long periods of time, generally does not deter an outdoor program because you can dress for it. Hot weather, though, above 95 degrees, may deter you somewhat. If you live in an area that is subject occasionally to such extreme conditions, be sure that you have an alternate indoor exercise to substitute during such weather so that your conditioning goes on. Running in place indoors is a good alternate to jogging outdoors on a regular schedule. Stationary cycling is a good alternate to walking and cycling outdoors.

The environment of your exercise area is important. If you live in a wet climate where it rains five out of ten days either seasonally or throughout the year, select an outdoor activity only if you are willing to go out in the rain regularly. If your environment is near a freeway or factory where the air is polluted heavily, you may want to select an indoor recreative exercise for your conditioning program. If you live where bicycling is hazardous because of heavy traffic, choose another activity. It may be pleasant, however, if you go to a park or area of clean air and serenity on a weekend occasionally, to ride on a bicycle trail or to take a walk through a wooded area.

Personal Preferences. Your goal is to get your body in good condition so that you have reserve power when you need it. You also want to enjoy your recreative exercise. If you are operating only marginally now, with little energy beyond that which you need for routine daily activity, the idea of beginning a recreative exercise program may appear to be beyond your endurance, making all exercise unappealing. You must select an activity and start just where you are if you are ever to improve. If you don't start an exercise program, you will forever live marginally with no physical resources to enjoy the extras of life.

At first you will be borrowing against endurance that you will develop in the future, and you may get discouraged. The human body responds quickly though, and sooner than you think you will be easily accomplishing your daily and weekly exercise goals with little effort. Once you reach increased levels of energy and endurance, you will never again want to live marginally with only enough steam to get through the workday.

Make your recreative exercise something you enjoy so that you will want to participate regularly the rest of your life. Start by investigating the side benefits of the various recreative exercises available to you.

In walking and jogging, for example, you may vary the route and learn a great deal about the neighborhood in which you exercise. You probably will meet the people in the neighborhood. If you like outdoor air, new acquaintances, and the excitment of what may be just around the corner, you may like jogging or walking. Bicycling is another recreative exercise that exposes you to new scenes. You are less likely to meet people than when you are walking or jogging, though, unless you join a bicycling club or unless others in your neighborhood are cyclists. However, if you like the wind in your face and the thrill of maneuvering under your own power, you will like bicycling.

After you've reached your desired level of fitness, add activities such as tennis, volleyball, and dancing, which are active recreative exercises that aid you in meeting people. The skill required in these activities frequently is attractive to those who like to work toward mastery while exercising. If the challenge of skill mastery appeals to you, you may enjoy these recreative exercises.

Swimming, rope skipping, stair climbing, skiing, skating, rowing — each have benefits to offer to make them attractive to you while you build the fitness of your body. You may even try several that you think you will like before you settle on one. When you are evaluating your choices, notice all the side benefits of each activity, the facilities, the environment, the equipment, and any items surrounding it that may make it more attractive and enjoyable. Make your choices those that truly suit your personality preferences.

ILLUS. 3-8 *Take into consideration all the aspects of exercises that make particular ones attractive to you.*

Photograph Courtesy of Cotton Incorporated

Age and Size. Age and size can make a difference in the rate at which you progress in your recreative exercise program. The usual plan of one-week steps may be changed so that the same level is maintained for two weeks before the next level is undertaken. This allows the heart and lungs a more gradual adjustment when it seems wise because of age or size.

It is important not to suddenly ask your heart and lungs to support an activity that is vigorous if for thirty or more years you have not made such a surprise request. Most people under thirty, who have participated in school activities and other youthful endeavors within the past ten years, can select almost any recreative exercise they wish at the rate suggested. Those over thirty should consider the present condition of their bodies and what they can and cannot do without undue strain from the beginning.

If you are a large person, either overweight or exceptionally tall, it takes more endurance from your heart to supply your body during exercise than it does for a person of normal or small size. A large person may need to progress at a slower rate than that given, taking two weeks at each level instead of one until the heart is built up to that endurance needed for the extra size.

If you are small or of normal size, the rate of progress given probably will feel only slightly tiring to you. Constantly try to increase your weekly rate, though, so that the conditioning effect works to your advantage in increasing the efficiency of your heart and lungs.

Enlist a "Buddy." Because your exercise program needs to go on whether you have company or not, it is a good idea to be able to function at your exercise program without a buddy so that you won't be dependent in case your buddy leaves or discontinues exercising for some reason. However, its always nice to have someone to do things with, and recreative exercise is no exception. If you have someone who is as conscientious as you are about your program, you can be of great benefit to each other for encouragement, especially when one of you seems to be a little out of sorts and wants to shirk the exercise program for the day.

There are several ways to recruit a buddy. If you have a friend who rides the same bus to work with you, suggest that the two of you get off a mile away from work and walk briskly on to your building each day. You will be doing him or her a favor in terms of health and the quality of life. If you regularly eat lunch with someone at work, suggest as an alternative that you exercise part of your lunch period, and picnic in the park during the remaining time. If you ride home on the bus with a friend, suggest that you get off a mile before your regular stop so that you can get in a brisk walk. Suggest to a friend who works in the same building that you climb stairs for exercise.

Rest

One of the adjustments young people make when they change a life style, for example, from the life of school student to that of an office worker, is in the way time is used. Having been a student for many years, the young person has experience in planning to meet school and private life schedules, and the routine is easy to plan. A new life as an employee is not quite so easy to plan simply because there is no experience in planning for an eight-to-ten hour day away from home without a break. Efficiency becomes the byword if all the routine chores of laundry, grocery shopping, apartment cleaning, personal care, ad infinitum, are to be done and time made available for pleasure. If the adjustment is not easily made, the area of life that usually suffers is the amount of rest time made available.

Frequently the lack of sleep can destroy the quality of the sleep you do get. If you've ever been too tired to sleep, you probably recall that it was a tense kind of fatigue — one that wouldn't let your mind or body relax. Your rest was plagued with unresolved problems about things you had done, hadn't done, or had done wrong.

QUANTITY OF REST

Sometime hair shampooing and hand laundry are put off until late at night in order to get in a movie during the week. It is one or two hours later than normal bedtime before these necessities are completed. The next day is one of sluggish movement, a lack of mental alertness, general poor job performance ability — all due to lack of rest. If this happens frequently, the work suffers as much as the worker, and the employer is sure to notice both.

The amount of rest you need each night depends upon your particular body mechanism. The amounts required vary from an average of six to ten hours of sleep per night. Take into account any emotional stress you may be subjected to when you are planning your rest time. Stress can be as exhausting as physical activity, and you should be alert to the additional rest requirement during stressful periods. A new job, for example, when you are learning a new routine and are concentrating constantly to catch all the activities of the job, will require additional rest time until you become accustomed to the new routine. Since the condition of your health also has an effect on how much rest you need, allow for additional rest time when you are ill or slightly ill. A cold may weaken your body so that it takes more energy to perform your regular activities, making you more fatigued than usual. Plan to get additional rest, both to allow the healing properties of your body and your medicine time to work and to allow rest time for the additional energy you are expending from your weakened position.

It is not wise to automatically assume that you are one of those people who can function well with only six hours of sleep. Try it for three nights consecutively and see how efficiently you can function each of the days. If you are not as alert and energetic as you normally are, increase the length of your night's rest for a few nights until you find the optimum length of time you require for sleep. Usually it takes two or three nights consecutively of the same number of hours' sleep to determine how much sleep is required. A six-hour night sandwiched between two eight-hour-nights sometimes may go unnoticed; whereas, three six-hour nights consecutively, if you are an 8-hour sleeper, may bring about undesirable changes in your disposition and demeanor. Avoid those undesirable changes by organizing your time so that you get adequate rest.

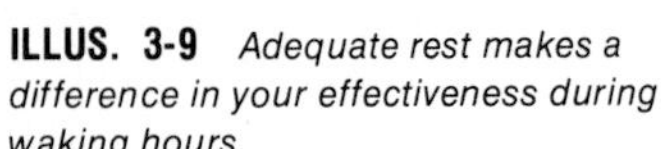

ILLUS. 3-9 *Adequate rest makes a difference in your effectiveness during waking hours.*

Photography by Terry Webb

QUALITY OF REST

The quality of your rest is as important as the amount you get. It is possible to be as exhausted in the morning as you were the night before if you have a night of fitful rest. There are, however, ways to improve your rest.

Recreative exercise will improve your rest by fatiguing your body. The fatigue you feel from tension and stress of the day's activity is not the kind that brings restful sleep. The fatigue you feel from walking two miles or jogging one mile is the kind that brings restful sleep. Complete muscular fatigue of the body can be brought about by recreative exercise that is enjoyed in a relaxing way. The enjoyment brings relaxation of the nerves, and the activity brings fatigue to the muscles. A good rest will follow.

Try to plan your day's activities so that important items that might haunt your sleep are not left undone at the end of your day. Learn to set priorities and to accept the fact that sometimes small things can wait until you sleep — soundly.

Avoid stimulating hot drinks and those with caffeine, such as coffee and colas, near bedtime if they seem to disturb your sleep. Avoid stimulating conversations and exciting books late at night if you have trouble getting them out of your mind at bedtime.

Do some calm meditating and slow, relaxing stretching to unkink your muscles when you recline in bed. Think each toe, foot, leg, finger, hand, and arm to sleep as you relax each one in turn. Allow only restful scenes to enter your mind.

You can improve the quality of your waking hours by making rest time a beauty treatment. Keep beside your bed several beauty aids that you use regularly. If your hands are rough and your heels are cracking, keep cream to smear on before you go to sleep so that your skin gets the benefit of the soothing emollients for several hours while you sleep. Keep eye cream, if you use it, close to your bedside so that you can put it on before you go to sleep. Also, just before you turn out your light is a good time to manicure your nails because you can allow your nail enamel to dry overnight. The longer the enamel goes without being disturbed before it is dry, the longer it usually lasts.

Cuticle cream, too, can be used just before you turn out your light. When you wash your hands in the morning, use the towel to push back the cuticle that has softened overnight. This procedure, practiced two or three times per week, saves time at your regular manicure as well as saving you dry, roughened cuticle in between times.

It is a good idea to stretch your body well before you get up in the morning. This is a gentle awakening of the muscles, increasing circulation and preparing them to bear the weight of your body without a shock. Getting up quickly before you have notified your muscles of what is coming and before the blood resumes its speeded up flow for daytime activity, can result in pulled muscles and weakness when you try to walk just after rising.

SUMMARY

The benefits of regular recreative exercise combined with adequate restful sleep influence all areas of your life. To be able to participate in all activities in which you are interested and to maintain good health, an alert mind, and efficiency in thought and movement can cause your life to become enriched and vitalized beyond mere routine into the limitless boundaries of imagination. Don't let a temporarily weakened body or a lazy attitude doom you to live among the ranks of marginal performers. Start your program of recreative exercise and sensible rest today.

Understanding Recreation and Rest

1. Why is leisure time activity important to your health?
2. What are the basic benefits of recreative exercise? The by-products of recreative exercise?
3. How can you know if you are making progress on the Aerobics program?
4. What common sense considerations are there in undertaking an exercise program?
5. Why is it necessary to participate regularly and how can you insure regular participation?
6. How can you decide on the amount of rest you need?
7. How can you improve the quality of your rest?

Chapter 4

Balance

Balance means that areas of your life bear the importance to you that they deserve. One area concerns your attitude about your appearance, the effect it has on people around you, and the amount of time and effort you expend to make yourself as attractive as you can be. In a more particular way balance, in this context, means that in movement you are graceful and flexible and that your body is in good proportion. The reference is to the balance that well-developed muscles contribute to your ability to stand, walk, and sit with grace.

Your attitude about your appearance shows in how well you take care of your body. There is a very good reason for the fact that people who are attractive have an edge in most competitive situations. It takes more discipline than natural beauty to make oneself attractive, and discipline is a desirable character trait in anyone. Another reason is that it takes intelligence and awareness to realize that by expending the effort required to make oneself attractive, much advantage can be gained. Without question, intelligence and awareness are desirable traits. On the other hand, one who does not take care of her body and whose appearance suffers frequently is thought of as undisciplined, unaware, or plainly unintelligent. A few years ago a slovenly appearance was a way of rebelling against "the system." Today, however, if one wants to succeed in a competitive world, she must be carefully aware of the necessity of good grooming.

Appearance reflects what you think of yourself. The more regard you have for yourself, the better care you take of your body. A well-developed exterior reflects the self-image you have mentally. If you think you are a worthwhile person, it shows in the effort you invest in developing yourself.

Closely related to your self-image is the image others have of you. If you consider yourself interesting, usually others feel the same way about you. They are influenced by the regard you have for yourself as it shows in your appearance and attitudes. Keeping your body fit by proper nutrition, exercise, and correct posture results in visible evidence that your self-image is good, and it will influence others in forming a favorable opinion of you.

Two added advantages of keeping your body fit and in good proportion are the facts that your clothes will be easier to fit and you probably will be weight-conscious. A body with symmetry and well-toned muscles is more nearly like the average size for its height. Clothes not only are easier to fit, but they look better.

ILLUS. 4-1 *A body with symmetry and well-toned muscles looks good, and clothes fit better.*

Photograph Courtesy of Cotton Incorporated

Exercise Benefits

One of the first places to start in self-improvement is with your form and its appearance. Movement, suppleness, and your shape are all tied to balance from another angle. Body symmetry is considered desirable in the shape of a human body. Both sides should be about the same. Symmetry is developed by exercising both sides of the body to correct any unevenness and to keep both sides strong so that one will not become a dominant side. The shape of the body that is desirable is one without excess fat but with some degree of fatty and muscle tissue to form round curves over the bones underneath. Most of the padding should be muscle because control and flexibility depend upon well-developed muscles. Only a thin layer of fat near the skin is considered desirable. Muscles characteristically assume a shape that is desirable; fat rarely does.

Movement and flexibility depend upon the development of muscles used in movement. Graceful movements will not be possible without well-developed muscles that both stretch and contract with ease. Stretching exercises combined with bending ones make the curves in your form gentle and flowing and enable your body to move lithely and with more of a floating flexibility than with rigid, board-like jerks.

BODY SHAPE

A body without exercise becomes lumpy with fatty deposits in inappropriate places. Muscle tissue is so shaped that when it is developed in place of fatty tissue, it provides a gentle curve where it is becoming and a firm, smooth look where it is desired. Fat has no orderly shaping; it generally just bulges if it occurs in large quantities. It isn't necessary to worry about developing unsightly muscles with exercise. You won't be able to do it without a weight-lifting program and the supplemental dietary foods for body building similar to those which professional football players use.

Shape Analysis. One of the best ways to determine whether or not you need exercise for reshaping your body is made visually by simply standing nude in front of your full-length mirror, observing bulges and hollows where there should be graceful curves. With a hand mirror check the side views and back view. After all, you are seen from those directions as much as or more than you are from the front.

Another check is to compare your relative measurements with those of the "average" body that is appropriately developed. Only your scale will tell you if you are too fat or too thin. However, your tape measure can reveal whether what you have distributed on your bones is distributed in an aesthetically pleasing proportion.

The first measurement is a wrist measurement just above the bone on the elbow side. The leg measurements correspond to this measurement. The thigh should be approximately three and one-half times the wrist measurement; the knee should be two and one-half times; the calf, two and one-fourth times; and the ankle, one and one-fourth times. Other proportional relationships should be: waist, eight to ten inches smaller than the bust; stomach (three or four inches below the waist), one-half to two and one-half inches less than the bust; hips, one to two inches more than the bust; thigh, five to nine inches more than the calf; and calf, five to seven inches more than the ankle.

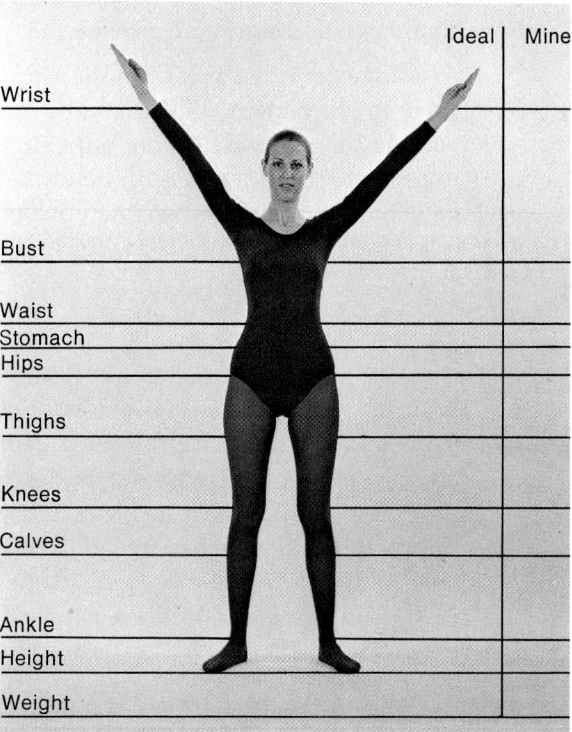

Photography by Terry Webb

ILLUS. 4-2 *Compare your shape to the "ideal."*

The proper way to measure is with a flexible tape measure that is kept parallel with the floor and even as you wrap it around your body. This bust measurement is taken over the fullest part of your breast with your bra on. The waist measurement is taken at the smallest part of the waist with the tape not pulled tight and without holding your breath. The hips, thighs, and calf should be measured at the largest part. The ankle is measured just above the ankle bone.

Shape Comparison. Examples of well-proportioned relationships have been computed below. Take your wrist measurement and follow the line across to compare your measurements with those listed.

WELL-PROPORTIONED RELATIONSHIPS

(INCHES, ROUNDED TO NEAREST ONE-EIGHTH INCH)

Wrist	Thigh	Knee	Calf	Ankle
4½	15¾	11¼	10⅛	5⅝
4¾	16⅝	11⅞	10⅝	5¾
5	17½	12½	11¼	6¼
5¼	18⅜	13⅛	11¾	6½
5½	19¼	13¾	12⅜	6⅞
5¾	20⅛	14⅜	12⅞	7⅛
6	21	15	13½	7½
6¼	21⅞	15⅝	14	7¾
6½	22¾	16¼	14⅝	8⅛
6¾	23⅝	16⅞	15⅛	8⅜

Waist	Bust	Stomach	Hips
20	28–30	25½–29½	29–32
21	29–31	26½–30½	30–33
22	30–32	27½–31½	31–34
23	31–33	28½–32½	32–35
24	32–34	29½–33½	33–36
25	33–35	30½–34½	34–37
26	34–36	31½–35½	35–38
27	35–37	32½–36½	36–39
28	36–38	33½–37½	37–40
29	37–39	34½–38½	38–41

ILLUS. 4-3 Well-Proportioned Relationships

BODY MOVEMENT

A well-proportioned body that moves without grace, flexibility, efficiency, and internal order is a shameful waste of beauty. Exercise aids the development of each of these areas.

Grace. Gracefulness is a balance between flexibility and strength. To check the gracefulness of your body, perform your everyday movements in slow motion to see if you can move with ease and grace.

Stand with your back to a chair, place one leg so that the back of your knee touches the chair, and without the use of your hands (since you are usually holding a handbag or a coat or both) very slowly lower yourself into the chair by bending only your knees and hip joints. Do not curve your back as you sit. The more slowly and smoothly you can perform this slow motion sitting, the better your flexibility and strength, and of course, the more graceful you are.

Now, without the use of your hands and with one foot slightly in front of the other, rise from the chair with the same slow motion. Remember to let the leg and thigh muscles perform the work. Do not curve your spine.

Climb stairs in slow motion speed without the use of your body movement to swing you up or down the stairs. Steady yourself with the use of the bannister, but do not allow your head and trunk to bob back and forth for balance or momentum. Let muscles that were designed for climbing and lowering your body do the work. Keep your spine straight. Good control gives a gliding feeling and graceful appearance.

If you have trouble with any part of these activities, you need to build strength and flexibility in the muscle masses that are weak.

Flexibility. You need flexibility in your body, especially in your spine and neck. If you are flexible in the trunk of your body, your walk will be smoother. Flexibility makes all movement more graceful and easier for you to perform. Check your flexibility with some bending, twisting, and stretching motions. Stand with your heels against a wall; twist the trunk of your body with your arm extended so that it touches the wall on the opposite side of your body. (Illustration 4-4) Now with your toes to the wall, extend your arm around your back at shoulder level, twisting the trunk of your body, trying to touch the wall on the opposite side of your body. You should come very close to touching the wall both ways without bending your elbows (Illustration 4-5). Turn your head in either direction as far as you can. You should be able to see easily behind you (Illustration 4-6). The flexibility of your legs can be tested by keeping one foot stationary and turning the other so that the toes of it touch the heel of the stationary one, and the toes of the stationary one come close to the heel of the turned one (Illustration 4-7). Try it for each leg. Those are the twisting tests.

ILLUS. 4-4 *With your heels close to the wall, alternately twist the trunk of your body so that your extended arm touches the wall on the opposite side of your body.*

ILLUS. 4-5 *With your toes close to the wall, twist your trunk, trying to extend your outstretched arm to touch the opposite wall.*

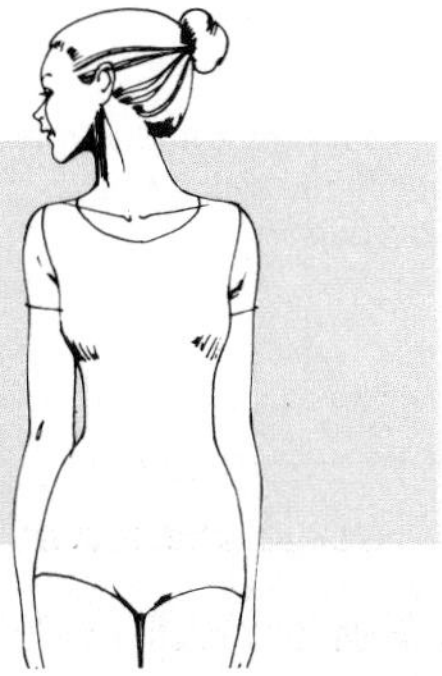

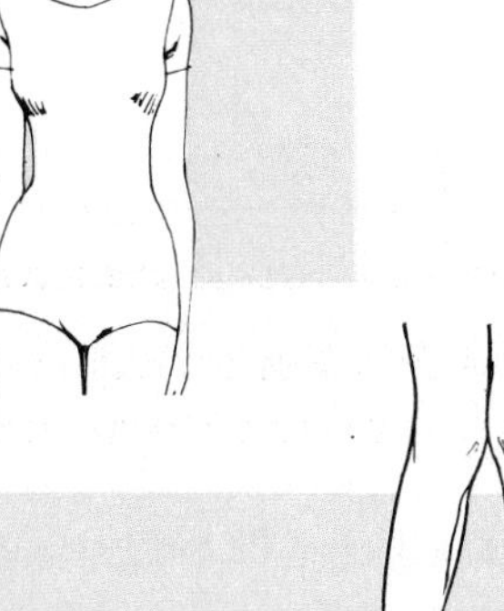

ILLUS. 4-6 *Turn your head in either direction as far as you can.*

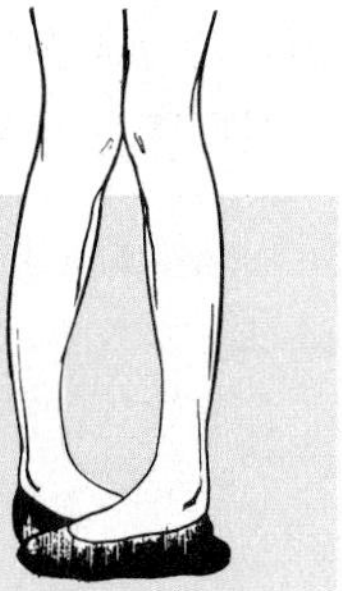

ILLUS. 4-7 *Turn your feet to touch toes of each foot to the heel of the other foot.*

Now, try the bending ones. Stand straight with your heels and the back of your knees close to a wall. Bend at the waist to see if you can touch your toes without bending your knees (Illustration 4-8, next page). Turn around now, facing the wall, bending backward at the waist. Do so slowly (Illustration 4-9). You should have some flexibility in the backward leaning position. With your back to the wall again, bend from the waist sideways, letting your hand reach as low on your leg as you can. You should be able to easily reach your knee on each side (Illustration 4-10).

Stretching tests for your spine require the help of someone to mark your contracting height to compare with your stretching height. Stand with your back against a wall and without bending your waist, knees, or neck make yourself as short as you can; have someone mark your height.

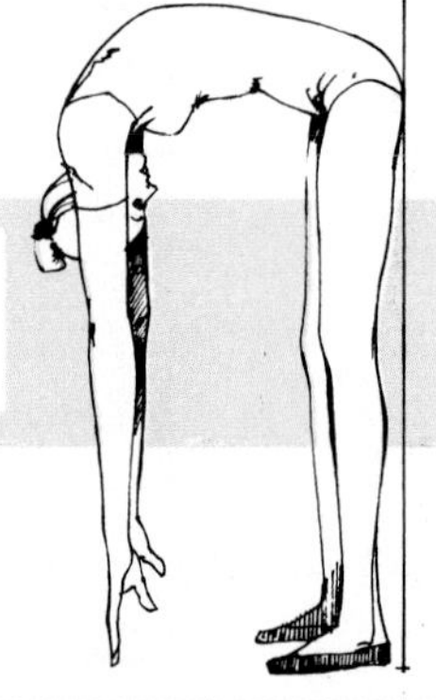

ILLUS. 4-8 *With your heels and the back of your knees close to the wall, bend at your waist to touch your toes.*

ILLUS. 4-9 *With your toes and the front of your knees close to the wall, bend backward as far as you can.*

ILLUS. 4-10 *With your back to the wall, bend sideways as far as you can.*

Now, without standing on tiptoes, stretch as tall as you can. There should be an inch or more difference. Record your scores (Illustration 4-11, below).

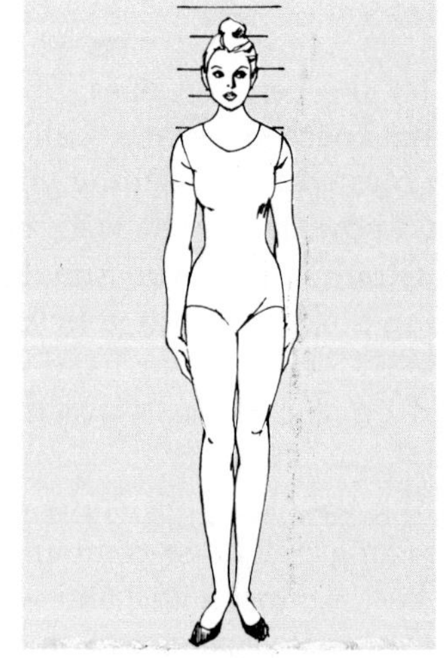

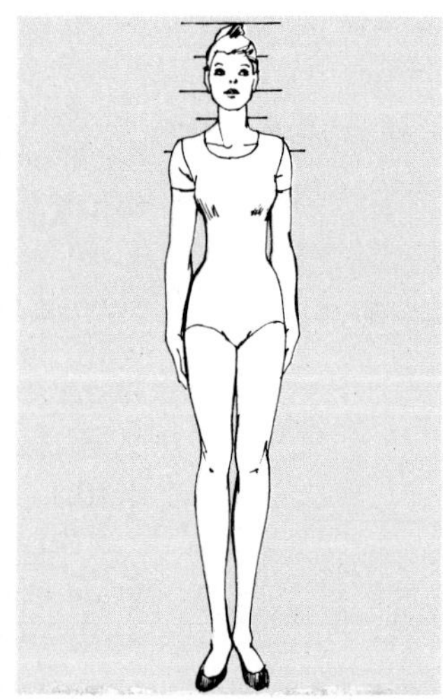

ILLUS. 4-11 *Use a ruler to measure your height as you "shrink" without bending your knees, waist, or neck. Measure again as you stretch to your full height.*

When you test your flexibility and gracefulness in slow motion, note carefully where the strain or lack of strength is in your body. Pinpoint and identify which muscle mass seems not to function as it should. If you are inflexible, note whether there is a roll of fat that keeps you from moving, or if it is a rigid spine or bone joint that won't move. The key to selecting the correct exercise for your particular problem is to feel the tension in precisely the area of your weakness or rigidness.

Static flexibility, the ability to stretch parts of the body as far as possible in various directions, and *dynamic flexibility*, the ability to make repeated rapid movements at a joint with very little resistance to the movement, are important to graceful movement in walking and in all movement as well as in the prevention of joint pains and aches. Poor flexibility results in stiff, awkward movement.

Efficiency. Exercise makes mechanical movement more efficient. Just as a car becomes more efficient when it requires less gasoline per mile, your movement becomes more efficient when it requires less energy for movement. The development of muscles in place of fatty tissue brings about such efficiency by replacing dead weight with working weight. Fatty tissue increases body weight, requiring more energy to maneuver it. Muscle tissue at the same weight contributes to the efficiency by facilitating movement with a minimum of energy.

Body Alignment. Proper body alignment depends on well-developed muscles. The balance of your body depends on your ability to center each part of your body over its supporting part. For example, the pelvic area centers over your legs in a particular way if your center of gravity is correct. In like manner, the rib cage centers over the pelvic area; the neck, over the sternum; and the head, over the neck area. All are designed to form a particular line so that the center of gravity for your body provides balance as you stand and move. If you are not able to maintain the appropriate balance because of weak muscles in your back, abdomen, shoulders, or neck, you put undue pressure on areas not designed to support parts of your body. If your head projects forward, the neck and backbone, which were uniquely designed to support your head, do not bear its weight. Your front neck muscles rather than the vertebrae and muscles in your back, support your head. You may, as a result, suffer muscular pain in your upper back because the muscles are constantly stretched to allow your head to assume its unnatural forward position.

If your pelvic area tilts forward, the muscles in your back near your waist will be stretched and vertebrae which should be straight will be curved, resulting in back pain. Your body is designed to work beautifully in a particular way. If you fail to maneuver it as you should, muscular and sometimes bone and joint disorders will occur. It takes well-developed muscles with strength to hold your body in its proper shape. Exercises to develop these muscles are available and they will help you avoid the uneasiness and pain that result from poor body alignment.

Energy Levels. Exercise stimulates the production of hormones that have an effect on your energy. Adrenalin and nonadrenalin are produced as a result of activity, and they release caloric energy to particular cells within the body, such as the heart, increasing its rate, blood pressure and blood sugar. These adrenalins are produced as a result of emotional excitement, such as stress, fear, and anger. A resulting caloric energy occurs. If activity is not undertaken to utilize the energy, unnecessary muscle tightening and increased heart rate occurs, damaging the body.

The physiological effects of stress are lessened by regular physical activity. The caloric energy released by adrenalin is used and the use of the energy is spread throughout the body, not taxing one particular area as it does when no activity is undertaken.

Activity increases the production of a hormone from the thyroid gland called thyroxin, which releases caloric energy, activating cells in all parts of the body. This increased metabolic activity lasts for several hours after the physical activity ceases.

Cortisone also is secreted as a result of activity. It acts on the tissue of the brain, stimulating better mental activity.

Exercise Plans

There are many kinds of exercise available for shaping the form of the body and developing muscular control. Isotonic calisthenics and isometrics are two of the finest. *Isotonic exercise* usually employs movement of muscles and joints, and sometimes the use of weights such as barbells, slant boards, and aids to increase the tension put on muscles exercised. *Isometric exercise* pits one muscle of the body against another for a certain period of time. Both kinds of exercise are very good.

The calisthenic form of exercise requires movement of the body by stretching, bending, pushing, pulling, twisting, and lifting. Usually it is done privately or in an exercise class. Isometric exercise requires little movement beyond pushing, pulling, or the conscious contracting of a muscle for a certain period of time. Both are designed to strengthen and tone the muscles involved. However, calisthenics, because of the movement, tend to be more beneficial in developing flexibility and suppleness. Yoga is a form of exercise that combines slow movement and the pitting of one muscle against another along with meditation, and it can be beneficial to an exercise program. The advantages of exercise along with the principles to be employed are important.

ISOMETRIC EXERCISE

Isometric exercises are simple and produce quick results. They require little time and no equipment. Frequently they can be done while you are sitting at your desk with no one noticing. This kind of exercise requires no particular type of clothing, and it causes little fatigue and no perspiring. It must, however, be accompanied by other kinds of exercise since it makes no contribution to cardiovascular endurance and little to flexibility.

Isometric Principles. Some guidelines to follow if you select an isometric program are:

- Select exercises that work all your major muscle groups that need strengthening.
- Hold each contraction for six to eight seconds.
- Use maximum effort for each contraction.
- Complete your entire group of exercises each day.
- Vary the exercises weekly so that different points in the muscle group are exercised on a weekly basis. Changing the angle of the flexion will accomplish this.
- Ordinarily, the breath is inhaled before the contraction, held during the contraction, and exhaled after the contraction.

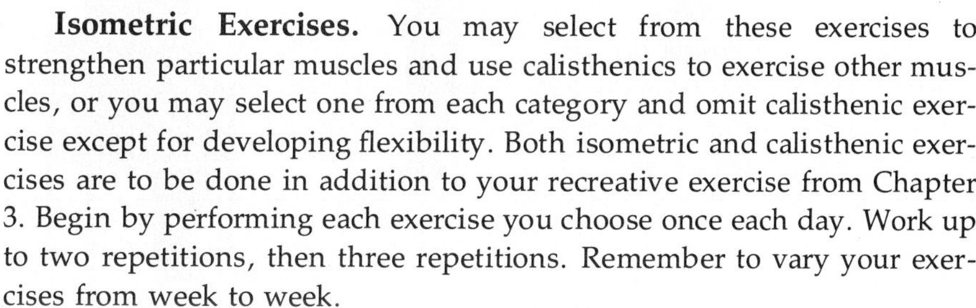

Isometric Exercises. You may select from these exercises to strengthen particular muscles and use calisthenics to exercise other muscles, or you may select one from each category and omit calisthenic exercise except for developing flexibility. Both isometric and calisthenic exercises are to be done in addition to your recreative exercise from Chapter 3. Begin by performing each exercise you choose once each day. Work up to two repetitions, then three repetitions. Remember to vary your exercises from week to week.

(1) Neck — Upright position (sitting or standing), place palm side of interlaced fingers against forehead. Push forward with your head and resist with your hands (Exercise 1).

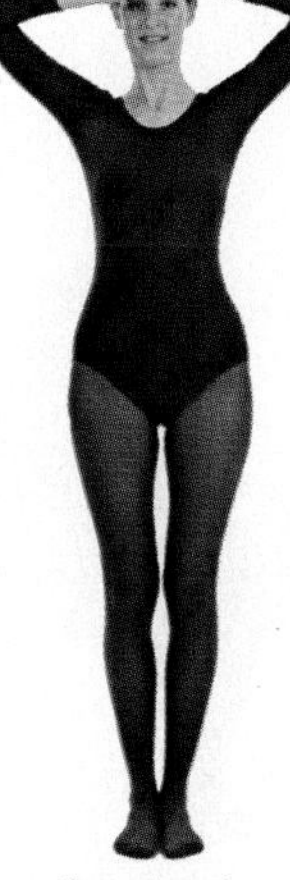

Exercise 1

Photography by Terry Webb

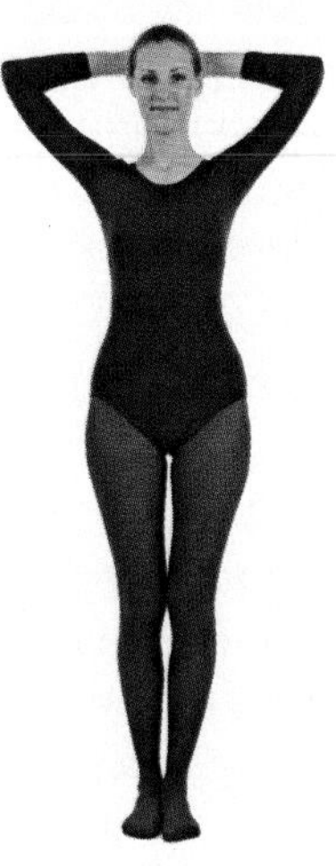

Exercise 2

(2) Neck — Upright position, place palm side of interlaced fingers behind your head. Push head backward resisting with a forward pull of the hands (Exercise 2).

(3) Neck — Upright position, place left hand palm on left side of head. Push with hand and resist with head. Repeat, using right hand and right side (Exercise 3).

(4) Shoulders and Arms — Standing, back to a wall, palms against wall at your side. Keeping arms straight and body still, push against the wall (Exercise 4).

(5) Shoulders and Arms — Sitting, grasp seat of chair at the sides. Pull on chair, resisting with buttocks and legs. Keep your spine straight (Exercise 5).

(6) Shoulders and Arms — Sitting, place palms on chair seat at sides. Keep spine straight and push with hands (Exercise 6).

Exercise 3

Exercise 4

Exercise 5

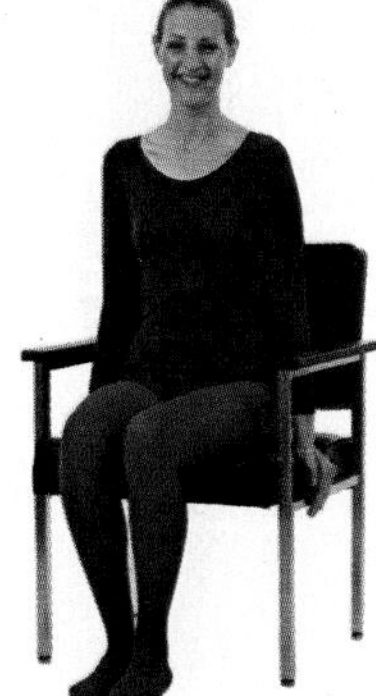

Exercise 6

Photography by Terry Webb

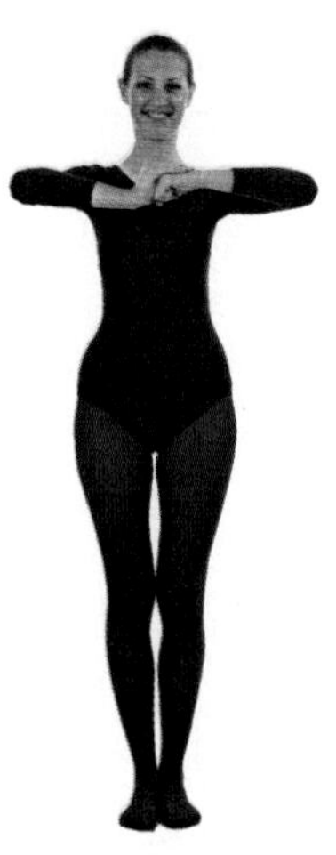

Exercise 7

(7) Shoulders and Arms — Upright position. Extend elbows to side shoulder level. Place fist of one hand in palm of other hand. Push with fist and resist with palm. Reverse hands, and repeat (Exercise 7).

(8) Chest and Arms — Upright position. Hands close to chest, palms clasped together. Push right hand, resist with left. Reverse hands (Exercise 8).

(9) Abdomen — Upright position. Pull stomach in against backbone as far as possible, using only stomach muscles (Exercise 9).

(10) Abdomen — Lying, face-up position, knees bent, feet flat on floor 8 to 10 inches from buttocks, hands on hips. Raise trunk to half-way sitting position and hold (Exercise 10).

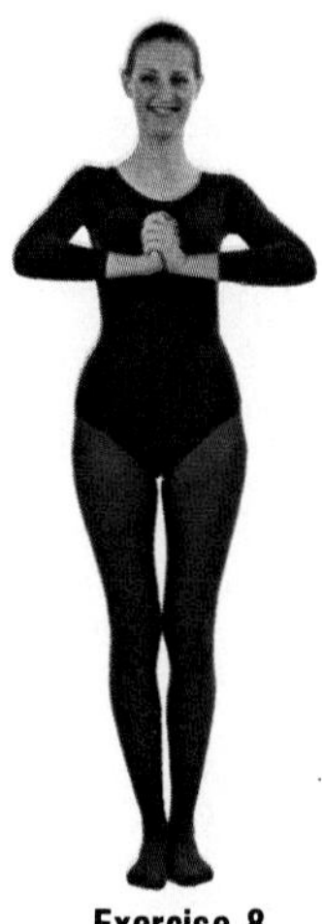

Exercise 8

Exercise 9

Exercise 10

(11) Abdomen and Back — Standing. Heels 3 to 5 inches from wall, back to wall, knees bent slightly. Using gluteal and abdominal muscles, push as much as you can of your back against the wall. As strength is gained, move heels closer to wall and straighten knees. This exercise is your major posture building aid for the pelvic area (Exercise 11).

(12) Back — Lying face-up position. Draw knees to chest, tightening abdominal muscles. Grasp legs below knees and pull them toward head (Exercise 12).

Exercise 11

Exercise 12

Photography by Terry Webb

(13) Back — Prone face-down position. Place lower legs under heavy bed or sofa. Knees straight, push heel against sofa or bed above (Exercise 13).

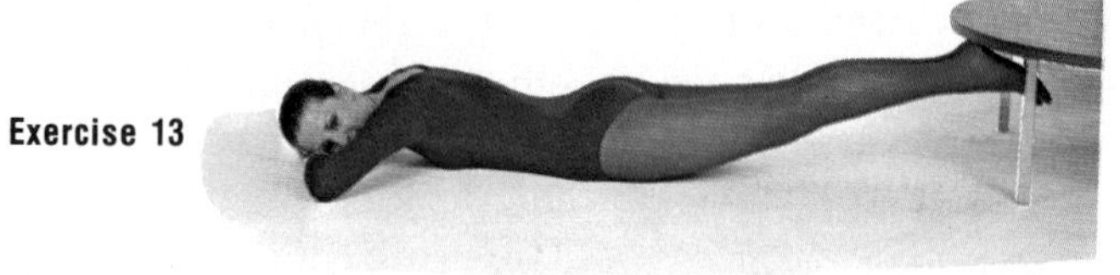

Exercise 13

Photography by Terry Webb

(14) Legs — Sitting position. Knees 10 inches apart. Extend arms, palms against sides of knees. Press with hands; resist with inner thigh muscles (Exercise 14).

(15) Legs — Sitting position. Knees 10 inches apart. Extend arms, palms against inner sides of knees. Press outward with hands; resist with thigh muscles (Exercise 15).

(16) Legs — Sitting position. Ankles pressed against outside of chair legs. Pull legs toward one another against the resistance of the chair (Exercise 16).

(17) Legs — Sitting position. Ankles pressed against inside of chair legs. Push legs away from one another against the resistance of the chair (Exercise 17).

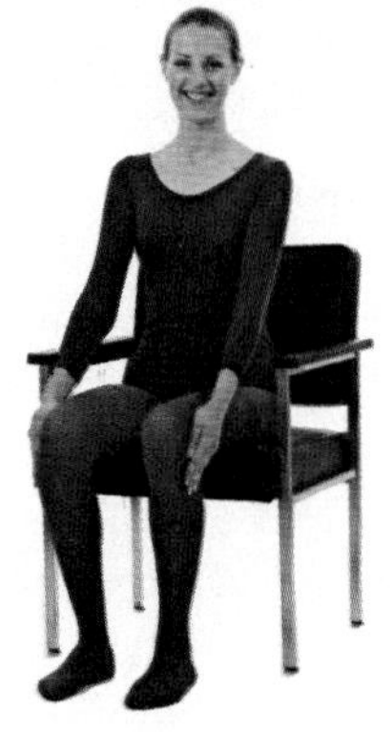

Exercise 14

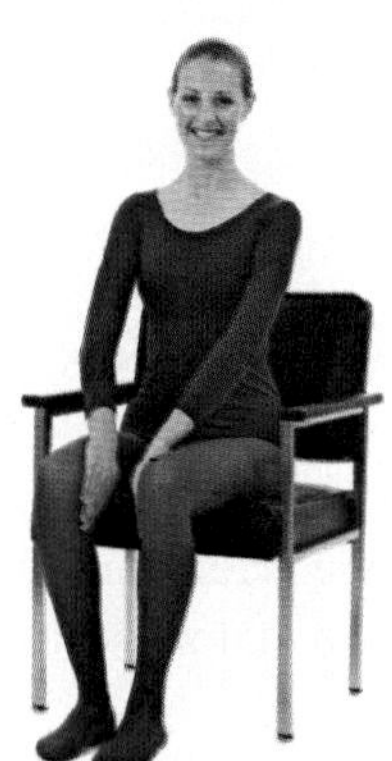

Exercise 15

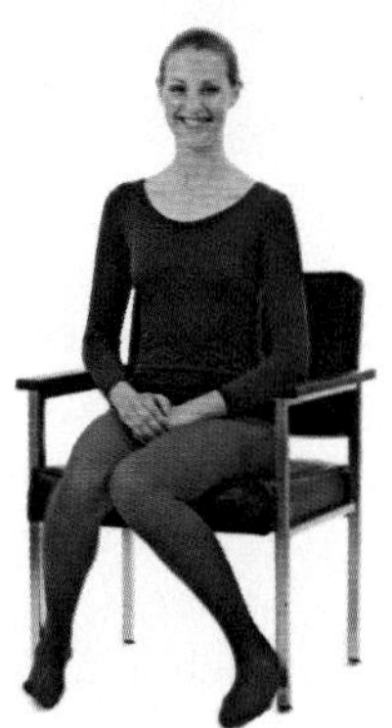

Exercise 16

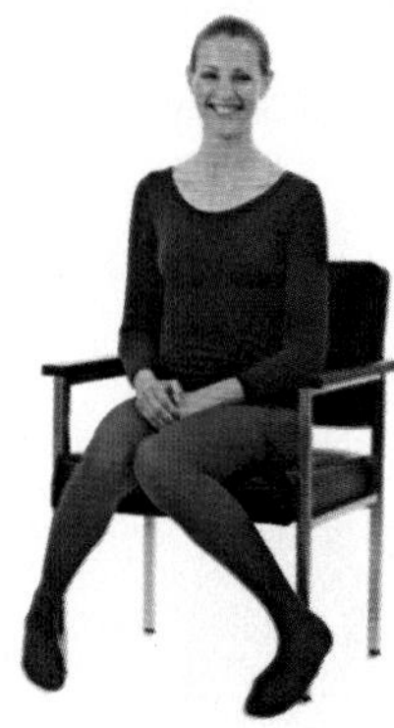

Exercise 17

Photography by Terry Webb

ISOTONIC EXERCISE

A good calisthenic program includes exercises to develop flexibility, coordination, muscular strength and endurance, muscle tone, and good body lines.

Isotonic Principles. To achieve desired results certain principles must be followed.

- Exercise groups equally on each side to insure balanced development and body symmetry.
- Select the appropriate exercise and number of repetitions to meet your specific goals. Strength is best developed by repeating two or three groups of ten to fifteen repetitions; whereas endurance is developed by increasing the repetitions to twenty or twenty-five but performing them without a break. Until you attain some strength, perform only one group of repetitions at a low number. Later, you may increase the number of repetitions per group to attain endurance. Or, you may increase the number of groups to two or three at a low number of repetitions for strength.
- A slow rhythmical pattern is preferable to a jerky pattern. After strength is developed, however, additional resistance can be added by speeding up the pattern somewhat. It must remain smooth, however, to accomplish the strengthening power.
- Correct form is necessary to achieve the desired results. The complete motion of the exercise is necessary to incorporate flexibility into the results. Poor form may strain muscles not designed to perform and may result in poor flexibility in muscles and joints.
- Breathe normally when you exercise. The basic rule is to exhale when you exert and inhale when you relax. This procedure may be reversed, though, when the exercise calls for expanding the rib cage while exerting.
- Plan to exercise regularly. Without regularity, more harm than good may be done. A Monday-Wednesday-Friday schedule is better than a slipshod schedule, but it is not as good as a Monday through Friday schedule. You may find exercise so invigorating and the results so encouraging that taking the weekends off may not be appealing.

Isotonic Exercises. Select from the calisthenic exercises the ones that fit your needs of flexibility, strength, endurance, or body shaping. Aids such as barbells (or homemade substitutes of plastic bottles with handles, filled with sand to a specified weight), slant boards, and weights may be used in many cases to increase the tension of the muscle mass being exercised. Aids usually produce faster results but certainly are not necessary to an effective program. The exercises for flexibility, strength, and body shaping will be similar. Those for endurance will simply be more repetitions so that the muscle increases its ability to withstand longer periods of tension.

(18) Neck — Lying, face-up position with head hanging off a bed or couch. Arms alongside body. Curl chin upward to chest, using neck muscles. Lower slowly. Vary exercise by turning head to right or left and raise head. 15 to 25 (Exercise 18).

(19) Neck and Abdomen — Lying, face-up position, hands at sides. Using tightened abdominal muscles and neck and chest muscles, curl head and shoulders off the floor. Hold this position for five to eight seconds. Return head to floor slowly. 10 to 15 repetitions (Exercise 19).

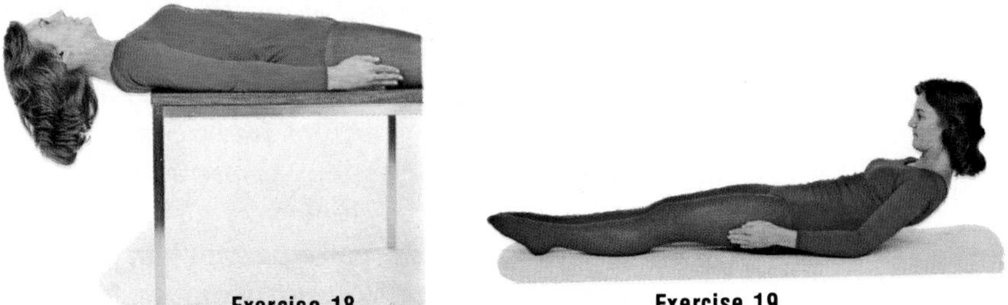

Exercise 18 Exercise 19

Photography by Terry Webb

(20) Shoulders and Chest — Standing position, feet shoulder-width apart, arms at shoulder level extended sideward, palms up. Moving arms upward to the back, make large circles. Turn palms down and reverse the circle. 15 to 25 each way. Weights may be used (Exercise 20).

(21) Shoulders, Arms, and Chest — Prone, face-down position, knees bent, feet raised from the floor, hands palm down placed under shoulders. Push body off floor fully extending arms. Keep spine straight. 10 to 15 repetitions (Exercise 21).

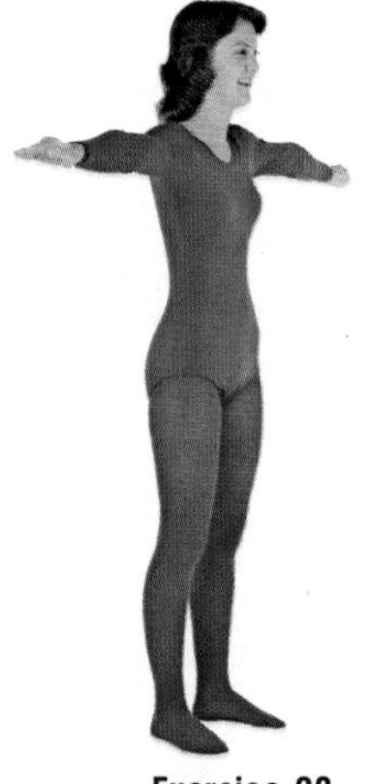

Exercise 20

Exercise 21

Photography by Terry Webb

(22) Abdomen — Lying, face-up position, arms extended sideward, palms down, knees drawn to chest. Keeping knees together, touch left knee to floor to left of your body, bring back to starting position, then touch right knee to floor on right side of body, return to starting position. 10 repetitions (Exercise 22).

(23) Abdomen — Lying, face-up position, legs straight, arms at sides. Keep small of back on floor, bring knees to chest, extend legs upward, return knees to chest, straighten legs on floor. 10 to 15 repetitions (Exercise 23).

Exercise 22 **Exercise 23**

Photography by Terry Webb

(24) Abdomen — Lying, face-up position, legs straight, arms crossed, hands grasping opposite shoulders. Roll up to a sitting position, lower yourself to lying position. 15 to 25 repetitions. This exercise may be varied by changing the arm position: arms may be extended above the head; arms may be above head with fingers laced behind head. Knees may be bent at a 45 degree angle. The more tension placed on the abdominal muscle mass, the quicker the results. Weights may be used in the extended arm position (Exercise 24).

(25) Back — Standing position, feet close together. Slowly bend, reaching with your fingertips to touch your toes. Keep your knees straight. 20 to 25 repetitions. Weights may be used (Exercise 25).

Exercise 24

Exercise 25

Photography by Terry Webb

Exercise 26

(26) Back — Standing position, feet shoulder-width apart, arms extended sideward shoulder level. Bend and twist, touching right hand to left toe. Return to starting position. Bend and twist, touching left hand to right toe. 15 to 25 repetitions. Weights may be used (Exercise 26).

(27) Sides — Standing position, feet shoulder-width apart, hands laced behind your head. Bend sideways as far as you can to the left, return to starting position, bend to the right, return to starting position. 10 to 15 repetitions each side. A weight may be held in the interlaced fingers (Exercise 27).

(28) Side — Lying, face-up position, arms extended sideways shoulder high, palms down, legs straight. Raise right leg to vertical position; keeping it straight, lower it to the floor on your left side. Arms, head, and shoulders are kept flat on the floor. Return leg to starting position. Repeat with left leg to right side. 15 to 20 repetitions (Exercise 28).

(29) Buttocks — Standing position, feet together, one hand on chair at side. Swing leg farthest from chair forward and up. Return leg to starting position, swing leg backward and up. Keep knee straight. Return to starting position. Turn to brace yourself with your opposite hand and repeat for the other leg. 15 to 25 each side (Exercise 29).

Exercise 27

Exercise 28

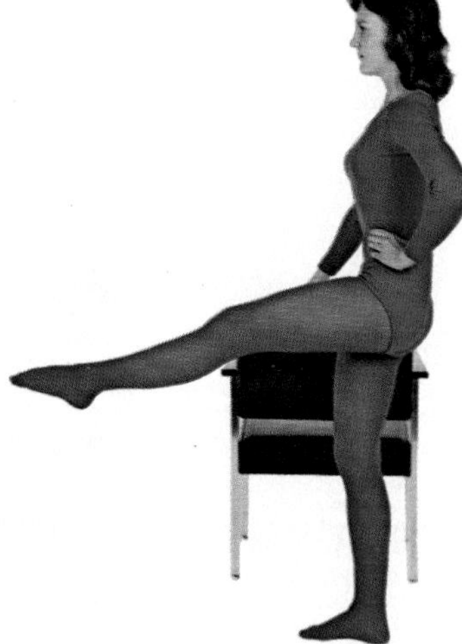

Exercise 29

Photography by Terry Webb

(30) Buttocks — Kneel on all fours (knees and hands). Attempt to touch left knee to head under body, then simultaneously raise head and extend leg back and up, arching back. Return to starting position. Repeat with other leg. 15 to 25 repetitions each leg (Exercise 30).

Exercise 30 *Photography by Terry Webb*

(31) Thighs — Standing position, right hand on chair, feet close together. Swing left leg sideward and up as far as you can. Return to starting position. Repeat 20 times and change legs (Exercise 31).

(32) Thighs — Standing position, feet wider than shoulder-width apart, hands on hips. Stretch to right, bending right leg, extending left leg. Return to starting position. Stretch to left bending left leg, extending right leg. 5 to 15 repetitions each side (Exercise 32).

(33) Thighs — Sitting position, leaning backward, bracing with hands behind, palms down, knees bent, feet lifted from floor. Alternately straighten each leg and return to bent position. 15 to 25 repetitions each leg (Exercise 33).

Photography by Terry Webb

Exercise 31

Exercise 32

Exercise 33

(34) Legs — Lying in side position, head resting on right hand, right elbow on floor. Lift left leg sideward as high as you can. Lower to starting position. Repeat 20 to 30 times each leg (Exercise 34).

(35) Calves — Standing position, feet together, hands on hips. Raise body on toes. Lower to starting position. This exercise can be varied by standing with the toe half of the foot on a thick book and alternately lowering and raising from the level position. 20 to 25 repetitions (Exercise 35).

(36) Calves — Standing position, hands on hips, knees half bent. Raise heels from the floor, balancing weight on toes. Lower heels to starting position. 15 to 20 repetitions (Exercise 36).

(37) Feet — Sitting position, legs extended, hands palm down behind body to brace you. Point toes as far as possible, return to upright position, curl toes toward body as far as possible, return to upright position. 15 to 20 repetitions (Exercise 37).

(38) Feet — Sitting position, feet resting on towel. Alternately with each foot pick up towel with toes and hold for 5 to 8 seconds. Release towel. 15 to 20 repetitions (Exercise 38).

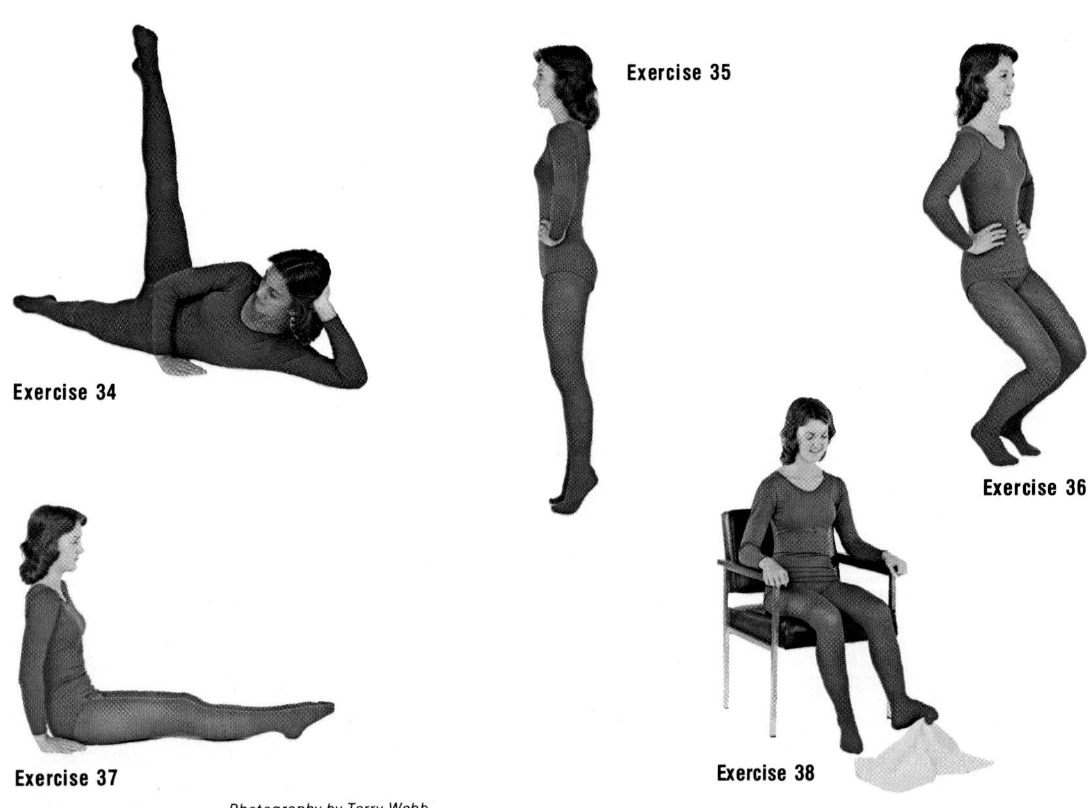

Exercise 35

Exercise 34

Exercise 36

Exercise 37

Exercise 38

Photography by Terry Webb

Any of the isotonic exercises performed with the hands and arms free may be done with weights for added tension on the muscles. Use either barbells, dumbells, or homemade weights. Plastic bottles, either of a curved shape or with a handle, may be filled with sand to a two and one-half to five pound weight and used effectively.

YOUR EXERCISE

The key to achieving results with exercise is to choose correctly the ones you need and to perform them faithfully. Go back to your tests of strength (graceful, slow motion movements) and flexibility and to your shape analysis. Note exactly what you want to improve and the shape you want to achieve. Select the appropriate exercises for those goals.

Remember that muscle strengthening (toning) can be done either with isometrics or isotonics. The more resistance you place on a muscle, the quicker results you will get. Therefore, the use of weights may provide faster results than you will get without them. The isometric form of exercise often is good to use at your desk or while you are watching television. It is a good resolution to make to yourself that for any thirty-minute period you spend in a sitting or lying position watching television, three minutes will be spent simultaneously in isometric or isotonic exercise. Concentrate in every case on putting tension in exactly the spot where you have determined there was inflexibility or weakness.

Exercise slowly. The longer tension is applied to the muscles being conditioned, the more conditioning effect takes place. When you bend, for example, bend slowly, forcing the weak muscles in your back and legs to control your body as you bend. In raising your body, require the same slow tension of the muscles in the opposite direction.

Stretching exercises improve both static and dynamic flexibility. A slow to moderate pace is required for both. Quick or jerky movements can negate the effect of the exercise and can pull muscles and possibly tear them.

Aids. Many people like to exercise to music. The rhythm of the music contributes to the rhythm of the exercise. Records to exercise by have been put on the market and you may find them useful.

Joining a television performer in an exercise show is often a good way to exercise. The encouraging words the performer gives you tend to spur you on when you are tired. The regularity of the show helps to keep you exercising regularly.

Non-Aids. Because exercise takes some energy and many people resist expending energy, short-cuts are constantly being advertised and sold. Most of the time they do more for your morale than for your body. Machines that shake, rub, bounce, and heat your body while you relax will do very little to turn fatty tissue to muscle tissue. They neither strengthen muscles nor make you flexible. Mainly, they increase surface circulation somewhat but not as well as recreative exercise does. The roughness of some machines can bruise and break small vessels causing unsightly discolorations in your skin.

A massage can be very relaxing to the muscles and provide stimulation to the skin. Pounding and kneading tissue, though, does not build strength and flexibility unless there is corresponding resistance, which is not provided during massage.

Sauna baths can be very relaxing and can produce perspiring, which temporarily lowers body weight by dehydrating it. (A sponge without water weighs less than one with water.) Saunas have been shown to produce side effects, however, that may be damaging to the heart if the baths are taken immediately after exercise.

Steam baths and whirlpools both can be very relaxing and are good for that purpose. They do not do any muscle building or body shaping.

SUMMARY

You can attain the body shape and movement you want. It is a matter of using what you know about nutrition and exercise. Achieving a beautifully balanced body is a matter of developing habits that benefit you throughout your life. Make your exercise plans now and incorporate them into your daily schedule. Within a month, you will notice a difference.

Understanding Balance

1. Why do attractive people have an "edge" in most competitive situations?
2. What are some ways to benefit yourself with exercise?
3. How does exercise contribute to graceful movement?
4. How can you become more efficient with exercise?
5. What does the center of gravity have to do with your posture?
6. How does exercise affect your level of energy?
7. How do isotonic exercises differ from isometric ones?

Chapter 5

Posture

The word *posture* refers to the various body positions you assume in performing everyday activities. The way you carry yourself affects your well-being in many ways. Many vague aches and pains are caused by requiring muscles to support parts of your body which they were not designed to support. Bones and joints can be permanently deformed by poor posture. The internal workings of your cardiovascular, respiratory, and digestive systems, among others, depend upon the proper functioning of the muscular and skeletal system in keeping your body in appropriate alignment.

Beyond the physiological systems, there are some aesthetic considerations that affect your success. Graceful presentation of your form is one of the most important parts of your personal development program. It gives you a feeling of poise and control that reflects to others your confidence in your personal worth, and it frequently communicates to others your feelings about them.

Basic Postures

Your body functions with both static and dynamic postures. The postures you assume in movement are dynamic; the ones without movement are static. The body positions that you use for standing, walking, sitting, sleeping, bending, pushing, pulling, and reaching are postures that depend upon your skeletal and muscular systems.

IMPORTANCE OF POSTURE

These intricate systems are designed to function in a particular way and that is where the problem frequently lies. If you have "just grown" without real direction or information about your posture beyond "stand up straight" admonitions from parents and teachers, you have not had real motivation to develop good posture. If any reason at all was given, it was usually for the "sake of beauty."

While it is true that good posture is essential to a well-groomed, well-presented form, there are other very important reasons to "stand up straight." Your health and your freedom from pain are two important reasons.

Because the muscles and bones are designed to function a particular way, they suffer strain and sometimes permanent disfigurement when they are continually misused. Poor posture can result in low back pain, strained muscles, permanently deformed shoulders, and curved spines.

If you have developed good posture already, you are unique. Most of us, without direction, assume whatever posture is most comfortable at the moment with little regard for the design of our bodies. These postures, be they good or bad, are habit forming. If you have somehow developed good ones, congratulate yourself. If you have developed bad ones, change them and retrain yourself before you do irreversible damage to your body.

The muscular and skeletal machinery of your body properly works in such a way as to provide for unobstructed internal functioning with little strain, tension, or possibility of injury. This superb design provides for efficient mechanical functioning; it also provides for beauty in form and movement. The presentation of your form in all postures is important not only to your health but to your self-image and the image others have of you.

STANDING POSTURE

Standing posture is a basic one and it influences all other postures. There is a center of gravity for your body in every posture. That center is the point at which the entire weight of your body is concentrated so that, if supported at this point, the body will remain in equilibrium in any position. That center, when your body is properly aligned in a standing position, passes through the midpoint of your body. Specifically, from a side view, this imaginary straight line passes through the earlobe, center of the shoulder, center of the hip, slightly to the back of the kneecap, and slightly to the front of the ankle bone (Illustration 5-1).

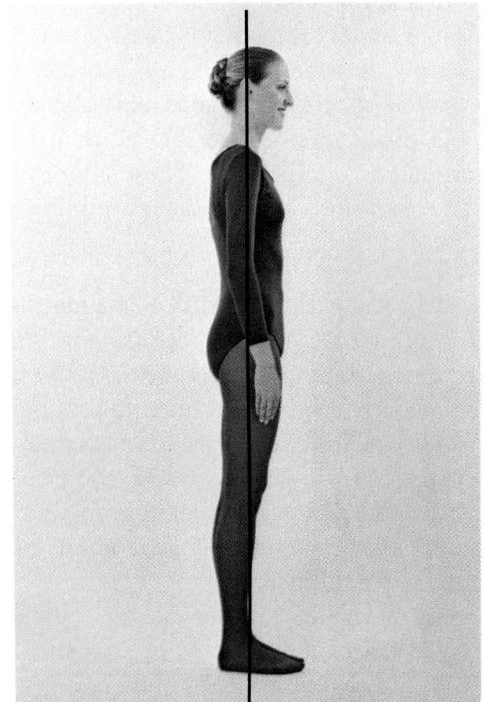

ILLUS. 5-1 *A line extended from your earlobe straight to the floor should pass through the center of your shoulder, the center of your hip, slightly to the back of your kneecap, and slightly to the front of your ankle bone.*

Photography by Terry Webb

Check Alignment. You can check that alignment by taping a string to the top center of your full-length mirror and allowing the string to fall freely, making a straight line through the center of the mirror. Align your body by positioning your earlobe along the line. Ask someone to help you position yourself and to evaluate your body alignment. From the front view, points to check are:

(1) Head and neck centered between your shoulders with shoulders relaxed and even.

(2) Pelvis and hipbones even and centered squarely over your feet.

(3) Feet pointed straight ahead.

From the side view, points to check are:

(1) Chin parallel to the floor.

(2) Shoulders neither too far back nor too far forward.

(3) Abdomen flat.

(4) Small of the back straight.

(5) Buttocks tucked under.

(6) Knees straight but relaxed.

If a single point is out of alignment, some other part of the body will disalign itself to make it easier for you to maintain your equilibrium. For example, if your buttocks are protruding abnormally, your stomach will protrude to maintain your equilibrium. If your head is held forward, some other part — probably your upper back — will be curved out abnormally to compensate. These abnormalities look unattractive, and they will strain muscles and disfigure bone structure, eventually causing you pain.

Correct Alignment. To assume the correct posture, develop a mental routine that you can perform anytime with or without a mirror. If you are strengthening your muscles with regular exercise, the correct posture will be easy to maintain once you assume it.

Unless you have skeletal malformations from too many years of poor posture or from genetic defect, good body alignment is not only possible; it is preferable to any other alignment.

(1) With your feet slightly apart, distribute your weight equally between them.
(2) Stand as "tall" as you can with comfort.
(3) Check your eyes to be sure they are focused neither up nor down, so that your head is level.
(4) Straighten your neck so that the chin is directly over the "u" shaped notch of the breastbone at the base of your neck.
(5) Shoulders are down and slightly back although not abnormally so.
(6) Straighten your backbone at the waist by tucking your buttocks slightly under and pulling your stomach up and in.
(7) Give your knees a little flexion so that they are not locked.
(8) Now, concentrate on how correct body alignment feels. Most of the time you must depend on how it "feels" for alignment since a mirror usually is not available. Also, the more comfortable you become with this aligned feeling, the more often you will notice when it is lacking.

Maintain Alignment. Part of the problem of body alignment is that of forgetting and falling back into bad habits. Some reminders you work out for yourself will help until correct alignment becomes more natural to you than misalignment. Some reminders that have worked for others are to mentally check posture:

(1) Every time you check the time of day.
(2) Every time you assume a new body position.
(3) Every time you speak.
(4) Every time you perform any other regular activity.

Others put "posture" signs on their home mirrors, inside desk drawers, on fronts of file cabinets, on the refrigerator, on the car mirror, and on other places that will serve as reminders. The best reminder, of course, is your body, which, through conscious practice, becomes accustomed to good alignment and feels uncomfortable when it is misaligned.

Placement of Feet. Maintain good alignment from your hip joints upward, but turn now to polishing the static standing posture of your form by changing your leg and foot positions to present a graceful line. The position of your legs and the slight turn of your head while keeping your torso and neck aligned properly can give you a graceful presentation. The idea is to avoid showing the "broad" view of a full front presentation. By rearranging your foot position and your face direction you can present yourself from the "thinner" appearing profile view.

Actually, only one foot is moved. The arch of one foot is placed against the heel of the other. In bringing the foot back, the body is slightly turned so that there is more of a profile view than a broader front view. You can vary the relationship of the arch to the heel to present your legs more attractively by placing the heel forward closer to the ball of the foot or by moving the heel back closer to the other heel. If your legs are very thin, position your foot so that most of the width of both legs is visible from the side view. If they are heavy, position your feet so that only the width of one leg shows.

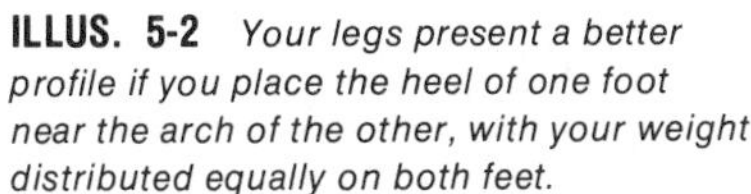

ILLUS. 5-2 *Your legs present a better profile if you place the heel of one foot near the arch of the other, with your weight distributed equally on both feet.*

Photography by Terry Webb

Arm and Hand Positions. The way you position your arms and hands when you stand can affect the profile you present and influence whether you appear plump or svelte. If your elbows are held so that there is no space between them and your waist, your waist looks thicker. If you fold your arms across your waist with hands resting on your opposite upper arms, fingers pointing upward, the look is more graceful than if the hands are tucked inside your upper arms next to your body (Illustration 5-3). If you clasp your hands in front of you, either clasp them high enough so that space appears between your elbows and waist or low enough so that the width of your arms appears mostly in front of your body instead of alongside it. If your arms are hanging down loosely at your sides, place them slightly in front of your body or slightly behind your hips so that they do not add width to your hips. When your hands are clasped, make it loosely. To clasp tightly makes you appear tense. Fingers interlaced loosely are comfortable and attractive. Hands on your hips can present a comfortable alternative. You will appear slimmer if you place your hands so that the fingers are in back and the thumbs are in front. The wrist is not sharply angled in the thumb-front position.

Exercises for Alignment. If you are unable to assume and maintain the correct posture, determine the exact point of deviation and analyze the reason for misalignment.

Your head should be erect, with your chin centered over the notch in your breastbone. The back of the neck should be straight, not curved or pushed forward. Your chin should be parallel with the floor. If your head is not held erect, you may be holding it forward (in a snapping turtle position) because the muscles in your neck are not strong enough to hold it erect. Exercises 1, 2, 3, 18, and 19, Chapter 4, will aid you in developing enough strength and flexibility to hold your head properly.

Your shoulders should be down, slightly back, and in line with your hips. If you have a curved upper back so that your shoulders slump forward and downward, the muscles in your chest probably are contracted and those in your back are stretched. Exercises 4, 5, 6, 7, 8, 20, and 21 will aid you in correcting this unattractive slump.

Your diaphragm should be pulled up out of your waist, leaving the abdomen flat. The small of your back should be flat, and the buttocks should be tucked under slightly. If your stomach protrudes and the spine curves at the small of your back, your back muscles have contracted and the stomach muscles are stretched. Exercises 9, 10, 11, 12, 13, 23, 24, 25, and 26 are designed to correct this particular problem. Exercise 11 is the most popular one for correcting the curved spine, and it does an especially effective job.

Legs should be straight with knees slightly flexed, not visibly bent. As you walk, leg muscle development or lack of it will be obvious.

ILLUS. 5-3 *If you fold your arms, keep your fingers pointing upward.*

Photography by Terry Webb

WALKING POSTURE

The posture developed for standing applies to walking. The straight line from your earlobe through your hips remains the same. Your legs simply swing from the hip joint in the way they were particularly designed to do. The arms should swing gracefully at your sides to maintain that delicately balanced center of gravity as your legs alternately swing forward.

Alignment and Movement. The idea is to stand tall, tuck buttocks under, keep shoulders low, take steps about as long as your feet are, and swing the arm of the same side back approximately the same distance as the length of the step. The swing of the arm is very gentle — not stiff or awkward. In fact, it should hardly be noticeable. The knees are kept slightly flexed. If they are stiff, the weight of the body is bounced on the cartilage of the knee, which eventually causes pain. If they are slightly flexed, the "bend" cushions the weight of the body, not allowing it to destroy the structure of the knee. A stiffened knee also will give a bouncing walk that jars your head. "Smooth" is the key word. If you glide along smoothly, your walk is correct. If your head or body is "bobbing," something is wrong.

Correct Walking Posture. Some of the common problems occurring in walking are:

(1) Feet that point out or in. Frequently this causes a "fanny wiggle" that is unattractive and is not healthy for the spine.

(2) A stride that is too long, causing the head and body to bob up and down at the beginning and middle of the long step.

(3) Feet kept too far apart. This looks like the walker is straddling a ditch and makes for an uncomfortable bounce of the torso. The feet should pass closely together, not touching but passing very closely, maintaining parallel lines.

(4) Too much bend in the knee, sometimes accompanied by slumped shoulders, giving the appearance of ancient ancestors who swung from trees.

(5) Heavy steps caused by striking the foot to the floor very hard as if to make an imprint in the floor. Actually, the heel should gently strike the floor first, followed by a roll to the ball of the foot from which you push off for the next step. The gentleness of the footwork provides the basis for a gliding motion of the upper body.

(6) Those who look like they are walking a tightrope, placing one foot directly in front of the other instead of maintaining parallel lines.

(7) Tiny steps that appear to be mincing the floor as the walker moves along.

(8) Hands clutched tightly and jerked back and forth. Your hands should be relaxed with fingers slightly curved. The swing of the arm should be from the shoulder in a graceful arc.

(9) Leaning the body backward or forward with each step. The chin should remain level as your body moves forward with a smooth, gliding motion.

Exercises for providing for a more graceful walk are designed to develop strength in the thigh muscles and flexibility in the hip, knee, ankle, and foot joints. Exercises 14, 15, 31, 32, 33, 34, 35, 36, 37, and 38 will help you develop the strength and agility you need.

SITTING POSTURES

There is a difference between collapsing in a chair and sitting in one. The tendency is to brace body weight with your hands and wrists on the arms of the chair and drop the buttocks into the chair. Indeed, that is practically the only way a seat can be taken if the thigh muscles are weak. It amounts to collapsing and is hard on the furniture as well as the person. Graceful, it is not!

Graceful Sitting. The most graceful way to sit is to approach the chair from an angle and walk closely enough to touch one leg to the edge of the seat of the chair. Then turn, allowing the back of your leg to touch the chair, placing one foot slightly in front of the other so that the magical center of gravity won't fail as you propel your body into the sitting position. Slowly bend only at the hip and knee joints. Keep the upper part of the body straight. Use your hands and arms if necessary only to guide yourself into the seat of the chair if the chair has arms. Otherwise, the hands and arms will not be needed during this maneuver. If you do not turn your head to look at the seat of the chair as you sit, your balance will be easier to maintain and you will appear less awkward and more sure of yourself. Allow the leg that is touching the chair to be your guide. Using this procedure usually places your buttocks on the front part of the seat of the chair. When your weight is on the chair, use your hands on the chair seat to gently lift yourself back into the chair so that the back of the chair braces your back. It is normal to lean forward when you talk from a sitting position, but it must be done from the hip joints, not the waist. A slumped, curved spine results from leaning from the waist.

Good sitting posture maintains the same alignment from the hips to the head as good standing posture. You should be sure that you sit well back into the chair, keeping your spine straight but allowing the back of the chair to support your back. Your thighs should rest on the seat of the chair almost to the bend of the knee, and your feet should rest comfortably on the floor.

The structure of the chair is important. A chair that has a seat too deep to allow you to sit back and bend your knees simultaneously will be uncomfortable. When you sit in such a chair, sit forward far enough to allow your legs to bend naturally from the knee; but concentrate on keeping your hips, back, and head aligned as if you were standing. This kind of chair simply will not support your back properly.

Leg Positions. Your legs may be crossed at the ankles and positioned slightly to the side of the body on the side of the front foot (Illustration 5-4, next page). If they are crossed near the knee, it must be well above the knee (Illustration 5-5). This is impossible if your legs are too fat or if the chair is so deep that the top leg cannot hang comfortably. When legs are crossed at the knee, the ankles are kept close together but not wound around one another. If the chair is low enough, the crossed legs may be moved slightly to the side of the lower leg. An exaggerated side placement is not pleasing and can throw the upper part of the body out of alignment.

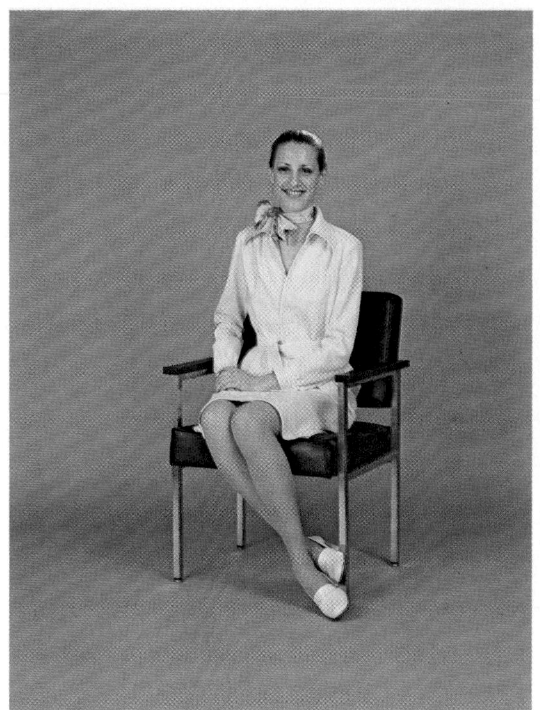

Photography by Terry Webb

ILLUS. 5-4 *Crossing your legs at the ankle and sweeping them to the side presents a graceful posture.*

ILLUS. 5-5 *If you cross your legs at the knees, keep your ankles close together.*

One of the most comfortable positions is to place feet, legs not crossed, flat on the floor, one foot slightly in front of the other, or to position feet with the arch of one near the heel of the other similar to the standing position (Illustration 5-6). However legs are arranged, it is of utmost importance to keep the head-through-the-hip area aligned.

Hand Positions. The position of your hands has nothing to do with bone and muscle support and alignment, but their placement can affect the poise you reflect. Hands are always held well back in your lap. Graceful positions include:

(1) Cupping your hands in your lap.
(2) Crossing your arms with fingers pointing upward along opposite upper arms.
(3) One hand palm up in your lap, the other hanging loosely from the arm of the chair.
(4) One hand palm up in your lap, the other resting on the chair seat, palm down.

Photography by Terry Webb

ILLUS. 5-6 *Placing the heel of one foot near the arch of the other, with the knees held close together, is a graceful way to sit.*

Graceful Rising. Using your hands on the seat of the chair, lift yourself to the front edge of the seat of the chair. With one foot in front of the other, use your leg muscles to lift yourself from the chair, keeping your back and head aligned. It is tempting simply to pump your arms on the arms of the chair to raise yourself. This maneuver looks more like a shoulder-building exercise than the graceful movement of a poised person. Using your leg muscles instead of your shoulder muscles to rise from a chair insures sure footing and control when you begin to move.

Correcting Sitting Posture. Posture as you sit is a habit you've formed like any other. These poor habits can be changed. Some of the common problems with sitting posture are:

(1) Bending at the waist as you sit. It is infinitely better if you bend only where you have joints designed for such bending. In this case those joints are the hip joints, where the thighs of your legs are joined to your torso. Keep the waist straight so that the spine is not bent out of shape as you sit.

(2) Slumping the shoulders. Shoulders should be kept level and in line with the hips. Slumping forward stretches the muscles in your back and contracts those in the chest.
(3) Crossing legs too close to the knees. Legs, if they are to be crossed at all near the knees, should be crossed above the knees to allow for proper circulation in the lower leg. The back of the knee should not be pressed hard against the thigh of the other leg because to do so will restrict circulation. Crossing the legs higher not only presents a more attractive view of your legs, but it puts much less strain on the cardiovascular activity in the leg.
(4) Letting knees fall apart when legs are crossed at the ankles. Sitting with your knees apart is unattractive from an aesthetic point of view. It gives your entire body the illusion of being wider than it is. If you stand or sit with knees apart, you widen the line of your body. When you cross your legs at the ankle, sweep your feet to one side so that your knees fall together naturally. Ankle-crossed legs are always easier to sweep to the side of the forward foot.
(5) Sitting with feet side by side. Although this posture will not harm your body, it is not as attractive as a slight variation. Place the arch of the back foot against the heel of the other, turning the back foot slightly so that the toes are angled slightly outward.

Sitting at a Desk. If you work at a job that necessitates sitting at a desk for long periods of time, concentrate on keeping the spine straight and the legs free so that good circulation occurs. Sitting on your legs restricts circulation and places the hip joint out of position. Be sure that your desk chair is at a height so that both feet rest on the floor with some freedom of the knees. Be sure that you can sit completely back in the chair so that the back of the chair supports your back and yet your knees bend easily at the front edge of the chair seat. For most people, an adjustable back on a desk chair is most comfortable when placed near the small of the back or at the waist. Placed higher, it seems to encourage waist bending which, of course, eventually results in low back pain.

If you find it necessary to sit for long periods of time at a desk, move about somewhat each hour to relieve any tension that may be building in your muscles. Some relaxing movements are:
(1) Dropping your chin to your chest and rolling your head from one side to the other, then making a complete circle of it.
(2) Lifting your shoulders alternately and making circles with them as you dangle your arms at your sides.
(3) Stretching your legs out under your desk and flexing your toes and feet, pointing them forward then backward.

(4) Pushing back your waist and the small of your back, humping them. Then push them forward arching your back a few times. Carefully return to the straight position to continue your work.

SLEEP POSTURE

Normally, one is not concerned about body alignment during sleep. You can, however, achieve more restful sleep if you pay a little attention to the way you position yourself as you recline. Probably the position that provides for the greatest muscle relaxation is reclining on your back with your head slightly elevated but not enough to strain or stretch your back neck muscles. Arms are positioned below the shoulders but relaxed. The lower back is not arched, but is kept very near the mattress. If the knees are slightly elevated the back will be easier to keep straight. A small pillow placed under the knees usually is very comfortable and provides the balance needed for straightening your back.

If you choose to sleep on your side, you can relieve the tension on your back by bringing the knees up slightly, either one or both of them. Also, you can avoid pain in your arm by making sure you do not put pressure on the upper part of it by pressing it under your body. Bringing both your arms to the front of your body in the side position usually allows for better balance of the body.

If you sleep on your stomach, you can keep your back straight by placing the small pillow under your stomach. The same small pillow used for your knees when you sleep on your back can be used for your stomach when you sleep on your stomach.

The more relaxed and comfortable you are when you fall asleep, the less you are apt to move during sleep, and the more refreshing will be the rest. Determine a comfortable position for yourself that is also good for your body alignment, and try it for a while. You should have fewer aches and pains in the mornings than usual.

BENDING AND LIFTING POSTURE

The same good body alignment you have developed for walking and sitting serves you in bending and lifting. The idea is to keep the line straight from your ear lobe through the center of your hips. In bending, you bend only the hip, knee, ankle, and foot joints. The back is kept straight (Illustration 5-7, next page).

The position of the feet is usually with one slightly in front of the other, for additional balance and support. Such foot placement causes one knee to be bent at an angle slightly higher than the other. The item you are lifting can then be lifted to knee height and simply held as you

ILLUS. 5-7 *When you bend, keep your back straight.*

Photography by Terry Webb

straighten your legs. Little strain is put on the back if it is kept straight at all times during the bending and lifting process.

If you are reaching up over your head, you will have more balance if one foot is slightly in front of the other rather than both side by side. Then if the object you are lifting shifts slightly to the back, you will have the back foot to brace yourself, preventing strained muscles and a possible accident.

CARRYING OBJECTS

When you carry any object, the closer you hold it to your body, the more balanced you will be while carrying it. If the object is heavy and is to be carried at your side, it may be necessary to lean slightly in the opposite direction for balance. Avoid trying to carry objects that are heavy enough to necessitate your leaning so much that it is visible. Such strain on your spine can cause pain and damage.

Try to avoid carrying items in front of your body. Not only are they cumbersome, but the temptation to curve your spine is greater. Back sprains and "slipped discs" are very often the result of carrying items improperly.

PUSHING AND PULLING

If you find it necessary to pull or push a table or desk slightly, use the same good body alignment you have developed for other activities. Keep your spine straight, and use the leg muscles to push or pull. The hip joint and leg muscles are infinitely better equipped to handle pushing and pulling motions than are your back muscles and spinal joints.

ASCENDING AND DESCENDING STAIRS

Ascending and descending stairs require the same head-to-hip alignment as walking does. The common alignment fault is to lean forward in ascending and to lean backward in descending. Your balance will be better if you keep your chin parallel to the floor and use your legs, bending at the hip and knees to propel yourself up and down stairs. To confirm your step, use your heel as you descend so that it will not be necessary to look down as you step. Use your toe as you ascend.

ILLUS. 5-8 *Lean neither forward nor backward when you ascend and descend stairs.*

Photography by Terry Webb

It is always a good idea to use the bannister. It should be used, however, more as a steadying agent than as a hoist for your body. Depend upon your legs to move your body, and use your arms and hands on the bannister only to steady yourself.

Polished Postures

Health, grace, and good form have been your concerns in developing basic postures. Polished postures are merely simple ways of doing things that might otherwise be awkward and of communicating your feelings. You can add to your poise and graceful movement by polishing your basic posture.

ENTERING AND EXITING

Opening a door, entering a room or car, and closing the door behind you can be accomplished, of course, in several ways. There is a way to perform each of those activities, though, that adds to your graceful movement rather than detracting from it.

Rooms. Grasp the door handle with the hand on the side closest to the hinges of the door. Open it wide enough to walk through face front. As you pass through the doorway and past the door itself, reach behind with your other hand to grasp the handle on the other side of the door and shut it. This procedure does not require any cumbersome turns that place your back to the direction in which you are moving.

Cars. Again, with the hand on the same side of your body as the hinges on the door, grasp the handle and open the door wide enough to allow you to stand close to the seat of the car. Face away from the seat. Using the back of your leg to guide you, lower yourself on to the car seat gracefully. When you are seated, swing your legs, keeping them together, into the car. Close the door.

PUTTING ON AND TAKING OFF

If you've ever gotten tangled up in your coat getting it on or off, you have probably wondered if there wasn't a better way. The easiest way, of course, is to get someone to help you. That isn't always convenient, though, and you can do it yourself gracefully.

Because you appear to be floundering if you sling your arms up and around, try to keep them quietly close to your body.

Putting On. Grasp your coat at the collar in one hand, holding it so that you can place your other arm in the sleeve. Release the collar as you get one side of the coat on, and reach down and around your waist (rather than up over your shoulder) to reach your coat behind you. Find the arm hole and push your arm through it as you lift your coat up on your shoulders.

Taking Off. Reach down behind your waist with both hands and grasp the sleeve of one arm with the other hand and pull the sleeve off your arm. Bring the free arm around to the front. Keeping your hand at about waist level, grasp both sleeves and remove the other one. As the coat slides off your arm, grasp the collar with your free hand and fold the sleeves neatly along one side of the front of the coat. If you are planning to carry rather than hang up your coat, fold it over your arm at the waist, keeping the sleeves tucked in.

CARRYING HAND ARTICLES

Women carry handbags most of the time, and often have other items to carry as well. The center of gravity is easiest to maintain if items are carried alongside you close to your body. Items with handles, such as handbags and brief cases, are easily held at your side. Usually the lower you carry them, the easier it is to maintain good posture. Try to avoid tucking items between your upper arm and your body or holding them in front of your body. One way tends to make you curve your body sideways; the other may make you slump your shoulders.

SENDING MESSAGES

The carriage of your body and the posture you assume are sending messages to people around you. The study of such communication is called *kinesics* or commonly, "body language." Although kinesics includes communication by facial expression, use of body space, and hand gestures as well as posture, only those messages related to your posture are discussed at this point.

The theory of kinesics is that each of us positions our body in such a way as to reflect how we feel at a given time. We change our positions to reflect changing feelings during an encounter. The key to using kinesics is to understand what various body positions indicate and what a change in body positions means in terms of a person's feeling defensive, open, suspicious, reassured, ready, cooperative, frustrated, confident, nervous, or bored. One value in learning about kinesics is in being able to analyze the messages you are sending to others by the way you position your body in static and dynamic postures. You can change these postures, if desirable, to reflect what you want others to "see" you saying. Another value is in developing your ability to interpret how others are responding to you.

The generalizations regarding the interpretations of posture are not always true because a person may be influenced at any given time by several factors outside his personal feelings about those around him. A woman may fold her arms occasionally, for example, not because she is defensive about what is being said to her, as it is normally interpreted, but because her arms are cold and that position makes her feel warmer. However, close observation of the positions you rather unconsciously assume are more often than not accurate indications of how you feel.

Overall Posture. Generally speaking, an alert, erect posture is interpreted as meaning you are interested, ready, and cooperative — that the persons with whom you are communicating deserve your utmost attention. A casual posture indicates comfort and enjoyment — that the persons with whom you are communicating may be taken for granted. Beyond the general terms of alert and casual, more specific indications of feeling are evidenced by parts of the posture.

Walking. The length of your stride in walking and the pace at which you walk are often indicative of various emotional states. Generally, the lighter the step and the quicker the pace, the happier the person is and the more ready she is to pursue her goals. The person who walks with lead in her shoes is perceived as sulky, and slow to move in making decisions. A person who half-heartedly shuffles along appears to be dejected, without goals or direction. A person who walks along with her hands in her pockets is believed to be secretive and critical. One who places her hands clasped behind her back reflects pensiveness, and one who walks along swinging her hands more than is normal communicates self-satisfaction and pompousness.

Hands. Your hands can indicate openness and sincerity when they are open and guilt, suspiciousness, and tenseness when they are clenched. When you rest your chin on your hand and your expressions are alert, you indicate that you are evaluating; but when you rest your chin on your hand and your expressions are bland, you indicate boredom. When you touch only part of your face with a finger, you indicate doubt. Moving your hand to the back of your neck or to scratch your head (when it doesn't itch) indicates frustration. Placing the finger tips of your hands together indicates confidence to the point of smugness, and rubbing your hands together shows expectation.

Arms and Legs. When your arms are crossed and your hands are clenched around the opposite upper arm you indicate defensiveness. Tightly clenched fists indicate tenseness and difficulty in relating to other people. However, when the hands are resting relaxed with the fingers pointing upward, the position may reflect a change of position only for the comfort of it.

Crossed ankles that are locked against the chair leg indicate a defensive holding back. Tightly crossing your legs at the knees with your arms across your waist indicates that you are closed to communication.

ILLUS. 5-9 *The quickness and lightness of your step may tell something about your emotional state.*

Photography by Terry Webb

Photography by Terry Webb

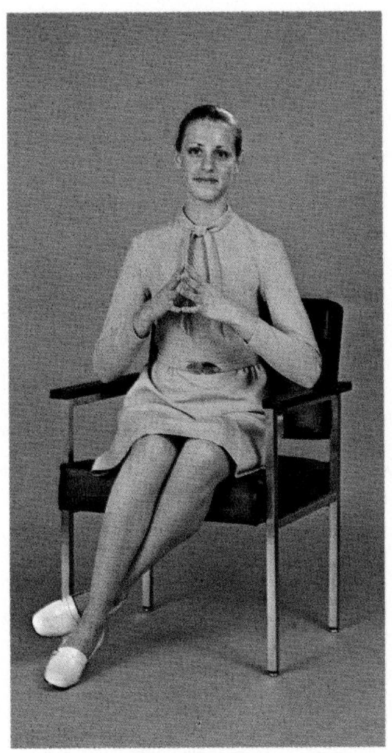

ILLUS. 5-10 *You may be indicating a smug feeling if you "steeple" your fingers.*

Photography by Terry Webb

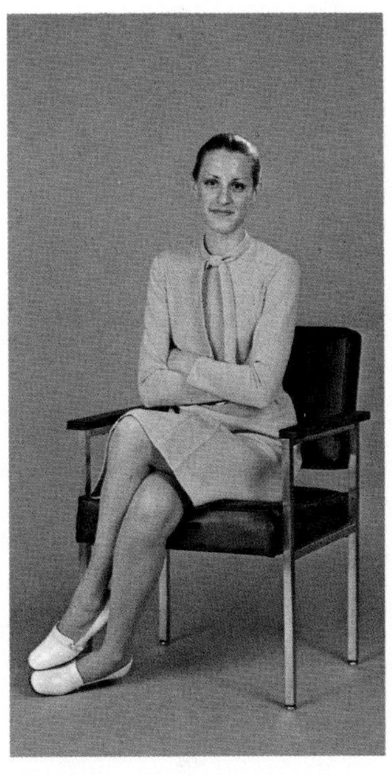

ILLUS. 5-11 *You may indicate a closed mind if you sit with your arms and legs tightly crossed.*

MAINTAINING POLISHED POSTURES

Alert posture without rigidity or fidgeting of any kind reflects the emotional state of self assurance and poise. Hands loosely clasped or cupped in the lap when sitting or near the waist when standing reflect an attitude that is open to possible communication. Walking with a normal stride, a "tall," alert look, and a gentle swing of the arms reflects uncomplicated control of the situation.

When you feel yourself assuming some other positions, analyze your feelings and deal with them positively so that you can release your energies in constructive activity.

SUMMARY

Posture can make a considerable impact on your life. It influences your health, reflects your attitude, makes an impression on the feelings of those around you, and, of course, changes your appearance. A complete checkup on your posture several times a day is worth the benefits that accrue to you for maintaining it.

Understanding Posture

1. Besides better appearance, what does good posture mean to your well-being?
2. Why should you worry about only one point of your posture that is out of alignment?
3. How can exercise influence posture?
4. Where do you bend to sit? Why?
5. What are some relaxing activities you can do if you sit for long periods of time at a desk?
6. How can you improve your posture as you sleep?
7. How can you communicate your feelings with your posture?

Projects for Part 1

1. Plan a three-day menu that you could follow that contains the correct amounts of protein, fat, and carbohydrates for maintaining your ideal weight, using the exchange system of dietary control. If you are overweight, make the three-day plan one that would enable you to lose approximately two pounds per week if you extended it over several weeks. If you are underweight, plan a menu that will enable you to gain at least one pound per week.
2. Make a recreative exercise plan for yourself covering six months. Describe the time of day, amount of time, and facilities you will need. Give alternate activities for bad weather days and for variety when you have reached the level of fitness you desire.
3. Analyze your own measurements and flexibility, and design a program for yourself for the next six months to correct any deviations from the average. Determine which exercise and the number of repetitions you would undertake.
4. Analyze your posture once each hour during a single day. Decide what improvements you need in alignment and what your image and communication are reflecting to others with your posture.

Part 2

Second Dimension Your Radiance

The second dimension of personal development includes the areas of complexion care, makeup, hair grooming, and the often overlooked areas of hand and foot care and fragrances.

You know already how your appearance affects the way you feel about yourself. More and more you will learn that it affects the way others feel about you, too.

The first subject in this dimension is the care of your complexion. You need first of all to become expert in cleaning and protecting your skin. The procedures and products you will need for this expertise are presented in detail.

Your face and hair are vital to your radiant look. You will learn to analyze yourself and to choose techniques, applications, and styles that enhance your most attractive features and balance your irregular ones.

The second dimension concludes with those areas of grooming that others are sure to note even if you don't – your hands, feet, and fragrance. These finishing touches are easy to master and very important to your overall grooming.

Chapter 6

Skin Care

Radiance begins with clean, well-nourished skin. Look at a baby's skin and you'll realize that all skin starts off pretty. Abuse by the environment and neglect by the owner can often change it to something less than beautiful. With proper care, you can preserve and restore much of the beauty with which your skin was born.

The importance of caring for your skin cannot be overestimated because all personal grooming begins with your skin. Not only do you strive for a clear, translucent appearance to your skin, but you seek to eliminate body odors and excessive body hair and to protect the natural beauty of your skin from abuse.

Basic Skin Care

Skin reflects not only your inherited characteristics but also your habits of eating, sleeping, exercising, and moisturizing. A coke and french-fried-potato diet will not nourish a lovely skin; neither will three hours' sleep per night followed by three cups of strong coffee. This all-important organ of your body rapidly reflects poor eating or rest habits. It usually serves as an advance signal of much more serious problems unless bad habits are corrected.

SKIN AND NUTRITION

The adage, "You are what you eat" is never truer than as it applies to your skin. This very visible part of your body makes a large contribution to the way you look, and what you eat makes a considerable difference in the quality of that contribution.

"Good" Food. The vitamin generally believed to contribute to fresh looking skin and sparkling eyes is vitamin A. It occurs mainly in green and yellow leafy vegetables and milk, not in potato chips and candy bars! (Illustration 6-1). The nutrient that facilitates the replacement of dying cells in your skin is protein. Protein occurs mainly in lean meat (not carbonated colas or cake!) Every day some skin cells die and are sloughed off. The dying, shedding, and replacing process is a continuing one, and your food intake daily should provide the nutrients required for such replacement.

Another important element in your diet is water. Your skin consists of large amounts of water — not stagnant water — water replaced continuously. One of the most important purposes of water in your body is to flush impurities and waste from your system. You can make your entire body, skin, digestion, and elimination systems function better by consuming six to eight glasses of water a day. It is often difficult to get the amount of water you need if you drink mainly from fountains. Make an effort to provide a glass for drinking water either at the fountain or at meal time.

"Not-so-good" Food. Some foods and liquids seem to harm your skin. Liquor and coffee cause skin problems, especially flushing, in some people. Over a period of time, the effect of flushing is to cause permanent redness in the skin. You can avoid flushing by diluting liquor (if you must drink it) in mixers and punches, and by drinking decaffeinated coffee of a reduced temperature.

Fatty foods, such as those that are fried, oily sandwich spreads, nuts, chips, butter, candy, olives, and avocados are believed to contribute to excess oil in very oily complexions. By substituting fresh fruit and vegetables for those snack foods listed, catsup and mustard for oily sandwich spreads, skim milk for whole milk, baking for frying, you will also be helping yourself in weight control as well as nurturing a beautiful skin. Foods with a high iodine content, such as shell fish and iodized salt, sometimes contribute to blemished skin problems. Chocolate seems to be another of the not-so-good foods for your skin.

Good nutrition for your skin means including meat, milk, milk products, and green and yellow leafy vegetables in your diet every day. It means eliminating foods that contribute to problems to which you may be vulnerable, such as flushing and blemishes. At first glance the foods to be avoided may seem to be the best of your meal and snack times. Tastes are acquired, not inherited or inborn. You can reeducate your taste preferences to those that make for healthier, more beautiful skin if you wish. Skin nutrition, like general nutrition, means eating to main-

ILLUS. 6-1 *Vitamin A occurs in green and yellow vegetables.*

Photography by Terry Webb

tain the good health of your body rather than eating to satisfy temporarily the desires of your taste buds. Choose foods that you have specific reasons to eat rather than those that appeal temporarily to your senses of taste, smell, and vision.

SKIN AND RELAXATION

If you are nervous and tense for long periods of time, your skin will reflect your discomfort. There will be no glow and no fresh looking skin simply because the nutrient-carrying blood cannot penetrate the constricted blood vessels to feed and regenerate the surface of your body. A heart that is not working at peak efficiency or blood vessels that are constricted near the surface of your body can rob your skin of the nourishment it needs (Illustration 6-2, next page).

Rest. Take a good look at your skin, especially your face, when you get up in the morning. Take another look when you begin to prepare for bed at night. Most skins look very different before and after rest. The older you get, the more obvious the difference. Rest for your body includes rest for your skin. Relaxing and sleeping allow muscles to rest and blood to flow freely into the tiniest capillaries, bringing oxygen and nutrients to nourish your skin. Without such rest, your skin competes with other organs of your body, such as your muscles and digestive organs, for those important nutrients. Without adequate rest, the skin may get only whatever is not burned as energy. If you are eating only marginally, other parts of your body may exhaust your supply of nutrients before your skin gets a chance at them.

Photograph Courtesy of Cotton Incorporated

ILLUS. 6-2 *Relaxation is good for circulation, which rids your skin of waste.*

Activity. Skin needs stimulation, too — not the vigorous rubbing and pounding that goes with a body massage (although that is better than no stimulation at all). The skin needs stimulation from an atmosphere that relaxes you in an activity that promotes vigorous blood flow, adequate oxygen intake, and elimination of waste. As you participate regularly in activity that stimulates blood flow and oxygen intake, you care for your skin.

A brisk walk or a game of tennis that causes your circulatory system to speed up its flow of blood to your cells promotes lovely skin. When your skin tingles and glows temporarily from increased activity, it means that additional nourishment has been brought by your blood to the skin surface. Relaxation is necessary to this kind of activity. A tense or nervous body constricts blood vessels, causing the skin to be cut off from this beautifying nourishment.

SKIN CLEANSING

No skin is radiant or well-groomed unless it is clean. Fortunately, with a variety of soaps and bath aids, cleaning your skin can be one of the most pleasant times of your day.

Baths and Showers. There are two effective ways to clean your body. One is a bath, the other a shower. A shower is more efficient for getting your body clean, but it usually is not as relaxing as a bath. Your bath can be a period of time for relaxing as well as for cleansing your body. If you do relax in a tub of warm water, do not use soap until just before you are ready to complete your bath. Lengthy exposure to soap tends to strip your body of oil and make it feel uncomfortably dry.

ILLUS. 6-3 *A bath can serve to relax you as well as to clean your body. If you plan to "soak," do not use soap until just before you complete your bath.*

Jean Naté

The temperature of the water you bathe in is important. Very hot water will be physically exhausting, cool water will be stimulating, and warm water usually is very relaxing. Most of the time a warm water bath is preferred before you retire at night, and a cooler shower is taken before you begin your day in the morning.

Soaps. The soap you choose is very important, and you should be cognizant of the needs of your skin in choosing the appropriate one for cleansing it. Soap loosens and removes soil, grime, body secretions, dead skin cells, and bacteria through a chemical reaction between fats and alkalis. Since soap is a combination of fats and alkalis, you can obtain soaps of various proportions of each substance. If you tend to have very oily skin, choose a milled soap that does not have extra fat in it. If you have very dry skin, select a soap that is superfatted or transparent with glycerine and extra fat. Synthetic detergent bars of soap are available and differ from soap because they do not leave a bathtub ring. They lather better in hard water areas than soap does.

The fragrance in soap has no bearing on its ability to clean. Choose a fragrance you like or one with no fragrance at all. Scented soap will impart fragrance to your lingerie if you store the extra bars in your lingerie drawer.

Bath Aids. There are many items available that are conveniently used for special problems during your bath. A brush for washing your back is good if you have problem skin there. A pumice stone for removing dry skin on your feet and elbows is conveniently used at bath time. Shaving, if you use that method of hair removal, is easily done when you bathe. A light oil applied to your skin or in your bath water just before you are ready to towel off the water imparts a luxurious feeling to your skin.

SKIN MOISTURIZERS

Normally your body has oil over most of its surface, which soap and water float away along with dirt and grime. If you do not produce enough oil to replace that which is lost in bathing, or if harsh weather is robbing your skin of moisture, you can become very uncomfortable. Your skin may become rough and chapped. Although any part of your skin may suffer, some particularly vulnerable areas are your face, hands, and heels.

Body Moisturizers. Many people find a bath oil dissolved in bath water useful in controlling dry skin discomfort over the entire body. An inexpensive and effective oil for this purpose is baby oil. You can add it to bath water or spread it on your rinsed, wet skin at the end of your bath or shower before toweling. The water of the bath or shower helps to disperse the oil over your skin. Scented bath oils are also available, and you can concoct your own by adding your favorite fragrance to a bottle of baby oil. The scent makes little difference, but the oil on your skin makes a big difference in your comfort and the care of your skin.

Body lotions designed for application to your skin after you have toweled can be used for the same purpose. Usually either a bath oil or a body lotion is used. Most people don't need both.

Face and Neck Moisturizers. Don't put bath oil or body lotions on your face and neck. They are special cases and require very light but

ILLUS. 6-4 *Oil in your bath water can help control dry skin.*

Johnson & Johnson

penetrating oil for good results. Creams and lotions for your face are usually designated for day, night, or under makeup. The difference usually is the consistency. Heavier creams are usually for use at night when you don't mind a shiny look. Day creams usually are lighter and are absorbed quickly so that they don't shine through your makeup. Under-makeup lotions usually are very light and feel very slick. They make it easy to smooth on makeup as well as to protect your face from dryness.

Very oily skins probably will need only the light under-makeup moisturizer for both day and night moisturizing. Normal skin or skin that is beginning to become drier will probably need an under-makeup moisturizer for day wear and a night cream. Dry skin can benefit from all three, especially during exposure to harsh weather.

There are specially formulated eye creams of a very light but very oily consistency. If the skin around your eyes seems much drier than that of the remainder of your face, this kind of cream may be helpful. Claims to prevent wrinkles are made for these creams; however, there is little proof of their value above regular face moisturizers and the benefit you get from keeping your entire face moisturized with the regular moisturizers.

Hand Creams and Lotions. Hand creams and lotions are a must for most people. The best of all worlds is to have hand cream available every place you are likely to wash your hands. Apply hand creams and lotions as if you were putting on gloves, stroking from fingertip to wrist (to the elbow occasionally if you need it). Put an extra dab on your elbows if they are rough and dry (Illustration 6-5). If you handle paper frequently, you may need applications of hand cream more often because paper tends to dry the hands and nail cuticle almost as badly as water. It is always wise to protect your hands when you are using harsh cleaners and detergents. If no rubber gloves are available, apply an extra heavy coat of cream to your hands before you start. If you have extreme problems with chapping and the skin cracking, you may want to try petroleum jelly smoothed on your hands and covered with old cotton gloves over night.

Leg and Feet Moisturizers. Dry, rough skin can be a big problem on your feet and legs. Not only will you suffer discomfort, but you will tear your nylon stockings on the roughened surfaces. Removing hair from your legs strips them of much of their oil, and you may need to use extra lotion after each hair removing session. Body and hand lotions as well as bath oils are good for your legs. Heels, as well as elbows, need extra attention when you are restoring oil to your skin. If the skin in either area becomes very dry, it cracks. This, of course, can be painful. Petroleum jelly is an inexpensive treatment, but body lotions are good, too. An application of either one every night is helpful until you have your skin in good condition. Unless your skin is very dry, or is exposed regularly to harsh weather, less frequent applications are needed to maintain the skin on your heels and elbows.

Basic Face Care

Your face presents skin of a very fragile variety. It needs special attention in cleaning as well as moisturizing. Because it is particularly vulnerable to blemishes, the careful control of acne through diet and cleansing is necessary for the face.

BASIC CLEANING

Cleansing creams that are specially formulated to react with makeup usually are more efficient at removing makeup than soap and water. Eye makeup is a difficult cleansing problem because the skin is so tender. Eye makeup that does not succumb to cleansing cream or soap and water frequently yields to baby oil or a special eye makeup remover solution. Baby oil or remover solution on a cotton ball is gently applied to the lashes, allowed to soak in, then very gently wiped or rinsed off (Illustration 6-6). Use a wet cloth or a dry, soft one rather than paper tissue to remove cleansing cream and debris from your face and eyes. Follow with a soap and water wash if you wish, then with astringent or freshener. Your skin will feel clean and refreshed.

ILLUS. 6-5 *Protect problem areas such as elbows from drying and cracking by keeping them lubricated.*

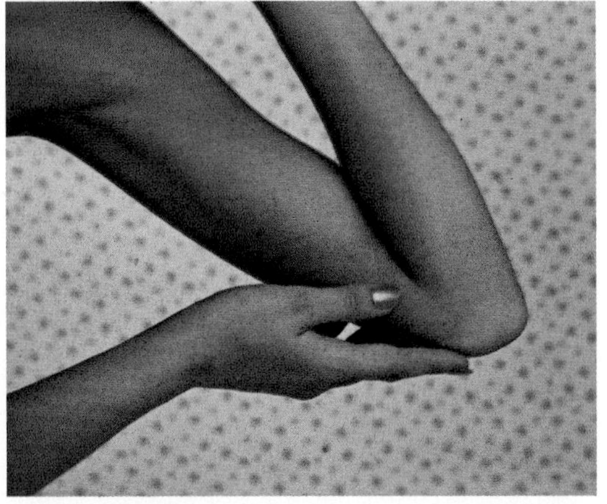

Johnson & Johnson

ILLUS. 6-6 *Carefully remove eye makeup with gentle cleansing agents.*

Johnson & Johnson

It is important not to abuse the skin when you are cleansing it. Gently apply the cream or soap in an upward circular motion with your fingertips or a complexion brush. Gently splash cool to warm water on your face to rinse soap off or gently use a wet cloth to remove the cream. Pat your face dry with a clean towel. Try not to rub it since your face skin is very tender and can be abused easily. Age and the pull of gravity give you wrinkles soon enough; don't let your fingers add to the damage.

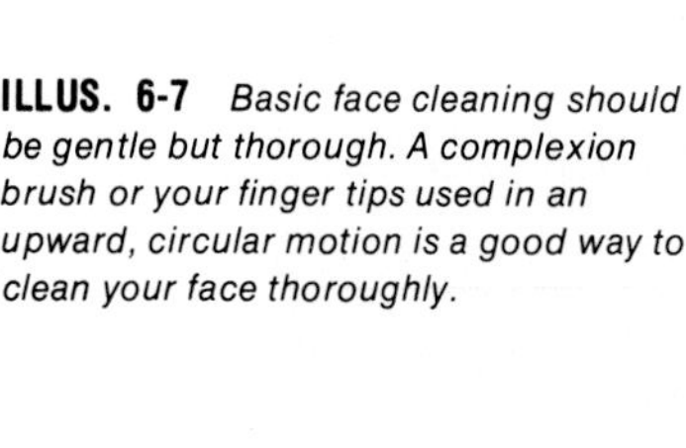

ILLUS. 6-7 *Basic face cleaning should be gentle but thorough. A complexion brush or your finger tips used in an upward, circular motion is a good way to clean your face thoroughly.*

Charles of the Ritz

Because your face skin is so sensitive and is subjected to dirt and grime in the air constantly, you may want to "treat" it occasionally. A facial mask is a perfect treat. There are oily masks for dry skin, normal masks for ideal skin, and drying masks for oily skin.

Ideally the mask will go on your face wet and will dry to either a clay type substance or a peel-off, flexible substance. As it dries, it closes the pores of your skin, cleaning them of debris and stimulating the circulation in your face. After you remove the mask, your face should feel clean, stimulated, and refreshed. Facial mask results are temporary and most cannot be used more than twice a week — less often if your skin is dry. They are ideal when you need a lift or when your skin looks lifeless from temporary abuses of a demanding day's schedule.

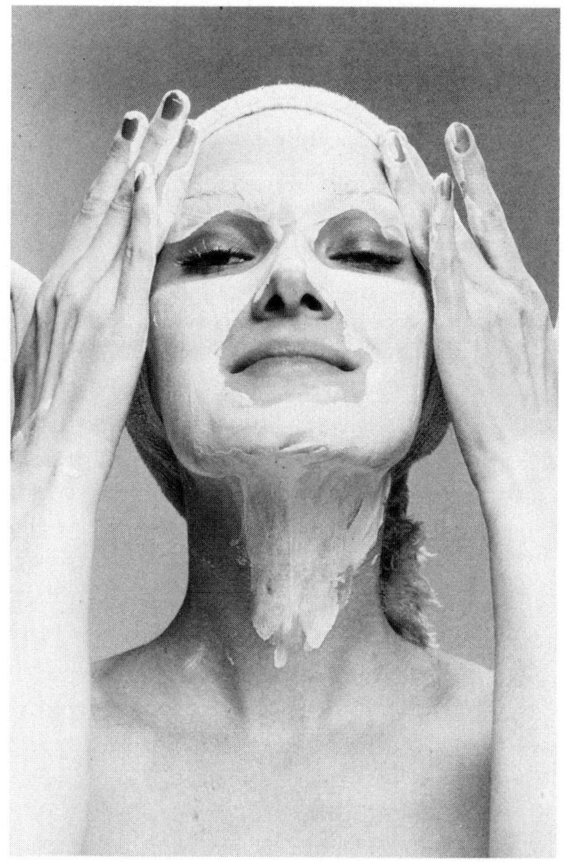

ILLUS. 6-8 *A facial mask can help in cleansing your face.*

Charles of the Ritz

CONTROLLING OIL

Complexions vary considerably according to the amount of natural oil that occurs and according to where it deposits itself on the skin. Each person's skin is slightly different and there are millions of degrees of oiliness. Not only do the differences among people account for varying degrees of oiliness, but each person throughout a lifetime experiences different degrees of oiliness in her own skin. Rather than trying to classify your skin in a particular category, learn how to treat all degrees of oiliness, so that throughout your life and on any part of your skin you will know how to contend with abnormal secretions or lack of secretions.

"Ideal" Oiliness. Characteristics of a skin with just the right amount of oil are a firm texture; radiant tone; fresh, transparent appearance; glowing color; a silky, supple look; no visible enlarged pores; and no flakiness. Other complexions usually strive for this "ideal" balance because the skin looks and feels better than it does with too much or too little oil. With care and attention, anyone can achieve the appearance of this kind of skin. The amount of care and attention needed is related to how much your skin varies in either direction from just the "ideal" amount of oil.

You care for your face according to how much oil occurs naturally on it. The frequency of cleansing, type of cleanser, choice of astringent or freshener, and moisturizers vary according to the degree of oiliness in your face skin. A skin with neither too much nor too little oil usually can take soap (mild soap) and water or it can take a cream or lotion cleanser. If soap and water are used, you may want to use a moisturizer immediately after cleansing to keep your skin from feeling taut. If either cream or lotion is used, you may want to use a freshener or astringent to clean and close the pores and to give a refreshed feeling similar to that obtained with soap and water. Depending upon its exposure to dirt and grime, this face should be cleansed once before bedtime and possibly again before makeup is applied in the morning. Sometimes astringent on a cotton ball will substitute for morning cleansing of this ideal skin.

An under-makeup moisturizer is used in the daytime under your makeup to allow you to smooth your makeup base on more easily and to keep it from changing color during the day. A night cream may be used in areas that are susceptible to wrinkling, such as the eye area and around your mouth.

Ideal skin may be a blessing you enjoy your whole life. More realistically, though, you probably will enjoy it for a short period of time between the oily teen years and the dry older ones. If you have it, check it carefully periodically, and do not take it for granted. Age has a way of changing skin, and you need to anticipate the damage it does. It is better to do what you can to delay it rather than try to treat it after it occurs.

Too Much Oil. Normally at puberty the oil glands in the skin become very active. You probably will have more oil from approximately age 12 to age 25 than at any time in your life. Frequently, the oiliest part of your skin is down the center of your face from your forehead to your chin. This area is known as the T Zone. The easiest way to check for

Revlon, Inc. Photography by Klaus Lucka

ILLUS. 6-9 *An ideal balance of oil in your face gives a firm texture and a radiant tone.*

oiliness is to wash your face carefully with soap and water, dry it, apply nothing to it, and check it approximately four to eight hours later. If it is moist with oil, it is oily. If it has a dry tight feeling, it is not oily. The problem is to achieve some oil but not too much. Too much oil contributes to blemishes, large pores, and flakiness and causes makeup to be discolored or absorbed. Too little oil contributes to dry, rough skin.

To control too much oil, there are many procedures you should follow. One of the first is to avoid fatty foods, such as fried foods, butter, nuts, and mayonnaise. These seem to contribute to the oil produced in abnormally oily complexions. Another procedure is to wash the oily skin two or three times a day with soap and lukewarm-to-cool water. Hot water seems to stimulate the production of oil. Soap removes oil and the dirt it attracts more efficiently than creams or cleansing lotions. Before makeup is applied, apply an astringent to tighten the pores of your complexion and to cool and refresh your skin.

Some special aids for very oily parts of your skin are available. A complexion brush can aid you in cleaning the oily areas. A brush more effectively cleans the pores that tend to be clogged with oil than your fingertips can. Small blotting papers are available that you can use throughout the day to blot oil from your face. These come in packages

ILLUS. 6-10 *If you have excess oil, it probably will be present at the points indicated.*

that can be carried in your handbag or placed in your desk drawer. Like all grooming aids, they should be used only in private and never at your desk. An under-makeup moisturizer that serves as a blotter-barrier to oil and keeps it from bleeding through your makeup during the day can help you keep your face looking fresh and oil free all day. It is necessary, of course, to keep your complexion fastidiously clean before and during the application of such preparations.

Extremely hot weather seems to stimulate the production of oil in oily skin. Take care to cleanse it more often and to blot the oil more frequently in hot weather if you are treating oily skin. Clay-type face masks and drying masks are good to use on oily parts of your complexion. They serve to remove the flakiness that occurs from excess oil as well as that which occurs from the natural deterioration of skin cells.

Too Little Oil. As you grow older or if your oil glands are not very active when you are young, you may find that you are troubled with dry skin. Dry in this sense means lack of oil, not lack of water. Dry skin is treated somewhat differently from very oily skin. A lack of oil makes skin rough and inelastic. While you still must keep it clean, you must also keep it lubricated. The first area of concern is to clean very dry skin without drying it out further. Creams and cleansing lotions are more effective in this than soap and water. If you feel you must use soap, choose a superfatted one. Refreshing lotions are better than astringents for tightening pores without drying.

ILLUS. 6-11 *If your skin is dry, carefully lubricate the areas indicated.*

A good procedure for dry skin is to use a cream or lotion to clean the skin, remove the cleanser with a clean, wet cloth, follow with a cool water rinse or freshener on a cotton ball, and apply a moisturizer.

An under-makeup moisturizer with an oil base will provide a surface that enables you to smooth on your makeup more easily and helps give you a dewy, fresh look. A night cream that is somewhat heavier is good to treat your dry skin at night. Particular areas of concern are around the eyes and mouth, where you will notice lines and wrinkles first. Lubricating with these under-makeup moisturizers and night creams seems to help in concealing the aging signs of wrinkles.

Frequently dry skin is rough and colorless. A mask that helps peel off the dead cells and that stimulates the skin without drying it is a good way to remedy these problems. Extreme weather, cold and hot, and very dry weather seem to take a toll on dry skin. If you know you are going to be subjected to extreme weather, apply extra moisturizer, such as a day cream, before you go out.

Your skin probably will not fit exactly into one category for all time. Good grooming and a radiant complexion merely mean that you know what to do for your skin whenever it shows signs of needing special care and that you regularly practice a routine of cleansing, freshening, and moisturizing that promotes the look of ideal skin.

CONTROLLING BLEMISHES

Blemished skin is a major problem for many young people. Before you can control or eliminate it you must understand what causes it. Because there is rarely a single cause, there is no single treatment that works infallibly for everyone. In many young people, blemishes are caused by oil that clogs the pores of the skin, forming blackheads. If these are not removed with vigorous, frequent washing, the oil that is continually produced collects in the shaft beneath the blackhead, is decomposed by bacteria that is present on skin, and becomes infected and swollen.

Depending upon the stage of development of the particular blemish you are treating, various procedures may be effective. To prevent blemishes from forming, it would be necessary to prevent the secretion of excess oil or to remove as soon as possible with thorough and frequent washing the oil that collects in the pores of the skin. Since the best way to reduce the production of skin oil that we know about today is to age the skin, cleansing it frequently seems more practical. A complexion brush or a wash cloth with a granular soap made for this purpose may make the washing more effective in removing these deposits of oil. The frequent washing also removes bacteria that contribute to the problem. Keeping your hands away from your blemished skin between washings will prevent the unnecessary introduction of additional bacteria to its surface.

After a blemish has formed, it must be treated carefully. If it is infected and swollen, permanent damage may occur in the skin if the blemish erupts spontaneously. Usually a doctor can treat severe cases of infection with antibiotics, and the doctor may choose to drain them under sterile conditions. You can care for occasional, small infections by keeping your body rested, nourished, and fastidiously clean. Since your body produces its own infection-fighting substances, your infection will heal itself if it is not severe. Your health must be good, though, in order for substances occurring normally in your system to kill the infection. The wastes will be carried away in your blood instead of erupting and scarring your face. If you have more infection than your body seems to be able to handle, it will be necessary to see a doctor for help.

Some doctors believe that certain foods contribute to and aggravate blemished skin. Often it is suggested that chocolate, carbonated water, colas, iodine (such as that occurring in shellfish and idiozed salt), and fats (such as grease that foods are fried in, butter, and nuts) contribute to the occurrence of skin blemishes. If you are seeing a dermatologist regarding your skin, follow the doctor's directions. If you are treating yourself, you may want to try eliminating these foods from your diet for six-to-eight weeks to see if your skin improves.

Sometimes you may experience blemishes at a particular time in your menstrual cycle. For these temporary breakouts, clean your skin frequently and carefully. Use a preparation designed to cover them under your makeup, and, by all means, never pick at them with your fingers. The introduction of bacteria to the irritated area may contribute to the problem.

There are some lotions designed to accelerate and facilitate the sloughing off of dead skin cells. Since these lotions are very drying, they may be helpful in removing the surface oil deposits that occur on the outer layer of your skin, especially around a blemish. They are referred to as renewal or sloughing lotions and should not be used all over your face daily — just on a blemished area.

Some skin eruptions are caused by allergies to food and substances in the air. A doctor can treat the cause of these eruptions.

Special Body Care

General procedures of body and face care get you on the right track to radiance. There are some special areas, though, that spark the glow you are seeking. Your smile for example, reflects more about you than you may want to show if your oral hygiene habits have been a bit lax. Getting close to others or even to yourself may be a problem if your perspiration control strategy is weak; and that "well-turned" ankle may be less than attractive if your hair removal techniques are slipshod. Two other areas that complete complexion care are protection of your skin from sun damage and treatment of discolorations.

ORAL HYGIENE

Your mouth is a special area of your body in terms of care. It should reflect a refreshing smile, clean, white teeth, healthy gums, and a sweet breath. The smile emanates from within, and you will learn about feeling like smiling in another dimension in this book. The clean, white teeth, pink gums and sweet breath you can attain with good oral hygiene.

Teeth and Gums. Usually a dentist can help you with any problems you have with your teeth or gums. Many people, however, need a check-up only once or twice a year and have their teeth professionally cleaned of built-up plaque and stains at that time. The rest is easy to do daily at home.

It is absolutely necessary to brush your teeth at least twice a day to clean them of food and plaque. More often may be helpful, especially if you eat sweet or gooey foods that deposit sugar or food on your teeth. Smoking, coffee, and tea may stain your teeth. Don't try to correct stains with vigorous brushing. Brush in a circular motion, being careful not to scrape back and forth over the same area. You can actually dig grooves in your teeth with the bristles of your brush by brushing improperly.

Food and plaque that collect between your teeth cannot be removed completely with a brush; therefore, you must floss your teeth either before or after brushing to get them completely clean. Dental floss is a strong, white, waxed string that you draw between your teeth to remove debris. It is available wherever you buy your toothpaste and toothbrush. Use it at least once a day. Toothpicks are dangerous to your gums and should not be used. They are never acceptable for use in public. It is better to carry a small container of floss in your handbag to use privately if you get food between your teeth.

ILLUS. 6-12 *Use of dental floss in addition to brushing is the surest way to clean your teeth thoroughly.*

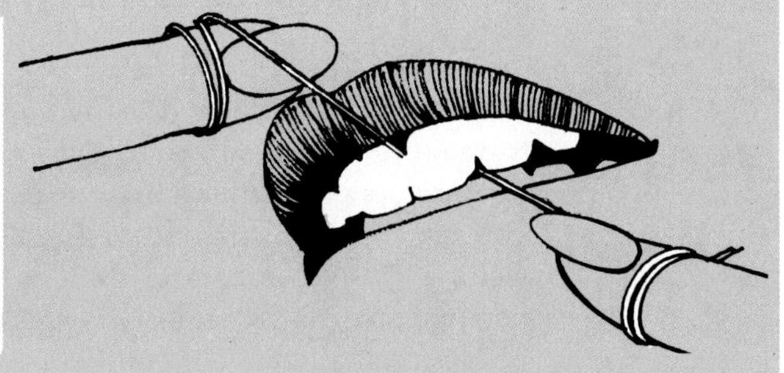

Only your dentist can treat gum problems. If you notice soreness or your gums pulling away from your teeth, consult your dentist. Early treatment of gum problems may mean a saving of much pain and eventually of your teeth.

Sweeth Breath. Your breath may be affected by many things: what you eat, your sinuses, tongue, teeth, gums, and the condition of your digestive system. It is not normal to have offensive breath. If you have it regularly, you should consider it the sign of a problem and start immediately to determine the cause and eliminate it. Bad breath is one of the most offensive of the body odors and definitely detracts from your grooming.

Foods with strong odors frequently leave an odor in your mouth and may contribute to bad breath long after you have cleaned the odor from your mouth. Brushing your teeth, rinsing your mouth thoroughly, and gently brushing your tongue will eliminate from your mouth any odor left from offensive foods. If the food odor still is apparent in your breath, an antacid tablet may aid in diluting the odor in your digestive tract.

Bad breath may result from sinus drainage. Frequently, an infection in your nose that accompanies a cold causes bad breath. Antihistamines are available to dry up the drainage of your sinuses and your nose and therefore are somewhat helpful in controlling the breath odor caused by this drainage. Breath mints actually do more to alleviate the bad taste such drainage leaves in your mouth than they do for your breath. They are better, however, than nothing at all for temporary relief.

Certain normal bacteria grow on your tongue. These in their normal balance do not cause bad breath. If you are under treatment with certain antibiotics, some of these bacteria may be killed. The result will be an imbalance that may cause bad breath. The doctor who prescribed the antibiotic can correct the condition.

Unclean teeth and unhealthy gums, of course, will cause unpleasant mouth odors. You know already how to clean teeth and care for gums. If you still suspect your teeth and gums as causes for unpleasant breath, consult with your dentist.

The condition of your digestive system affects your breath. An acid stomach can cause bad breath, and people with diabetes or other internal disorders frequently suffer bad breath. Ulcers in the stomach and improper elimination can also cause bad breath. Frequent acid stomach and the other problems described, of course, should be treated by a doctor. Control and/or cure of any of the conditions eliminates the resulting bad breath.

If bad breath is caused by something you can correct, there is no reason to tolerate it. If it is a symptom of a more serious problem, consult a doctor without delay; and use temporary breath fresheners and mints until it is corrected permanently. Remember, though that breath mints, fresheners, and gargles are temporary. You want permanent control of your mouth scent. There are few more offensive odors than bad breath. Sweeten yours by correcting the problem that is causing it. You can do yourself no greater favor in terms of human relations.

Vogue Pattern Service

ILLUS. 6-13 *Clean, fresh breath can enhance your confidence in all situations.*

BODY ODORS

It is unrealistic to consider yourself well-groomed if you have a body odor. Most body odors are caused by perspiration under your arms and in the genital area. The bacteria present on your skin most of the time are the cause of many body odors. They thrive in damp, warm places, decomposing body secretions such as perspiration, and causing the characteristic perspiration odors that are so offensive. You can easily control ordinary body odors with products available today, frequent bathing, and some special tips.

Perspiration is a secretion that forms on the surface of your skin to maintain your body at a constant temperature by evaporative cooling. Like other secretions and excretions, though, if it remains on your skin, it can harbor odor-producing bacteria. Bathing is the only way to control the bacterial odor after it has occurred. Once the bacterial decomposition of perspiration has taken place, producing the resulting odor, scented creams and sprays will not work. Only a bath will eliminate the odor.

Underarm Odors. There are two ways to avoid underarm perspiration odor: antiperspirants and deodorants. Both the amount of perspiration you produce and the amount of bacteria on your skin can be reduced considerably with these products.

You can reduce the amount of bacteria present in this vulnerable area of your body by using a deodorant that kills bacteria in the area in which it is used. Bacteria grow easily, however, and deodorants must be applied frequently to keep the bacteria growth under control. Perspiration causes a major problem other than odor; it circles your clothing. The best way to control the amount of perspiration you secrete is to use an antiperspirant. Antiperspirants actually are astringents that reduce the amount of perspiration you secrete for several hours. It is possible now to purchase products which are an antiperspirant and deodorant combined. With these most people can easily control the amount of perspiration and the growth of bacteria in the underarm area, completely avoiding underarm odor. For most effective protection, the products should be applied immediately after you bathe. If you have shaved your underarms during your bath, however, and your skin is tender or nicked, wait a few hours before applying your antiperspirant.

If you have a problem of excess underarm perspiration that cannot be controlled with an antiperspirant, your doctor may be able to help you. Tension sometimes increases perspiration, and foods with strong odors are said to influence the odor of perspiration as well as that of your breath. If there seems to be absolutely no way to control the production of perspiration, you can wear underarm shields to protect your clothing. To be effective, though, use deodorant under them and wash the shields after each wearing.

Other Areas. Frequent bathing and clean underclothing usually control perspiration odor in the genital area. Currently there are no deodorants or antiperspirants considered entirely safe for this area. Most people do not find it necessary to remove the hair in that area. If you have persistent vaginal secretions that create undesirable body odors, consult a doctor. While some secretion is normal, discolored and odorous secretions other than menstruation are not. During menstruation, when you perspire more than usual, bathe more often and change tampons or pads frequently to keep any body odor under control.

BODY HAIR

Body hair, like scalp hair, has been a subject of concern for many years. Men seem to desire more of it; women, less of it. In our culture it is customary to remove the hair under one's arms and on the legs. Removal of underarm hair makes your deodorant and antiperspirants more efficient. Removal of leg hair makes your legs look better in nylon stockings. Hair growing on the face usually is bleached. It may be permanently removed professionally, tweezed, or cut close to the skin with scissors.

Leg and Underarm Hair. There are several ways to remove body hair, and the method you choose depends upon how much effort and money you are willing to put into the process.

Shaving is probably the most commonly used method of hair removal for underarms and legs. Either a safety razor or an electric one will do the job. If you use a safety razor, lather the surface with soap or shaving cream carefully. Draw the razor across the surface against the grain of the growth of the hair. Rinse the razor frequently to clean the blade. This kind of shaving probably is most easily done in the shower or bath. If you use an electric razor, the surface should be dry. You can prepare the skin surface for more efficient shaving by using a pre-shave lotion that makes electric shaving easier. Electric shaving is more effective if you draw the shaver across the surface in a direction opposite to the growth pattern of the hair. Usually legs are shaved from the ankles to only a few inches above the knee. If you have dark hair higher on your leg that shows when you wear a bathing suit, it probably will be more comfortable to bleach the hair than to shave it unless your complexion is quite dark, making bleached hair noticeable.

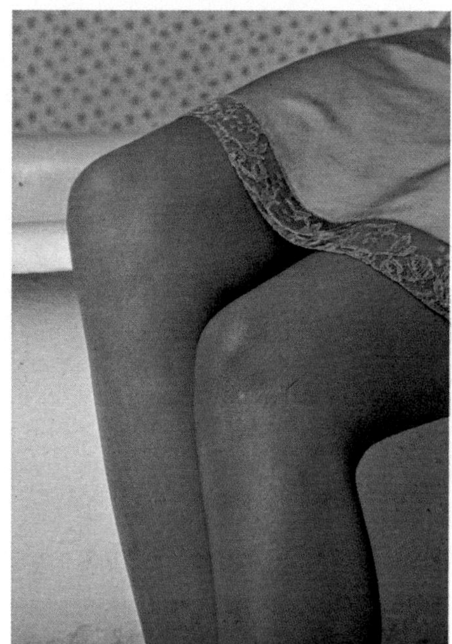

ILLUS. 6-14 *Legs that are free of hair are more attractive than those showing hair.*

Johnson & Johnson

Waxing and tweezing are two ways to remove hair. Both pull the hair out by its roots and usually are not used to remove underarm hair. In waxing, heated, softened wax is spread over the surface and allowed to dry. The wax is then peeled off the skin, pulling the hairs out, leaving a smooth hair-free surface. This can be painful, somewhat like tweezing. Tweezing, though, is too tedious to use on large areas and usually is confined to your eyebrows, where only a few hairs are removed at a time.

Chemical depilatories are available for removing hair, but you should test these chemical substances in a small area of your skin before you use them on a large one. A test consists of covering a one-inch area of the skin according to the manufacturer's directions, rinsing it, and waiting 24 hours. After 24 hours if there is no redness or irritation, the product is safe for your skin, and you can use it over the entire hair surface. Chemical depilatories dissolve the hair to just below the surface of the skin. The skin is rinsed, taking off the depilatory and the dissolved hair. Hair regrowth takes a little longer with depilatories than with shaving.

Facial Hair. Shaving, waxing, and depilatories can be used for underarm and leg hair. They should not ordinarily be used on your face. Facial hair can be removed professionally by electrolysis, or you can do it by tweezing, although this method sometimes causes irritation. Facial hair other than eyebrows can also be trimmed close to the skin with sharp fingernail scissors or it can be bleached. Facial depilatories may be used after careful testing if other methods are unsatisfactory.

Electrolysis is the permanent removal of hair with the use of electricity. You cannot do it yourself; it must be done professionally. It is about 80 percent effective the first time. Therefore, you will need to repeat about 20 percent of the treatment for complete removal of the unwanted hair. Electrolysis can be used for hairlines, eyebrows, other facial hair, and any body hair you desire removed permanently. Compared to other procedures, this one is more expensive.

Bleaching should not be done around the eyes. Other facial hair, however, can be bleached as well as body hair. Peroxide that is somewhat stronger than that used for cleansing minor cuts and wounds must be used. Scalp hair bleaching products may also be used, provided you test them first and follow the directions very carefully. There are also products specifically made for bleaching face and body hair.

SUN DAMAGE

Deliberate exposure of the skin to the sun, specifically to its ultraviolet rays, is quite possibly the most damaging activity undertaken by people in the name of beauty. Although suntanning and sunbathing are popularly associated with beauty and health, they actually should be considered as a period of time you set aside to age your skin.

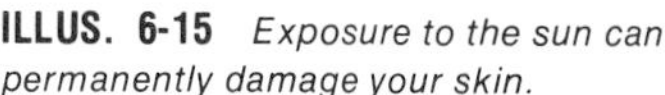

ILLUS. 6-15 *Exposure to the sun can permanently damage your skin.*

Johnson & Johnson

Tanned skin is the result of a permanent chemical change in the cell of the skin. With exposure to the sun, the blood vessels dilate, turning the skin red. The blood produces a substance in these dilated vessels that forms blisters and swelling. The tan that finally occurs in some people is a protective barrier the skin forms to prevent further damage to its cells.

Additional exposure adds damage to damage, and the chemistry of the cell can never be restored. The outermost cells are sloughed off in the normal course of time and replaced by new, normal ones. Deep sunburning though, alters cells deep within the skin that affect the texture, making it thick, rough, inelastic, lined, and leathery. Nothing can change it, and it will not heal. This kind of damage from the sun is permanent.

You can probably see some effects of the sun on your skin already. Compare an area like the back of your hand that is routinely exposed to sun to an area of your body that has never been exposed. There are ways to delay the aging effects of the sun. Shade yourself as often as you can from direct sunlight. When you cannot shade yourself, use a sunscreen which can be obtained at your drug store. Sunscreens are different from suntan lotions. Sunscreens, if they do the job properly, do not allow sun rays to penetrate the barrier they make; suntan lotions do allow the rays to penetrate (Illustration 6-16).

You can have tanned skin safely with the use of skin bronzers. There are two kinds. One is temporary, like makeup, and can be washed off. The other is more permanent. While it becomes lighter with bathing, all

ILLUS. 6-16 *Protect yourself with sunscreens when you are exposed to sunlight.*

Bain de Soleil

of it does not disappear until the cells of the skin die and flake off. Both of these preparations are satisfactory and easy ways of obtaining a tan without damaging your skin.

SKIN DISCOLORATIONS

Dark areas of skin on your face, neck, and hands can be a problem. Often these discolorations are caused by exposure to sunlight. If you curtail that exposure, sometimes the dark areas fade to their natural color. They also occur often as a result of chemical changes in the body during pregnancy and as a result of taking a birth control pill. Usually the skin returns to normal after pregnancy and when the use of the pill has been discontinued. Dark, rough, or ashy areas can occur because of dry skin.

Bleach creams have been formulated to treat these isolated discolored areas, but the preparations available for home use rarely have a lasting effect. The easiest way to treat the discolored areas, if they are not too bad, is to use a concealing cream beneath makeup. Although temporary, this procedure is satisfactory for most people. If yours is a particularly bothersome problem and none of the home remedies seem to correct it to your satisfaction, consult a dermatologist.

SUMMARY

Every age certainly has its beauty, but just as a too-young dress looks bad on an older person, too-old skin looks bad on a younger person. You want to reflect the best of skin for your own age — not a thickened, wrinkled, sagging skin before your time. Be alert to the needs of your skin. Establish a daily routine that includes the care your skin needs, and practice it faithfully. Well-groomed, cared-for, beautiful skin is your first step toward all-over radiance. Make it a good start.

Understanding Skin Care

1. How does nutrition affect your skin?
2. How does relaxation affect your skin?
3. How do you choose a skin cleanser or soap that is right for your skin?
4. What determines the best way to clean your face?
5. How can you control excess oil on your face?
6. Why is it dangerous to allow a blemish to erupt?
7. What causes bad breath? How can you correct it?
8. What causes body odor? How can you control it?
9. What effect does sun bathing have on your skin?

Chapter 7

Face Definition

An important part of your second dimension is your face. Your facial features express your mood and personality. Well-groomed people have always known that the "no makeup look" meant that the colors were well chosen and subtly applied, never omitted. Very few faces actually have smooth, even-textured skin that needs no enhancement or protection. The ones that look that way are just lucky enough to belong to people who have mastered the art of enhancing and protecting them through makeup. You can have one of those faces with a smooth, clear complexion, just the right balance of color in just the right places, emphasizing your best features, if you want it. To make it easy for you, all the products you will need are discussed along with selection and application techniques.

Each of the products discussed plays a special role in your makeup routine. Consider carefully the purpose of each one. Before you select a cosmetic, try the product at the cosmetic counter of a local store that supplies testers. You can make cosmetics work for you by practicing your makeup procedures during a free evening or weekend, streamlining your techniques, and getting the correct placement and amounts for your most attractive face. Making up your face after you have learned all the techniques should take less than fifteen minutes of your day, a very small investment for such rich returns in all-day radiance.

Before you put anything on your face, be very sure you have read and followed the suggestions in the preceding chapter on taking everything off your face. An absolutely clean, freshened face is the beginning of the look you seek. Since many of your cosmetics are applied with your fingertips, wash your hands before you begin.

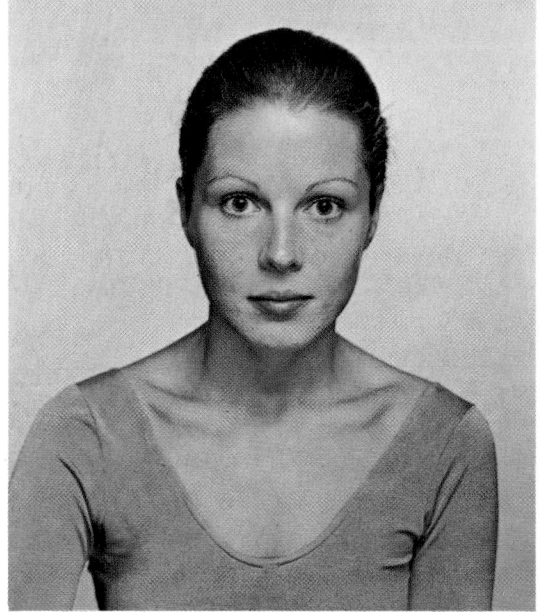

ILLUS. 7-1 *Begin your makeup routine with a clean, freshened face.*

Photography by Terry Webb

The procedures described in the first section are basic ones that will help you get started. Later, you can concentrate on tailoring your makeup to balance and camouflage imperfections, using the special techniques in the second section.

Basic Techniques

For your daily makeup routine you will use under-makeup moisturizer, foundation, powder, cheek color, eye shadow, eye liner, mascara, and lip color. Each of these products is available in many forms for your various needs. Carefully observe what is available and how to use each product.

UNDER-MAKEUP MOISTURIZER

Under-makeup moisturizer is a prime coat for your clean face, preparing your skin to accept your foundation. The wearability and colorfastness of your foundation will be enhanced by the use of an appropriate under-makeup moisturizer. Your clean face will benefit from the protection of this moisturizing film even if you have oily skin. Under-makeup moisturizer also provides balance between oily and dry parts of your face, giving your complexion a uniform texture and appearance.

Selection. Your needs for moisture will probably change from year to year and season to season. Fortunately, under-makeup moisturizers are available in many formulas to satisfy your changing requirements. Experiment with testers at your local cosmetic counter until you find the right formula for you. The moisturizer should dry quickly, leaving your skin smooth and soft. It should not make your face oily, but it may make it slick.

There are several kinds of moisturizers. Most are creamy liquids that can be poured onto your fingertips. (You should never put your fingers into the bottle or jar because to do so would introduce bacteria into the unused part, contaminating it.) Most under-makeup moisturizers are white, but colored ones, designed to improve skin tones, are available. Pink moisturizers can brighten dark, sallow skin; blue will brighten light, sallow skin; and light green will tone down threadlike, prominent blood vessels.

Application. Under-makeup moisturizers are applied with your fingertips to your face, forehead, neck, and ears if they are exposed. Use upward, outward strokes.

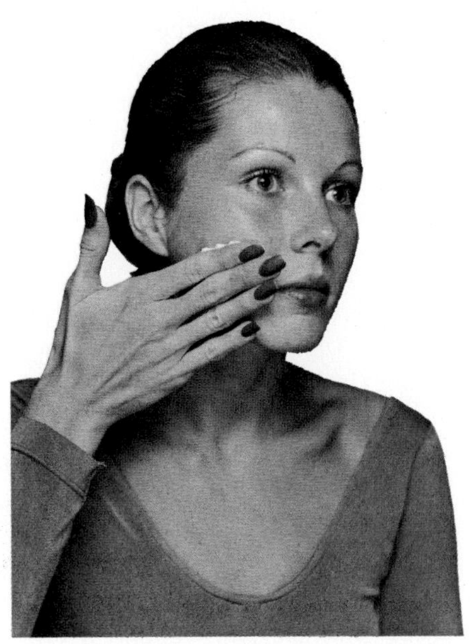

Photography by Terry Webb

ILLUS. 7-2 *Apply under-makeup moisturizer to your face before you apply foundations.*

FOUNDATION

After applying under-makeup moisturizer, you are ready for your foundation. The purpose of a foundation (sometimes called base) is to give your skin uniform color and texture. Slight imperfections in your complexion will be covered, giving you a smooth, even "canvas" on which to define and emphasize your best facial features.

Selection. Selecting a foundation includes decisions about form, color, formula, coverage, and finish. Consider your complexion coloring and problems when making each decision.

Foundation comes in liquid, cream, gel, and pancake forms. Apply liquid and cream formulas with your fingertips, but remember not to put your fingers into the bottle or jar. Pour the liquid onto your fingertips. Use a wooden or plastic spoon to get cream and gel foundation out of the container. Pancake foundation, especially good for oily skin, is applied with a wet cosmetic sponge.

The color of your foundation should be selected to match the color of your skin as nearly as possible. Experimentation is the surest way to select the right color. Most cosmeticians at department stores and drug stores have testers available that you can sample on your skin. With their help, apply several shades to your face. (You can "test" on the back of your hand, but your face is better.) Check them in direct daylight with a mirror to select just the right one for your own complexion. Make a note whether the shade you choose is a rose, beige, pink, cream, or brown tone, and be guided in the future when you change brands or kinds of foundation. You may need to change the color of your foundation seasonally as your complexion color changes.

Foundations come in nonallergenic, medicated, and astringent formulas. If you are experiencing frequent blemish problems, try one of these formulas. In general, the medicated and astringent foundations have a more drying effect on your skin than the normal formula. The nonallergenic formula does not contain the substances to which people are commonly allergic.

Foundations are available in varying degrees of coverage. If you have near-perfect skin, a translucent foundation to provide protection and a glow will be best for you. Gels and water-based liquids frequently are the most translucent of foundations. Oil-based liquids and creams provide the coverage needed by most people. Pancake provides the best coverage for blemished skin.

A matte or shiny finish foundation formula is available. Matte finish foundation usually does not require powder because it is considered to be an "all-in-one" (foundation and powder) formula. Most foundations, however, give some sheen, which may be worn as is or changed to a matte finish with the application of face powder.

Application. Foundation is applied to your entire face and on your neck and ears if they are exposed. Do not try to cover your face all at once. With your fingertips or a wet makeup sponge, begin with your forehead, cheeks, nose, chin, ears, and neck. Place "dots" of foundation at strategic places (Illustration 7-3), and blend them over your face.

Apply foundation sparingly to the hairy parts of your face, such as your upper lip and near your hairline. Very carefully blend the color into these areas, removing with a tissue any foundation that appears matted by the hair. There must be no line of demarcation between the foundation and natural skin. There should be an illusion of a smooth, even, unblemished complexion. If you have difficulty achieving this illusion, you may have chosen the wrong color. Too light a color foundation gives a chalky appearance. Too dark a color is impossible to blend without lines of demarcation.

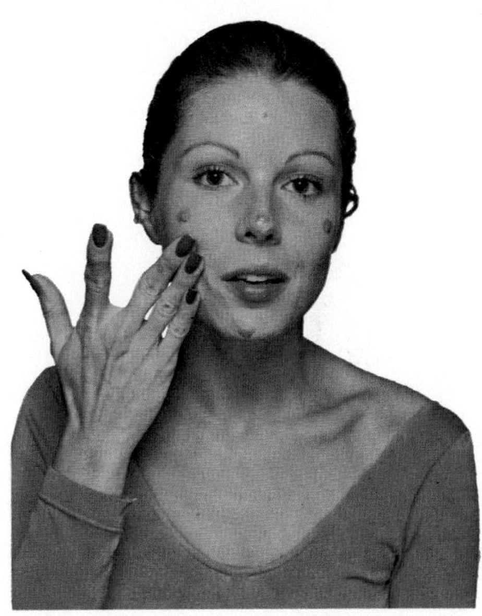

Photography by Terry Webb

ILLUS. 7-3 *"Dot" your foundation on, then blend carefully with a wet cosmetic sponge or your clean fingertips. Avoid any downward pull on the muscles of your face.*

FACE POWDER

Face powder is applied to set your foundation. It can provide a sheen, matte, or luminescent finish and can be obtained in loose or pressed form. Loose powder is most efficient for use at your makeup table. You may want to carry pressed powder in your handbag for quick touch-ups during the day. Don't confuse pressed powder with pancake foundation. They serve different purposes.

Selection. Face powder is available in colors and in a transparent form. Transparent powder adds no color. If you select a colored powder, which gives a slightly heavier look, it should match your foundation. When cream or liquid cheek color has been used, transparent powder is especially recommended because it cannot distort the color. Face powder is sometimes omitted entirely to achieve a "sheen," which fades into and out of popularity.

Application. Apply the powder carefully with a clean puff, brush, or cotton ball over your entire face, or just in the oily sections, such as your forehead, nose, and chin (Illustration 7-4). Pat the powder on; do not rub or stroke. Carefully blot with a tissue near your hairline, on your chin, and especially around your neck to avoid soiling your collar. Blotting is a pressing motion, not a rubbing one. Powder may be omitted in the drier areas of your face and where you have facial hair. Brush the powder away from your eyebrows and lashes.

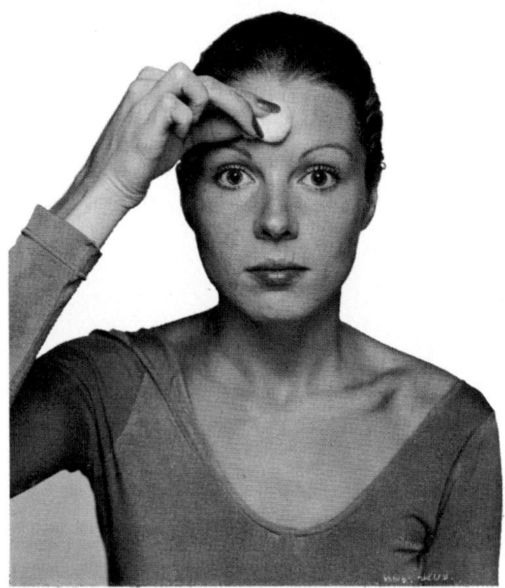

Photography by Terry Webb

ILLUS. 7-4 *Pat powder on the oily, shiny parts of your face.*

CHEEK COLOR

The purpose of rouge and blush is to contour your face and give you a healthy glow.

Selection. Rouge and blush are available in a large array of colors from light pink, to peach, to dark brown. Your color choice depends on the color of your complexion. Choose a pink tint if you are fair, a pink-orange ("peach") or blue-pink ("plum") if you have a medium or dark complexion. Darker tones are for darker complexions and provide more of a contouring effect than a brightening one.

Cheek color comes in liquids, creams, and gels that are applied before your face powder. Powder blush is applied after the powder.

Liquids can be poured or squeezed onto your fingertip and gently applied to your cheekbone. Creams and gels should be scooped from the container with a cotton-tipped stick or a wooden or plastic spoon and placed on your fingertip. Powder blush that is brushed on with its own applicator is easiest to apply but has less staying power.

Application. To apply, you begin at the high point of your cheekbone, approximately aligned with the center of your eye, and move out toward your ear to the hairline. Cheek color should not be near your nose or eyes. It is applied no lower on your face than even with the bottom of your nose. A triangle with softened corners is the usual shape of the cheek color (Illustration 7-5, next page). Blend the edges of the color carefully so that no lines of demarcation are visible. The color should be more intense in the center of the area to which it is applied than it is near the edges.

EYEBROW COLOR

Eyebrow color is available in brush-on powder or pencil form. Brush-on powder is used to lighten brows that are too dark while pencil is used to fill in brows that are too sparse. Eyebrows should be within one or two shades lighter or darker than your hair color. Brows and lashes can be permanently dyed or bleached. However, this procedure should be left to a professional in your beauty salon.

Selection. The eyebrow color you select depends upon whether you wish to lighten, darken, or fill in sparse brows. Blondes, greys, and greyish-browns can be used to good advantage to lighten dark brows. If you wish merely to fill in sparse brows with an eyebrow pencil, choose a color that matches the natural color of your own brows. Do not try to

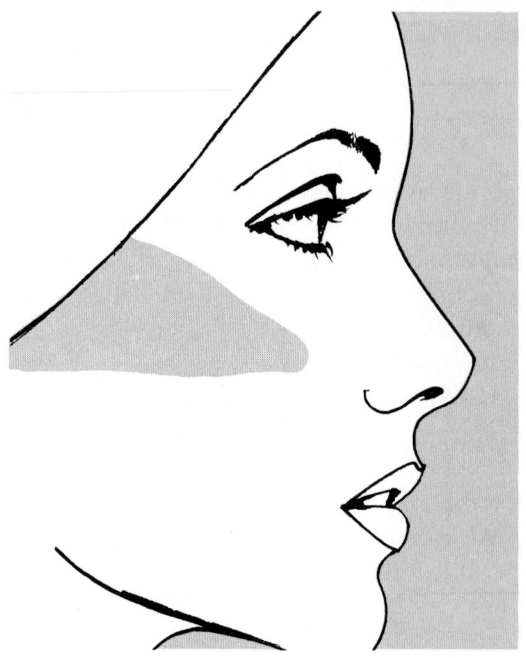

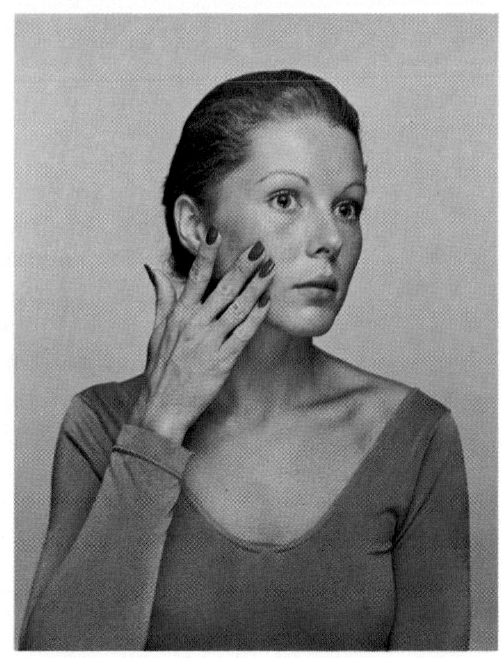

Photography by Terry Webb

ILLUS. 7-5 *A triangle with softened corners is the usual shape of color on the cheek.*

darken your brows more than two shades darker than your hair. Carefully keep both powder and pencil off your skin.

Application. Apply powder with a brush, and blot with a tissue. To apply the pencil to shape and color the brow, use short, feathered strokes. Very light, short strokes are vital to a natural look. Be careful not to curve the outermost corner of your brow down around the outside of the eye. To finish and soften the brow, brush gently with cotton or your fingertip (Illustration 7-6).

EYESHADOW

The purpose of eyeshadow is to highlight and enhance your eyes and complement your costume. It is worn between the brow and the lashes of the upper lid.

Selection. Eyeshadow is available in stick, cream, powder, gel, and cake form and in matte and frosted finish. The most enduring fashion shades of shadow are brown and grey. Today, however, many colors are available and are considered fashionable. The color you choose may be keyed to your ensemble, using blue shadow with a blue dress, green

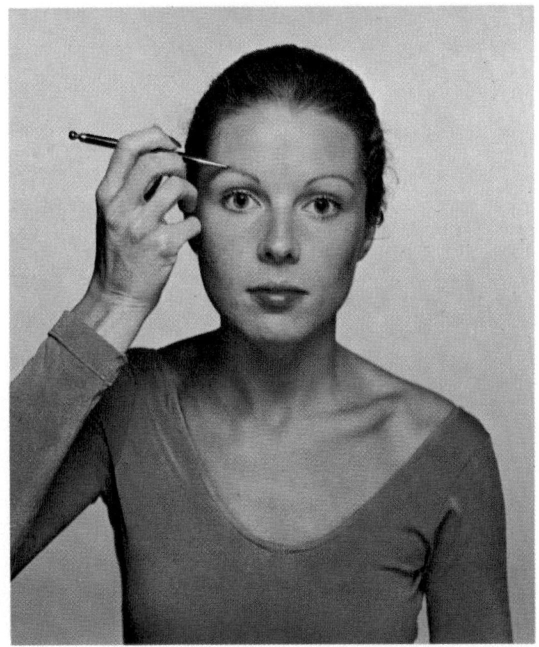

Photography by Terry Webb

ILLUS. 7-6 *Short, feathered strokes make a natural looking brow.*

with a green dress, etc.; or the color may be keyed to your eye color, blue for blue eyes, green for green eyes, brown for brown eyes, etc.

Application. Different colors and various placements can give you a variety of looks. If you select an eyeshadow cream or gel, stroke on a band of color from the inner to the outer corner of the eye (Illustration 7-7, next page). With your fingertip, blend the color upward and outward, making certain that the deepest color tone is closest to the lashes, blending and shading off as the brow line and outer portion of the eye area are reached. Cake and powder shadow are applied with a brush or a sponge. Apply from the inner to the outer portions of the eye, blending and shading to the brow line. Remember to make the color very subtle. A hint of color is usually much more flattering than strong, harsh colors.

EYELINER

Eyeliner is used to outline your eyes, emphasize their shape, and make the lashes appear fuller. It is available in many colors in cake, liquid, or pencil forms. The use of eyeliner fades into and out of fashion; however, it is usually appropriate for use on the upper lid.

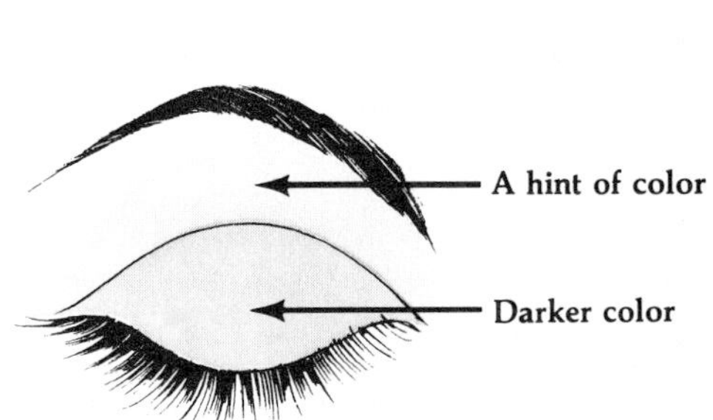

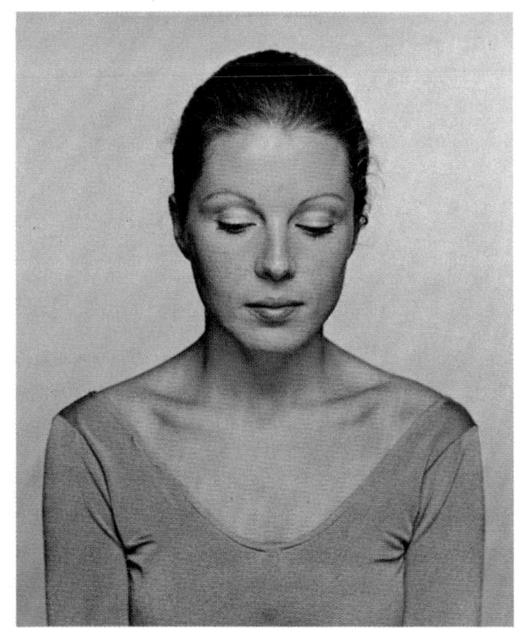

Photography by Terry Webb

ILLUS. 7-7 *Stroke eyeshadow on your lid so that the color is darkest near your lashes and lighest near the brow.*

Selection. Eyeliner is available in various colors. Usually, blondes, brunettes, and redheads find brown liner suitable for most occasions. Only people with dark complexions and eyes can use black liner.

Application. To apply liner to the upper lid, look down into a mirror; hold a brush or pencil so that your hand rests on your cheek. With your free hand, gently pull your lid taut by placing pressure on the outside corner. Starting from the inside corner of your eye, draw a very *thin* line across the lid as close to the lashes as possible (Illustration 7-8). As you reach the outer corner, the line should become thinner. You may extend the line a very short distance (less than one-quarter inch) beyond the outer corner of your eye in a straight or slightly upward direction. The cake and liquid forms of liner are applied with a brush. The pencil is applied directly to your lid. Keep your pencil sharp, but use the side or flat of the point, not the point itself.

If you want to try liner on your lower lid, begin with small dots along the lash roots. Carefully check your appearance in a mirror. If your eyes look too small, or if you have a stark, harsh look, remove the liner from the lower lid with oil or cream.

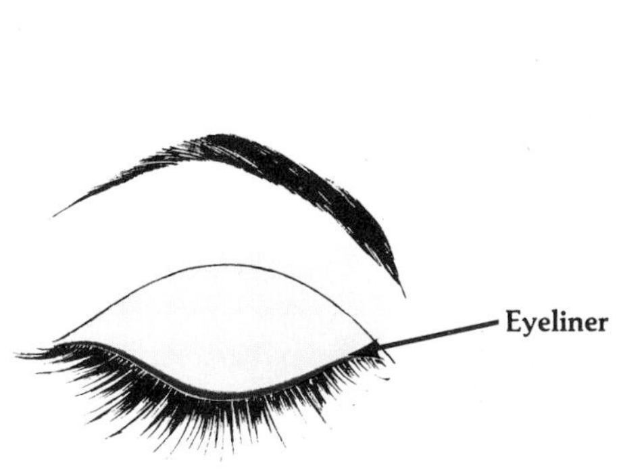

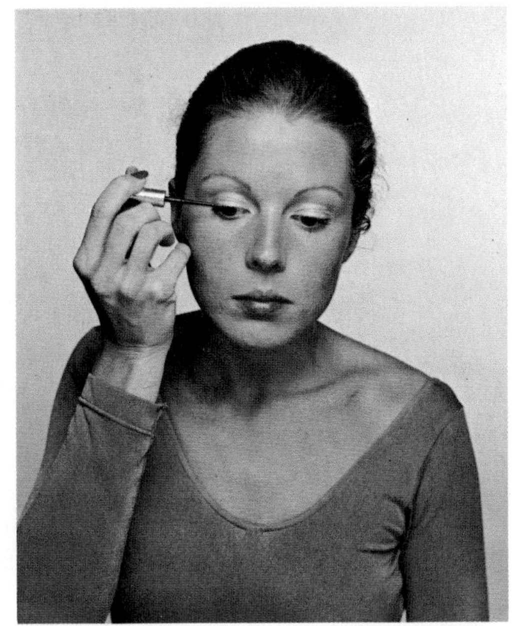

Photography by Terry Webb

ILLUS. 7-8 *If you use eyeliner, make it very thin and close to your lashes.*

MASCARA

Mascara is used to color the lashes uniformly, making them appear thicker and longer. It is available in cake, cream, and liquid form. Some liquid mascara has tiny fibers that lengthen and "fatten" the lashes. Apply mascara with either a brush or a stick applicator that comes with the liquid.

Selection. The color of mascara you wear depends upon your eye and hair color. Usually black mascara is good only for people with very dark hair and eyes. Most brownettes, redheads, and blondes fare better with a lighter color mascara. It is wise to start with a dark brown for daytime and save the colors to dramatize your leisure-time wear. Dark greens, dark blues, and plum colors are just a few colors that are available for special effects.

Application. To apply mascara, brush the lashes upward and outward (Illustration 7-9, next page). Don't forget to color the top of the upper lashes. For more color, allow the first application to dry and apply

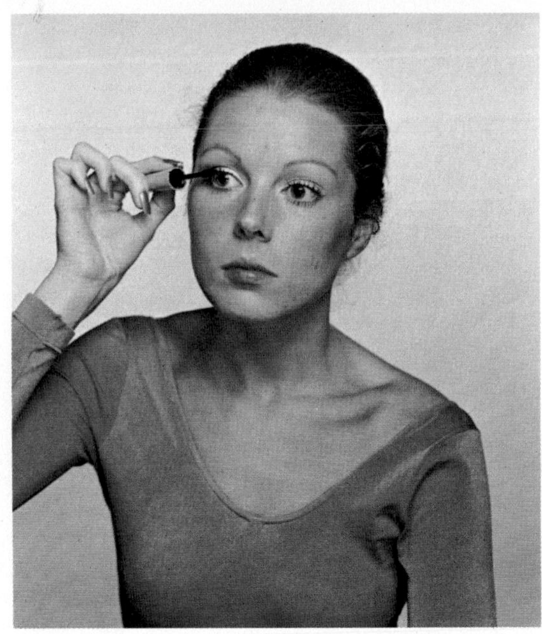

Photography by Terry Webb

ILLUS. 7-9 *Brush lashes upward and outward. Be sure to apply mascara to the top side as well as the underside of your lashes.*

another coat. Mascara should be applied sparingly, if at all, to lower lashes. Mascara applied on lower lashes tends to smear on the skin just below your eye; so be careful to keep this area clean throughout the day if you wear mascara on your lower lashes. Before your mascara dries, use a clean lash brush to separate the lashes for a full, natural look. After your mascara dries, place a tissue under your lower lash and brush upper and lower lashes again to remove loose makeup and prevent it from falling on your face or in your eyes during the day.

Eyelash Curling. After your mascara is dry and you have brushed away any debris, you may want to use an eyelash curling appliance for a flattering, wide-eyed look. Gently squeeze the lashes with the curler and hold for ten to thirty seconds. Practice with this appliance will make you expert in curling your lashes.

LIP COLOR

The purpose of lip color is to shape and emphasize your lips. Your mood is usually expressed by the way your lips look. It is important that lip color be applied correctly and kept fresh throughout the day.

Selection. Lip color is available in gel and cream form. The color you wear may be keyed to the color of your costume or of your complexion. Experimentation with a tester at your cosmetic counter is the best way to select a lip color. Dark and bright colors fade into and out of fashion. For daytime wear you probably will find lighter shades most flattering.

Application. Apply lip color with a lip brush (Illustration 7-10). Using a brush instead of the gel stick itself reduces the bleeding of color and improves wearability. Put plenty of cream or gel on the brush bristles to make an even line. Keep your lips closed but relaxed and draw a firm outline on half of the upper lip from center to outer corners. Next, open your mouth stretching your lips taut and retrace the line to fill in all lip creases. Complete the upper and lower lips. You may fill in with the brush or with the stick. DO NOT BLOT. Today's formulas do not require blotting; indeed, the texture and gloss are distorted when you do blot them. Along with the lip color, a clear gloss or conditioner may be applied either beneath or on top of the color. The use of such a conditioner or gloss gives a sheen that is flattering to most people, and it protects your lips from harsh weather.

Each time you reapply your lip color, carefully tissue off the remains of the last application. Lip color is most attractive and remains true in color longer when it is applied to clean lips.

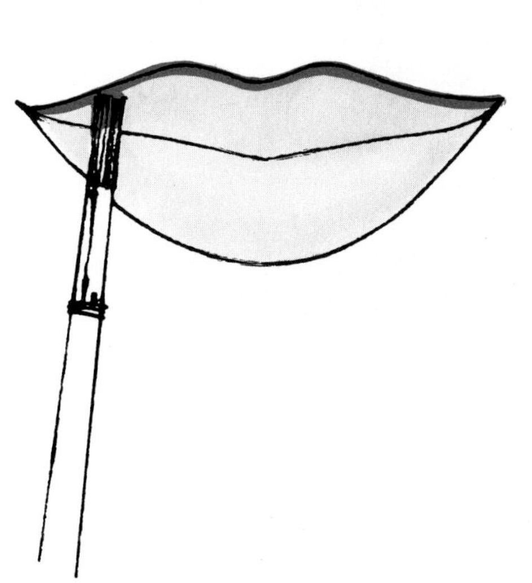

Photography by Terry Webb

ILLUS. 7-10 *Using a brush, outline your lips with color. Fill in with either the gel stick or the brush.*

Shaping. The most desirable lip shape is upper and lower lips that are approximately equal in size. If yours are not, you can create some illusion by outlining the fullest lip just inside the natural line and outlining the thinner one exactly on the natural line. Do not try to compensate for unequal lips by putting lip color outside the lip area. The skin around your lips is somewhat different in texture from your lips, and the color will not look the same as it does on your lips. You will merely look as if you made a mistake in applying your lip color.

YOUR BASIC MAKEUP ROUTINE

If you are just learning about makeup procedure, you need to practice the basic techniques in this section. Actually, your routine is easy and fast once you learn it.

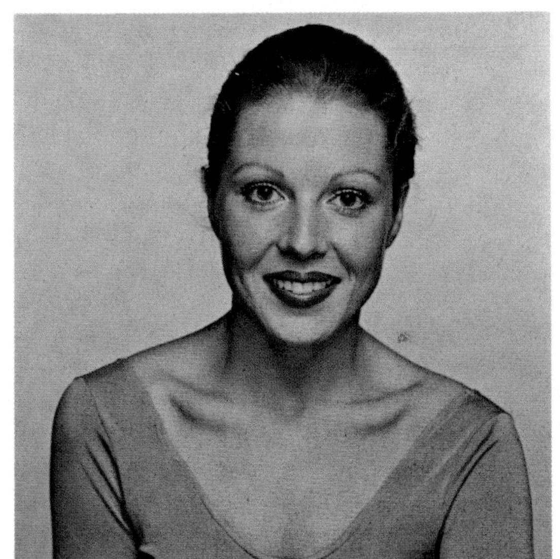

ILLUS. 7-11 *With just a little practice, you can have a radiant face.*

Photography by Terry Webb

If you follow the steps below, you probably will spend less than 15 minutes a day in making up your face.

(1) Start with a clean, freshened face and clean hands (Illustration 7-12).

(2) Apply under-makeup moisturizer (Illustration 7-13).

(3) Apply foundation (Illustration 7-14).

(4) Apply cheek color and powder (Illustration 7-15).

(5) Apply brow color.

(6) Apply eyeshadow (Illustration 7-16, next page).
(7) Apply eyeliner.
(8) Apply mascara and curl lashes.
(9) Apply lip color (Illustration 7-17).
(10) Check your face for lines of demarcation (Illustration 7-18).

ILLUS. 7-12 *Start with a clean, freshened face and clean hands.*

Fashion Fair

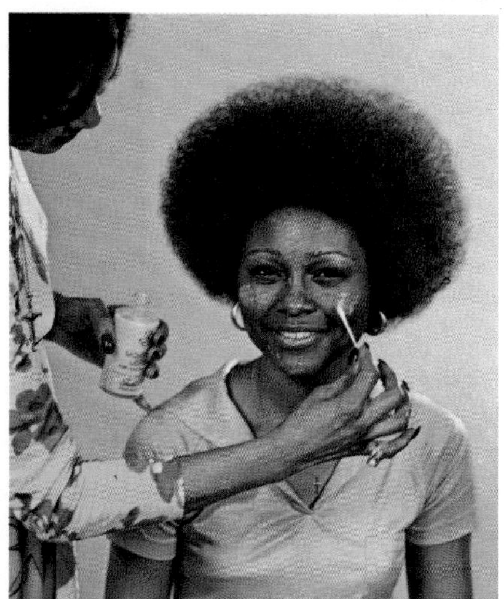

ILLUS. 7-13 *Apply under-makeup moisturizer*

Fashion Fair

ILLUS. 7-14 *Apply foundation.*

Fashion Fair

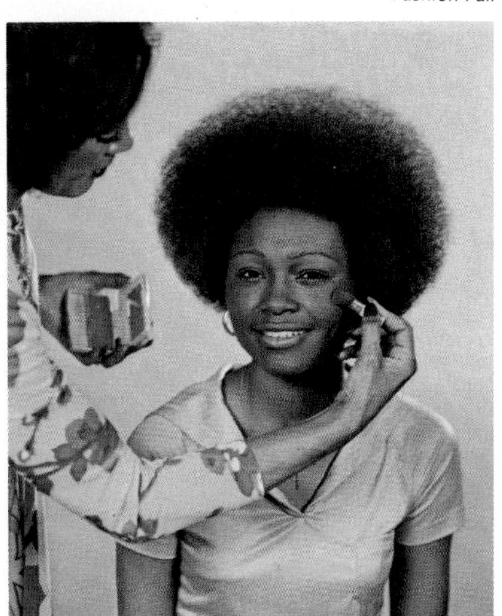

ILLUS. 7-15 *Apply cheek color and powder.*

Fashion Fair

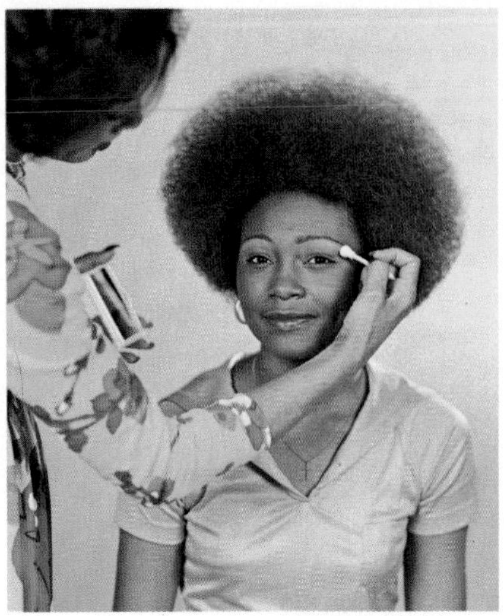

ILLUS. 7-16 *Apply eyeshadow and eyeliner. Apply mascara and curl lashes.*

Fashion Fair

ILLUS. 7-17 *Apply lip color.*

Fashion Fair

ILLUS. 7-18 *Check your face for lines of demarcation.*

Periodically throughout the day, especially if you eat, you will want to tissue off remaining lip color and reapply it fresh. You may want to lightly powder a shiny nose, chin, and forehead if you have excess oil in these areas.

Special Techniques

When you have mastered the basic techniques of makeup application, you will want to tailor your makeup to fit your own special needs. Some of the makeup procedures you can use for this purpose are: contouring, shading, highlighting, glossing various parts of your face, tweezing your eyebrows, and adding false eyelashes.

OVALIZING YOUR FACE SHAPE

The oval-shape face has been designated as the most desirable face shape because most hairstyles, necklines, and collars are attractive with it. Other face shapes are as interesting and attractive, but they usually need some camouflaging via makeup, hairstyle, and dress to balance their irregular features.

Take a good look at your face with your hair pulled back. Study your jaw line and decide whether your face is most nearly oval, square, oblong, or round (Illustration 7-19). If your face is oval, you probably have no irregular features. However, if it is not oval, you should learn to ovalize it, using highlight, shader, blushers, and gloss. In a later chapter you will learn which hairstyles contribute to ovalizing your face.

ILLUS. 7-19 *Study the shape of your face to discover any variations from an oval shape.*

Supplies. To contour your face successfully, you must practice at home and check your face carefully in strong daylight before you make contouring a regular part of your routine. The supplies needed are a darker shade of foundation, rouge and/or blush, a white or very light pink highlighter, and a gloss. Remember, when you contour, that light shades attract attention and make the area look larger. Dark shades generally diminish and de-emphasize the surface to which they are applied. A glossy surface attracts attention to itself.

All contouring colors must be *subtle*. In contouring, it is the subtle contrast of light and dark colors carefully blended that accents your most attractive features, diminishes your less attractive ones, and balances your face.

Applications. Any face shape can use a "wide-eyed" look by applying white or light shadow just below the brow, a light line of dark shadow from the crease to the bony ridge of the eye socket, and eyeshadow color to the upper lid. As in all contouring, the key is to carefully blend the contrasting light and dark shades so that no lines of demarcation are visible.

Contour shading to add width to the cheekbone area is achieved by applying a light highlighter just under your eye area, a cheek color on your cheekbone, then a darker shade of color (a brown or bronze) just below your cheek color in the "hollow" of your cheek (Illustration 7-20).

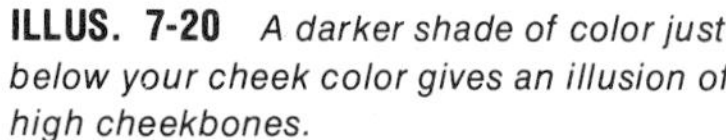

ILLUS. 7-20 *A darker shade of color just below your cheek color gives an illusion of high cheekbones.*

Lanvin — Charles of the Ritz *Photography by Bob Richardson*

To de-emphasize the shape of your jawline if it isn't oval, apply shader or a darker foundation on the areas of your jaw that make it a shape other than oval. Draw attention away from a jawline that is too wide by highlighting the center of your face. Examples of these balancing techniques are diagrammed in Illustrations 7-21, 22, 23, and 24. Use them as a guide. Your own face probably will not conform exactly to any picture. Study your own features and decide where you should place emphasis (highlighter) and where you should camouflage (darker foundation).

After you have completed the contouring, apply a clear gloss in the areas you wish to emphasize. Petroleum jelly or a commercially prepared glossing product can be used. Areas that can be emphasized with a gloss are your lips after lipstick has been applied, the highest point of your checkbone, your eyelid, and the area just under your brow.

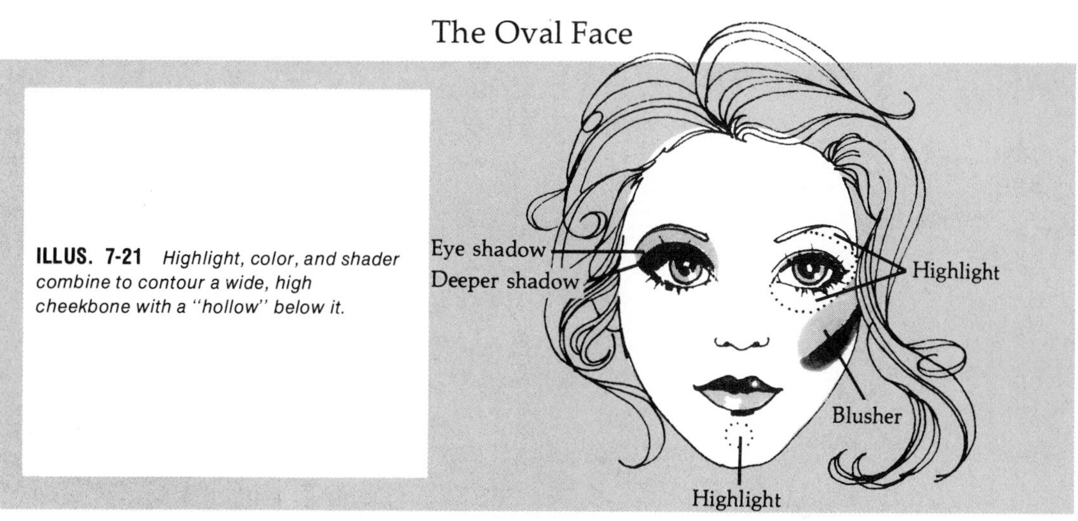

ILLUS. 7-21 *Highlight, color, and shader combine to contour a wide, high cheekbone with a "hollow" below it.*

The Square Face

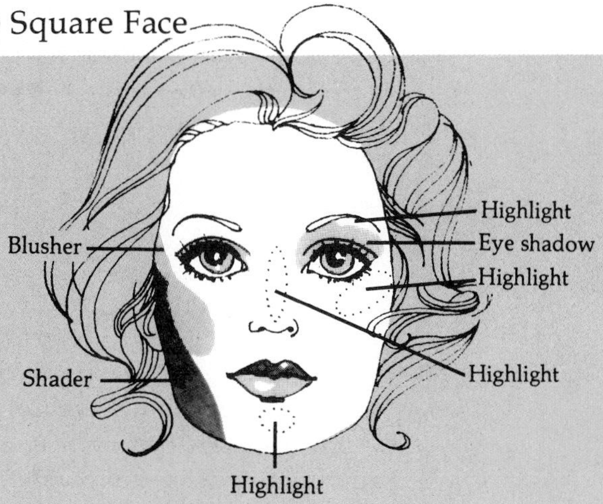

Highlight
Eye shadow
Highlight
Blusher
Highlight
Shader
Highlight

ILLUS. 7-22 *A shader softens and diminishes the square corners to give an oval illusion. Cheek color applied at an angle to the jawline and highlight to the center of the face draw attention away from the corners of the square face.*

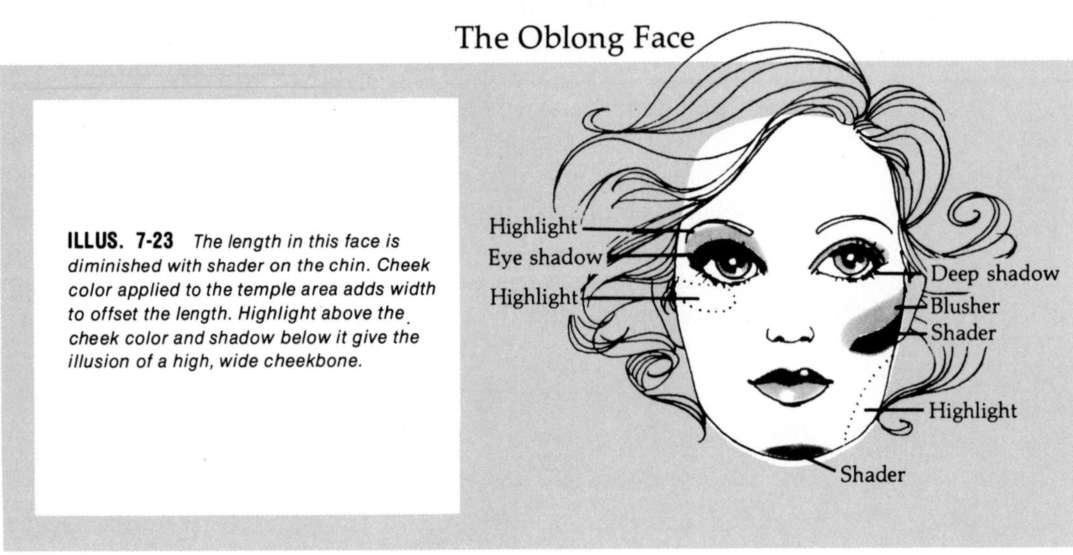

ILLUS. 7-23 *The length in this face is diminished with shader on the chin. Cheek color applied to the temple area adds width to offset the length. Highlight above the cheek color and shadow below it give the illusion of a high, wide cheekbone.*

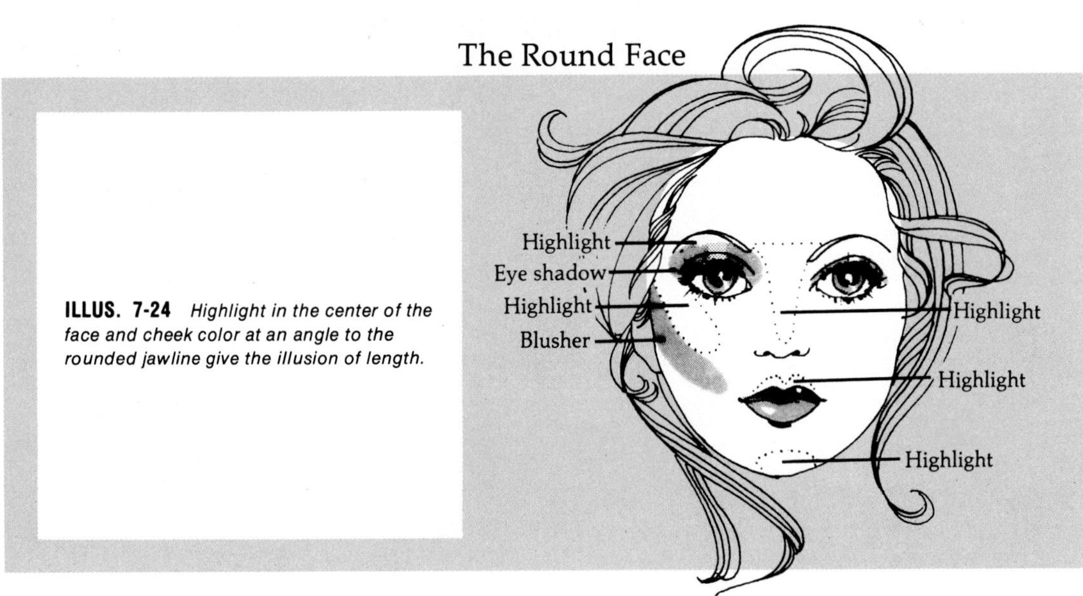

ILLUS. 7-24 *Highlight in the center of the face and cheek color at an angle to the rounded jawline give the illusion of length.*

SHAPING YOUR EYEBROWS

The shape of your eyebrows can help balance your facial features. Eyebrows are shaped by tweezing. First, it is important to tweeze stray hairs from under the browline (Illustration 7-25). Depending upon how quickly your brows grow, you should establish a regular schedule for tweezing these stray hairs. For some people, the routine will be nightly, for others, weekly, for most, sometime in between. Tweezing should be done after your face has been thoroughly cleansed. Use a little astringent or alcohol on a cotton ball to apply after the hairs have been removed to reduce the chance of irritation. The proper procedure for tweezing is to grasp the hair near its roots and gently pull in the same direction in which the hair grows.

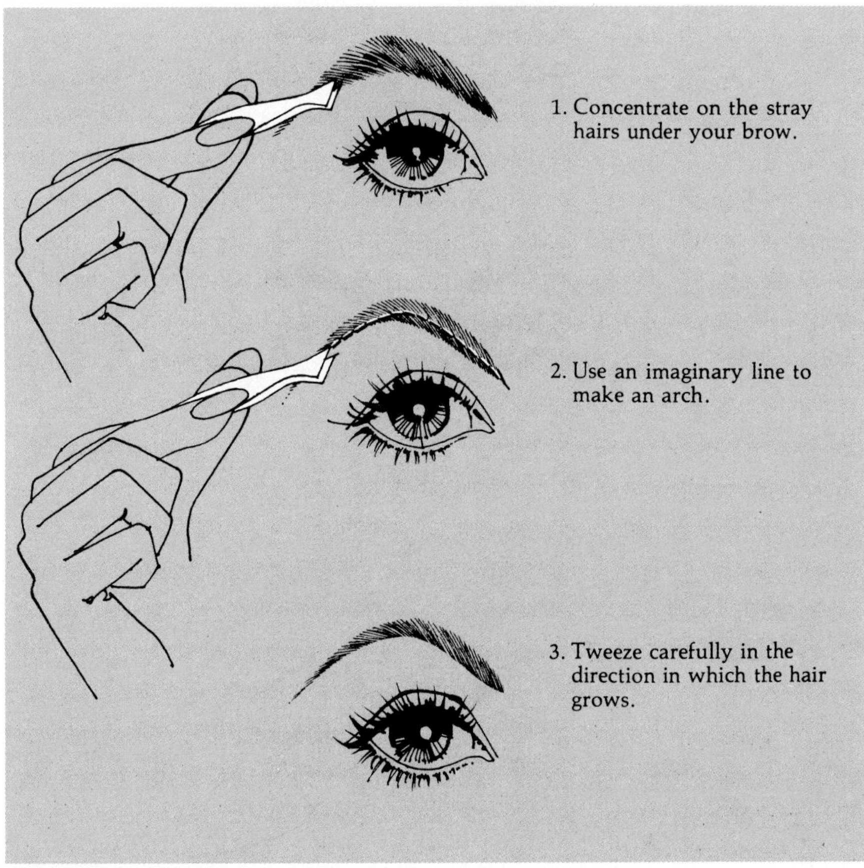

ILLUS. 7-25 *Tweeze stray hairs from under your brow by pulling carefully in the direction in which the hair grows.*

The Arch. Your facial features as well as the relative placement of your eyes will dictate the shape of your brows (Illustration 7-26, next page). The tweezing to be done to brows on a face with a narrow forehead and close-set eyes begins near the nose. The brows should not extend closer to the nose than just outside the inside corner of the eye, and they should be arched very close to the outer edge of the brow.

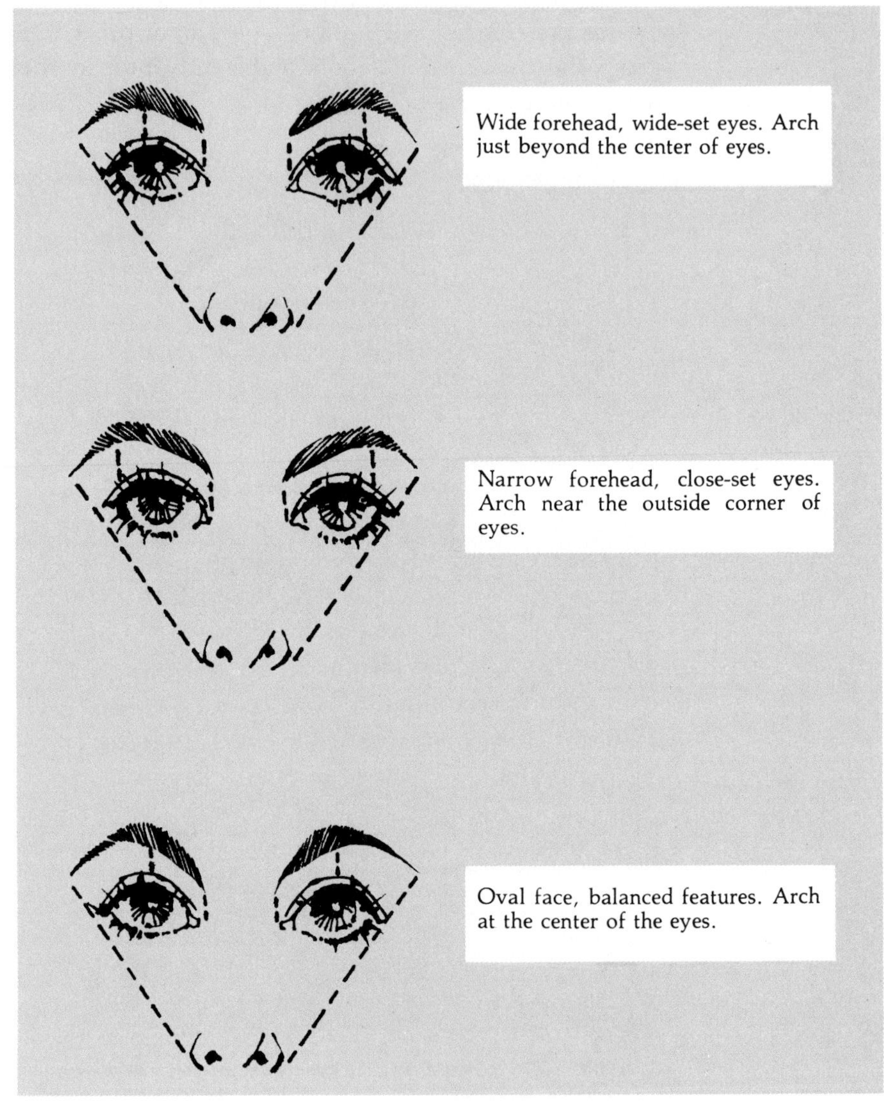

ILLUS. 7-26 *Your arch should be no closer to the center of your eye than the center of your iris.*

The broad face with wide-set eyes and a wide forehead should have brows that extend much closer to the nose with the arch just beyond the middle of the eye.

The oval face should have brows that begin and arch in a slightly different arrangement. The arch will be approximately at the center of the eye, and the brow will begin near the inside corner of the eye.

The Length. For all face shapes, the brow should not extend beyond an imaginary line extended from the corner of the nose through the outside corner of the eye. Measure this line with a pencil when you tweeze, as shown in Illustration 7-27.

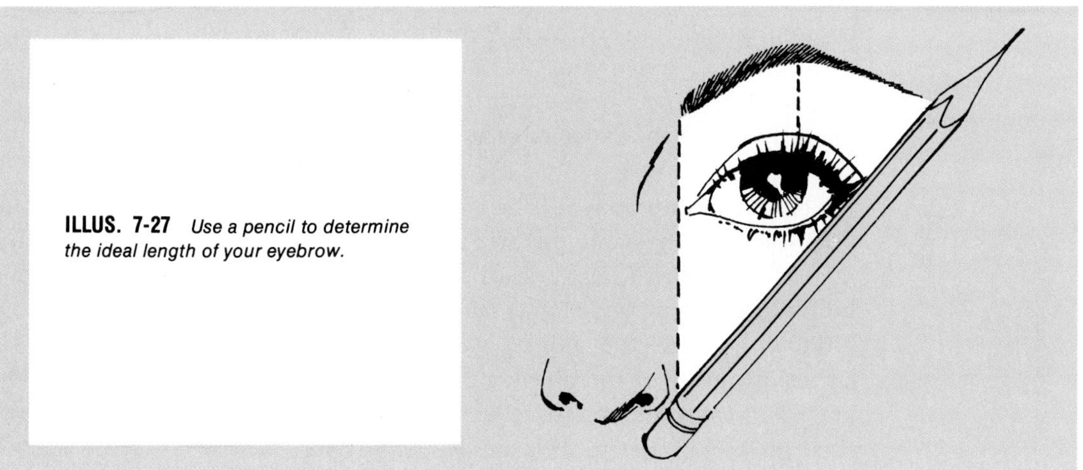

ILLUS. 7-27 *Use a pencil to determine the ideal length of your eyebrow.*

FALSE EYELASHES

False eyelashes are becoming more and more popular for daytime wear. They are available in many lengths, densities, and colors. You should select a color and density to match your own. Lashes that are very much darker or very much thicker than your own will never look natural on you.

Trimming. You may need to trim the length from the hairs in your false lashes. Trim them one hair at a time, and make them slightly uneven like your own. You probably will need also to trim the lashes to fit the width of your own lid. Actually, you should make them just slightly narrower than your lid, to give a natural look. False lashes are applied with waterproof surgical adhesive that does not dry hard. You should carry the adhesive in your handbag for emergency repairs any time you are wearing your lashes. A pair of blunt-edge tweezers are useful in handling the lashes.

To measure the lashes, hold them with your tweezers against your eyelid. Trim them only on the edge with the longest lashes. This cut edge should always be the outer edge. Cutting automatically designates a left and right lash. Do not get them mixed up.

Application. To apply the lashes, use a pin or toothpick to dab a small amount of surgical adhesive, available from a drugstore, in a thin line along the false eyelash strip. Let it set for 20 to 30 seconds. Look down into a mirror, exposing your lid as if you were applying eyeliner. Hold the lashes with your tweezers by the outer edge. Press the lash, beginning at the inside corner, to the edge of your own lid. Try to place the lashes just above your own lashes and not on them. You may need to practice this procedure several times before you are expert. To remove the lash, grasp the outer edge with your tweezers, and peel it off. Keep your lashes in a case with a curved surface.

Bottom lashes may also be worn. They are applied just beneath your own lashes in the same manner as your upper lashes. You may find that instead of a strip of false eyelashes for the bottom, clumps of lashes glued individually along your lower lash line are more flattering and more comfortable. To make the clumps, cut a strip of old lashes or a strip of lower lashes into two- or three-lash clumps. You may need to trim some of the length off the lower lashes to achieve a natural look. The clumps may be used instead of a strip of lashes for the upper lid also. They are usually used on the outer edge of your eyelid.

Although your eyes should be completely made up before you apply the lashes, you may want to reapply eyeliner and mascara after your lashes are in place. A *light* coat of mascara on false lashes gives a natural looking blend to your own lashes. All old mascara and adhesive should be cleaned off your false eyelashes before you wear them each time.

Storing. Clean your false eyelashes before your next wearing by peeling off the remaining adhesive and removing mascara with alcohol. Adhesive remaining on your own lid can be removed with oil.

If you desire more curl in your false lashes, especially to match the curl in your own lashes after you have curled them, store them rolled in a tissue around a pencil secured with aluminum foil. If your lashes are too curly, press them flat in a book for storage.

YOUR SPECIAL NEEDS

If you have troublesome blemishes or dark circles, cover them by using a stick of dense color approximately the color of your skin before you apply your foundation. These covers are made especially for this purpose. Apply your foundation over the cover, blending it with your foundation.

If you have especially oily skin, obtain blotting papers at your cosmetic counter to use periodically during the day to blot excess oil from your face.

For special occasions (evening only) you may want to use cosmetics with glitter and luminescent properties. They are available with a golden hue as well as with sparkle. Such cosmetics are most effective when used sparingly on the cheekbone or on the eyelid. Carefully avoid placing such eye-attracting makeup on your nose or forehead.

For travel, you will need small bottles of your makeup. If you cannot obtain them, purchase small plastic containers for travel. They are much lighter in weight than glass, and you can seal them more effectively by pressing the sides so that air is forced out before screwing on the lid. The suction produced when the sides are released keeps the lid on tight while you are traveling.

Most makeup products are available in nonallergenic formulas. Actually, nonallergenic means that the manufacturer has taken out the chemicals to which most people are allergic. They may or may not be the ones to which you are allergic. Frequently allergies are caused by substances other than your makeup; but because the rash or irritation appears on your face, you tend to think it is caused by your makeup. It may be wise to examine other possibilities before blaming your makeup.

If you feel that your regular facial features make you unattractive, study your face carefully. Determine what you can emphasize — eyes, high cheekbones, a well-shaped mouth — and practice contouring techniques to call attention to that area. Use the diminishing techniques to draw attention away from those irregular areas. Perfection of contouring techniques to emphasize one area of your face will obscure the areas you don't want noticed. It takes only one well-defined characteristic in a face to make it memorable. Only you will know of the irregularities; others will not.

SUMMARY

The purpose of makeup is to enhance your appearance by defining your attractive features and balancing your irregular ones. With the techniques you have learned, you are ready to develop just the right balance for yourself. Subtle application with practice in your free time is the way to adapt makeup to fit your own needs. Don't be afraid to try. Wear your "face" a few hours before you decide for or against a new application; and remember that too little makeup, as well as too much, will deprive you of the most attractive face you can have.

Understanding Face Definition

1. What is the purpose of under-makeup moisturizer?
2. What is the "no makeup" look?
3. Why would you use a foundation?
4. What is the purpose of makeup?
5. Eyebrow color is available in both powder and pencil forms. Describe the use of each one. What would you choose?
6. To what should eyeshadow color be keyed?
7. How do you apply liner?
8. Why do you brush your lashes after mascara is dry?
9. Why and how do you use a brush to apply lip color?
10. After you learn the basic techniques of makeup application, what can you do to tailor your makeup to your own facial features?

Chapter 8

Hair Halos

Hair has been of great importance in the lives of people throughout the ages, at least from Samson's time forward. It has recently been a form of expressing one's protest against the ills of society. Hair actually is a protective covering for your head. What you do with that covering in terms of keeping it clean, healthy, and arranged, though, can make a great difference in your personal appearance.

The most tempting solution to the problem of caring for your hair is simply to wash it, dry it, and let it hang straight from a center part or frizz it if it's curly. While a child of five or even a teenager of fourteen may look her best at home or perhaps at school with unarranged, unstyled hair, most of us don't. Hair simply requires more attention and care to present the well-groomed appearance expected for success in today's competitive world.

Basic Care

To have the best looking hair you can have, you must have clean, healthy hair. You may need to learn corrective procedures, too, if you have hair that is hard to handle or that has been abused. Shampooing and corrective techniques may open a whole new world of hair wear for you because, with good care, your hair can become more like that which you have admired on others.

SHAMPOOING

One of nicest things you can do for your grooming is to shampoo your hair well and regularly. Shampooing is more than wetting, pouring on a little soap, and rinsing. You can learn to give yourself a really good shampoo with very little effort.

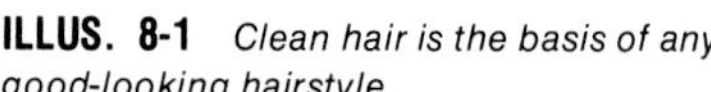

ILLUS. 8-1 *Clean hair is the basis of any good-looking hairstyle.*

Alexandra de Markoff

Before you wet your hair, brush out all the loose spray, dirt, and dust, along with any backcombing you may have in it. If you are washing your hair in the shower, brush your hair back so that it will require a minimum of rearranging once it is wet. If you are bending over the sink to wash it, brush your hair forward.

A wide-tooth comb is handy to have beside you when you are shampooing your hair. You can comb conditioners down through your hair, making sure that each hair is coated and that the ends are saturated.

When you wet your hair use warm — not hot — water. Hot water seems to have a drying effect on dry hair and to stimulate oil gland production in oily hair. Warm-water-saturated hair is ready for shampoo. Start with your scalp, sudsing it and rubbing it with your fingertips — not your nails — to remove any scale and dirt. Add more shampoo if you need it, and clean your hair next, working from your scalp to the ends. Try to work quickly because leaving shampoo on too long seems to dry your hair out. If your hair is not exceptionally dirty or oily, one soaping is sufficient.

The rinse should be warm-to-cool water, if you can stand it. The rinse cannot be too well done. Rinse and rinse and then rinse some more. This is where most people shortchange their hair — soap left in dulls the hair and makes it tacky so that it attracts dirt and grime. What a mess! Try a cold water rinse at the end of your shampoo to give your hair shine.

Gently squeeze the water out of your hair, being careful not to pull or twist any of it. Wet hair is very fragile. Wrap a towel around your hair and let it soak up the excess water. Gently blot it with the towel, trying not to tangle it. Avoid rubbing the hair strands together when they are wet. After your hair is towel-dried you can use conditioners, cream rinses, and setting lotions if you wish.

The shampoo you use should suit the needs of your hair. There are shampoos designed to combat excessive oil, dryness, and dandruff; and you can get shampoo designed for use on hair that is colored. There are even some made for use without water. They are rarely satisfactory for regular use, though, and are used mainly when you cannot possibly wet your hair.

CORRECTIVE PROCEDURES

You probably will not go through life completely satisfied with your hair. Either its condition, texture, bulk, oil, flaking scalp, curl, or color will not be to your liking. Perhaps the products you select to groom it will not perform to give you the desired results. Prepare yourself for these periods of discontent by learning what is available and what you can expect from the products you use on your hair.

Conditioning. Conditioning does not heal or permanently change abused hair. It does add strength, though, and helps prevent further damage or breaking. Hair that has been subjected to harsh weather or to chemicals, such as those used to permanently curl or color it, needs to be conditioned approximately every four to six weeks. The chemicals used for coloring and curling penetrate the hair shaft, causing tiny breaks in it. Conditioning temporarily fills these tiny breaks, giving some strength to the hair, making it smoother looking and usually more manageable. The longer and more often hair is subjected to chemicals or weather, the more often it needs conditioning. The ends of the strands need more conditioning care than that part which has newly grown from the scalp. Concentrating the conditioner where your hair is in poorest condition corrects damage without softening the hair too much near the scalp, where you may want more body.

Conditioners are applied to your hair after you shampoo, rinse, and towel-dry it. They may be left on for twenty to thirty minutes with or without heat, or they may be required for only two or three minutes. The hair is then flushed with cool-to-warm water, blot-dried again, and it is ready for hairsetting lotion.

Conditioners work by coating the hair shaft to make it much smoother. If they are designed to stay on for twenty-to-thirty minutes, they penetrate the hair shaft, adding strength. If they are designed for two-to-three minutes or less, they merely are coating the shaft. It is possible to get a buildup of the quickie conditioners if you use them after every shampoo. If you notice a dulling near the ends, or if they seem sticky when they are dry, you may need either to refrain from using conditioners for a while to allow the buildup to be stripped from the ends or begin using a vinegar or lemon rinse to strip the buildup. The occurrence of buildup depends upon how porous your hair is and the chemical makeup of the particular conditioner you are using.

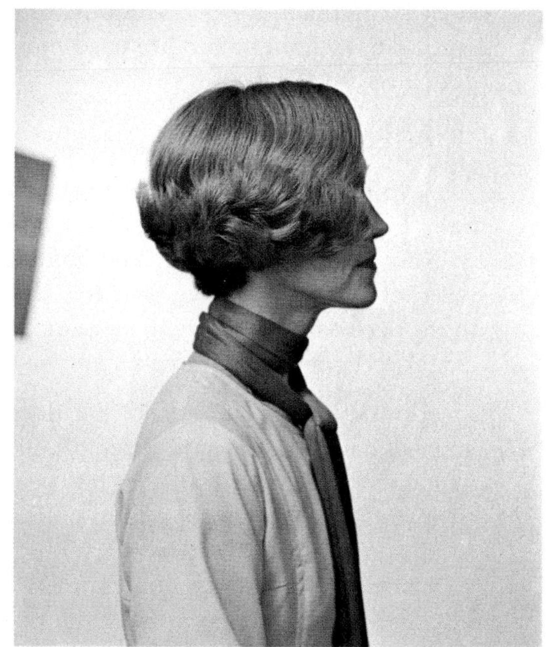

ILLUS. 8-2 *Conditioning colored hair is imperative.*

Hairstyle by Travis Johnson *Photography by Terry Webb*

Texture. *Texture* refers to the fineness or coarseness of your hair. Too much or too little texture can be controlled with products designed especially for that purpose. Texture or manageability can be added to fine hair with products labeled as "body builders" or "texturizers." These products add a coating to the hair shaft, making it seem to have more bounce of its own. You can accumulate a buildup of texturizers on your hair, making it dull, if you use them regularly and if your hair is very porous. If this seems to be happening, refrain from using the texturizer for a couple of shampoos to see if the shine returns to your hair.

Too much texture or coarseness can be tamed with a cream rinse, which makes coarse hair much softer. The cream rinse is rinsed in your hair after you shampoo it. Try to keep the texturizers and cream rinses away from your scalp. They were intended for your hair, not your skin.

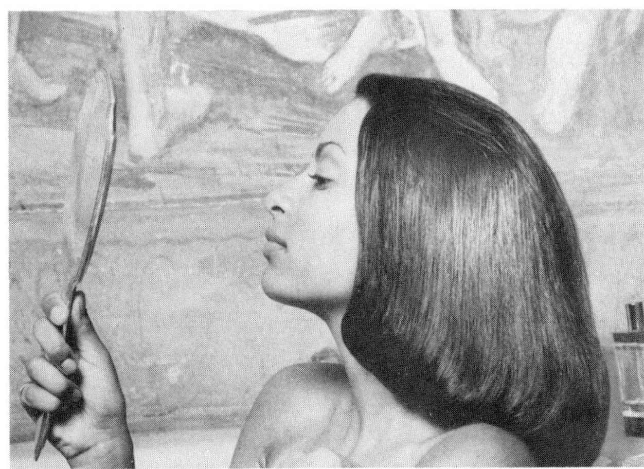

ILLUS. 8-3 *Too much texture can be tamed with a cream rinse.*

Walter Fountaine, Director of Glemby Specialists, Glemby International

Bulk. Closely related to texture is the bulk of your hair. Bulk refers to the relative amount of hair you seem to have — thick or thin. Most of us lose up to 50 hairs a day, but these are replaced continuously since new ones are growing constantly. Few people are satisfied with the amount of hair they seem to have growing on their heads. There are some products to help give the illusion of more hair, but few to give the illusion of less hair. "Body builders" coat the hair, causing it to appear fuller (Illustration 8-4, next page). Also, you can color your hair, which tends to make the hair shaft swell, seeming to give it more bulk. Hair cuts and styling are important in reflecting more or less bulk in your hair. Hair-setting lotions frequently add bulk to your hair by coating it, especially near the scalp. It is important to keep hair setting lotions off the scalp itself, though, because they tend to flake off your skin when they are dry, making it look as if you have dandruff.

Oil. Hair is frequently either too oily or not oily enough. If it is too oily, frequent shampooing is a must. Use shampoos and aids designed especially for oily hair. Avoiding cream-based rinses, shampoos, and grooming aids will help control oil, too.

ILLUS. 8-4 *Body-builders can change the appearance of bulk of your hair.*

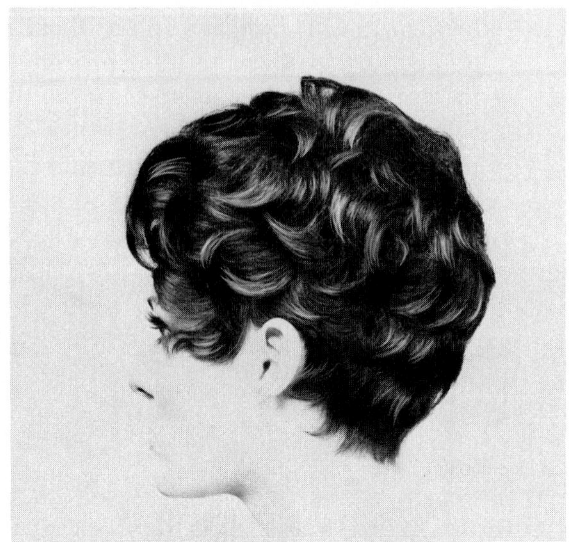

Hairstyle by Travis Johnson

If your hair is too dry, allow longer periods (up to a week) between shampooing. Use cream-based rinses and grooming aids designed for dry hair.

A vinegar or lemon rinse frequently makes oily hair more manageable but tends to cause dry hair to become even dryer. Very hot dryers are bad for both oily and dry hair. The hot air seems to stimulate the overactive oil glands in oily scalps and to further dry the hair shafts of dry hair without activating the lazy oil glands of the scalp. Warm air is best for drying your hair.

Dandruff. A dandruff problem is shared by many people. There is no known cure for dandruff. It is believed to be excessive flaking of the skin cells of the scalp, and there is no way to prevent it. You should shampoo when your scalp begins to flake. Massaging your scalp gently with your fingertips before shampooing may loosen scale that may be ready to fall so that you can shampoo it out. Use of dandruff-control shampoos will help control your dandruff, but they will not cure it. With continued use, your scalp may build up tolerance for the active ingredients in your dandruff-control shampoo, making it lose its effectiveness. Switch brands if your shampoo seems to quit working. Be very careful about allowing the "fallout" to rest on your clothes. A bit of flaking scalp on your collar or shoulders makes you look very untidy.

Curl. The permanent curl in your hair can be increased or decreased at your pleasure — almost. There are, of course, permanent wave solutions that alter the structure of your hair shaft to make it straighter or curlier. These, applied to your hair when it is rolled on a permanent wave rod, will permanently curl your hair. Applied to your hair while it is pulled straight, these solutions will permanently straighten your hair. The permanence of either process depends upon the strength of the solution. The main consideration is not how long your hair remains either curled or straightened but how much of the chemical it can take without damaging the hair. Very curly hair must take much abuse if it is to be permanently, very permanently straightened. Very straight, lank hair, likewise suffers strong assults from powerful solutions if it is to be very tightly curled. The point is, don't try to permanently change your hair too much in either direction. Select a style that uses at least a degree of curl or straightness that is native to your hair shaft so that you won't be tempted to damage the shaft with strong solutions in an attempt to permanently curl or uncurl it. Once hair has been permanently curled or straightened, it should not be redone until new hair grows out and all the hair already exposed to the solution has been cut off.

Walter Fountaine, Director of Glemby Specialists, Glemby International

ILLUS. 8-5 *Hair can be permanently straightened.*

Hairstyle by Travis Johnson Photography by Terry Webb

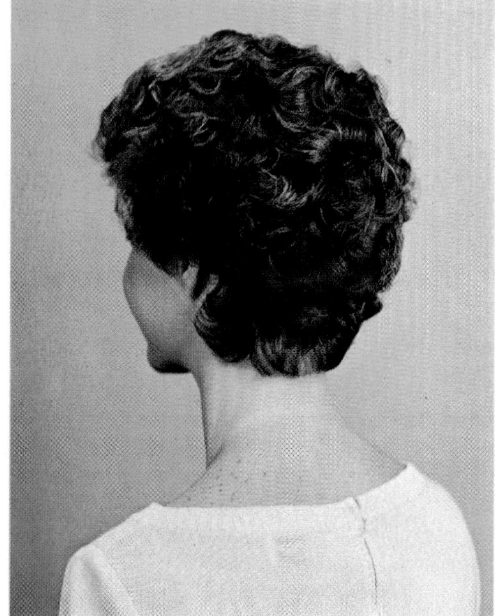

Hairstyle by Travis Johnson Photography by Terry Webb

ILLUS. 8-6 *Hair can be permanently curled.*

Color. At some time in your life, you probably will want to change or alter the color of your hair. There are some basic principles of permanent hair coloring that will help you to make and execute these decisions.

You can have very pretty highlights and colors with little trouble if you stay with your own basic color. Coloring can be a great deal of trouble, however, if you are a dark brunette who decides to change to flaming red or blonde. The new growth of hair (approximately one-half inch per month) must be colored as soon as it begins to show. However, if you are a dark brunette who simply has added red or auburn highlights, or who has frosted parts of the hair blonde, you may not need to retouch the hair for several months. Because coloring is a chemical treatment that can damage your hair, it is better not to select a color very different from your own so that the treatment will not have to be repeated frequently.

If you wish to change your hair color, be sure first of all that your complexion will be complemented by the color you select. If you are dark complexioned, do not try to change your hair to a very light red or blonde. If you are in doubt about how a color will look with your complexion, try on a wig of that color, and check your face in daylight and artificial light. Frequently it is necessary to change your makeup colors to a shade darker or lighter when you change the color of your hair. Sometimes it is helpful to darken or lighten your brows. While your wardrobe colors may remain basically the same, you may find that brighter or darker hues of your basic colors will complement your new hair color.

There are several disadvantages to changing the color of your hair. Frequent coloring without regard to regular conditioning can permanently damage your hair. You will need to use a shampoo that is formulated for colored hair so that it will not strip the color each time you shampoo. Conditioning must be done at least once a month, perhaps more often. Most people need to condition when they "touch up" the new growth of hair which occurs approximately every four weeks.

The advantages to coloring your hair depend upon how it improves your appearance and the manageability of your hair. As you age, lighter hair tends to look better with your complexion and may be well worth the effort it takes to maintain it. If your hair is fine and thin, coloring it will give it more body because the chemicals in the coloring process swell the hair shaft. If can also make your hair dry and coarse, though, and you must be alert to these problems.

You can achieve some of the advantages without many of the disadvantages of coloring your hair by frosting or streaking it. Coloring in this manner does not require a touch-up as frequently as an all-over color does, yet it gives your hair new drama and some body. Many people find it necessary to refrost or restreak the hair only at four- to six-month intervals instead of four- to six-week intervals for all-over colored hair (Illustration 8-7, next page).

When you decide to change the color of your hair, decide whether you wish to go lighter or darker or whether you simply want the highlight effect of streaking or frosting. If you are going lighter or highlighting you will be involved in a two-step process unless your hair is very light already. This will involve stripping your hair of its color (the first step) and adding the color you want in the form of a toner (the second step). If you are already very light and want only to go a bit lighter, or if you want to darken your hair, you will probably be involved only in a one-step process. In a one-step process the chemical agent that causes the color to penetrate the hair shaft is mixed with the color itself and both are applied at the same time.

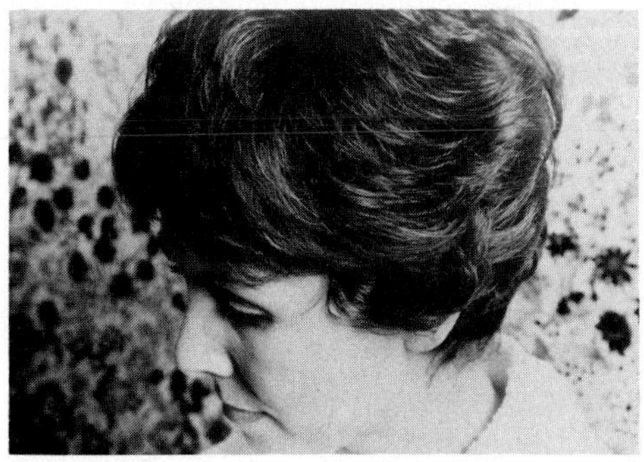

Clairol Quiet Touch

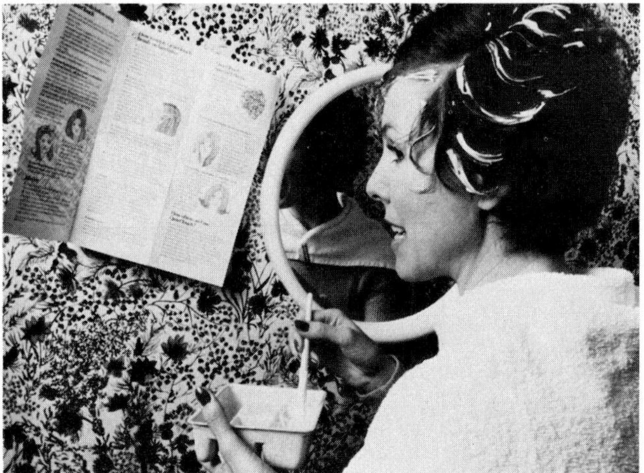

Clairol Quiet Touch

ILLUS. 8-7 *Frosting or streaking can change the appearance of the color of your hair.*

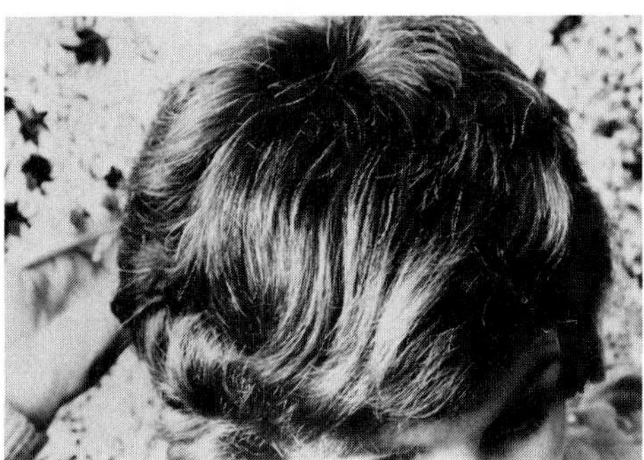

Clairol Quiet Touch

It is wise to let a professional hair colorist permanently color your hair for the first time. The hair colorist will want to "patch test" you for allergic reactions to the chemicals, and you will want a "strand test" before you actually submit to the color change. The patch test can save you much physical discomfort if you are allergic to the chemicals used. The strand test, in which a small amount of your hair is colored as a test to see how the color turns out before you do all of your hair, can save you much emotional discomfort if you do not like the resulting color. Hair that is permanently colored cannot be changed at will; it must have a resting period between color changes. You will have to live with whatever you get, at least for a while.

ILLUS. 8-8 *Be sure your complexion is complemented by the color of your hair as this girl's is.*

Hairstyle by Travis Johnson *Photography by Terry Webb*

Temporary Color. There are coloring products designed for temporary changes. Instead of penetrating the hair shaft, stripping and replacing your natural color, they simply coat your hair, covering your natural color. Only slight changes can be achieved if you are trying to lighten because your natural color shows through the coating.

Temporary hair coloring products are designed mainly for covering gray and restoring faded color. They may last only until you shampoo again or through four or five shampoos, depending upon which kind you select.

Basic Styling

If you are to look your best everyday, no one area of grooming requires more thought, planning, and attention than your hair and its styling. Yet, becoming adept at handling and styling your own hair can yield more results in personal self-confidence with less effort and expense than any other area in grooming. It is a matter of getting to know your hair and yourself well, so that the style you select meets all your needs, and learning to execute that style with a minimum of effort.

STYLING AIDS

A professional hairdresser can do things for your hair that you cannot do as well for yourself. You owe it to yourself, however, to learn all you can about keeping your hair as attractive as possible between visits to your hairdresser. It will take a little practice to learn to use some of the products and aids that will help in caring for your hair, but your reward will be pretty hair — every day.

Comb and Brush. The comb and brush you've been using all your life are your most basic tools. Be sure that the teeth of the comb and the bristles of the brush have rounded ends. That is the main criterion. They can be plastic, rubber, or some natural substance; the substance makes little difference. The teeth on your comb should be spaced far enough apart to comb through your hair easily but close enough, of course, to arrange your hair. If your hair is heavy, thick, or very curly, try a synthetic brush which is stronger than a natural bristle one. Force yourself to replace your comb or brush when they show signs of wear, such as bristles or teeth with jagged or sharp edges. These can damage your hair. Hair grooming aids should be washed as often as your hair is. Combs and brushes other than those with wooden handles can be immersed in warm, soapy water to be cleaned. Use a fingernail brush to clean your comb, and swish your brush back and forth in the water to clean it. Rinse them carefully and dry them on a towel.

Clips, Pins, Combs, and Barrettes. Grooming aids for holding your hair in place should simply have smooth edges, and, in the case of rubber bands, they should be covered with fabric so that they cannot tangle and damage your hair. When you use such hair arranging aids, it is important not to pull the hair tightly and to vary the placement. You can pull your hair out by its roots if you put a great deal of pressure on your scalp in the same spot day after day. Keep clips, pins, combs, and barrettes clean. Throw them away when they have lost their spring or develop sharp edges.

Heated Curlers and Curling Irons. Heated curlers and curling irons are aids for curling and smoothing your hair. Heated curlers come in several sizes and may be mist, dry, or conditioner curlers. Curling irons may be with or without steam. It is a good idea to plan to use end papers to protect the ends of your hair from drying out if you use hot curlers or curling irons regularly on your hair.

To smooth your hair with a curling iron, start near the scalp on a section of hair and pull the hair smoothly through the iron. The heat tends to straighten and smooth the hair. If you want a slight "bend" near the end, take one or two turns and hold it for a few seconds. Curls that are set with heated rollers and curling irons need to cool completely before they are combed. A longer lasting set can be obtained with mist or a heat-activated setting lotion than with dry heat.

ILLUS. 8-9 *Curls set with curling irons should cool completely before combing.*

Clairol Crazy Curl

Rollers. Rollers for setting wet hair are made of various materials and in many sizes. There are two kinds of materials that rollers are made of that are gentle to your hair: (1) magnetic, smooth plastic and (2) wire-mesh without brushes. Your style determines the size you need. Usually rollers are clipped in with metal clips, but pins will work if they do not pull your hair.

The correct amount of hair for each roller is the amount of space the roller takes up when placed against your head. It should rest on the area where the hair that is wrapped around it grows. Be sure that when you put a roller in your hair you do not roll it tightly. The strain on the roots of your hair may damage them. Carefully enclose the ends of your hair in end papers, and smoothly wind the hair and papers around each roller so that you will not crimp the ends of your hair unattractively.

Hair Dryers. A home hair dryer is a good investment. There are three main kinds. A hand-held blow-dryer is used for drying hair before it is set or while you are setting it with a comb or brush. A flexible bonnet-type hair dryer is one that is designed to be placed over hair that is set wet on rollers. Bonnet dryers will work but they do not distribute the air as evenly as the third kind of dryer, a hard-hood type similar to that in a beauty salon.

A hand-held blow-dryer usually has several heat settings for drying your hair. Usually you comb your hair with a wide-tooth comb in the direction opposite to the way you will eventually set it, while you let the warm air blow it dry. It is best to dry a small section at a time. Trying to dry thick sections at one time tends to burn the outer hair, leaving the under hair slightly damp. You can severely burn your hair with a hand-held dryer if you hold it too close or too long over one section of hair. Many people blow-dry their hair prior to setting it on hot rollers. Others blow-dry, combing the hair into place as it dries so that it does not require a set. Your haircut determines which method you should use.

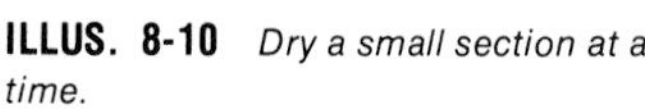

ILLUS. 8-10 *Dry a small section at a time.*

Clairol Progun 1000

Bonnet and hood-type dryers should have warm air settings because too much heat may damage your hair. The curls should be cooled before they are combed, and you can plan for this by turning the dryer to "cool" a few minutes before you are ready to comb.

Setting Lotion. Most hair styles last longer when setting lotions are used. Even if you are blow-drying your hair prior to setting it or while you set it, setting lotion combed through towel-dried hair will give you a longer lasting and more manageable set.

Some lotions are conditioners and setting lotion in one and are not designed to be rinsed out before setting as most conditioners are. These combination lotions are good for occasional use but may build up and dull your hair if they are used too frequently.

Hairspray. Hairspray fell into disrepute when it was used to construct monument-type hairstyles that could not be combed. When used correctly, however, it can give you hours of well-groomed hair through wind, rain, and sleet. Don't be afraid of its ill-gotten reputation. Try it on your hair a little at a time, holding the can 10 to 12 inches from your hair so that it lands in a fine mist wherever you need control.

HANDLING PROCEDURES

The less you have to handle your hair to keep it well-groomed, the better it is for your hair. The key to well-groomed hair every day, without excessive wear and tear from handling, is to get an expert cut of a good style for your particular hair and become an expert in setting and arranging it so that it stays put without frequent handling.

Haircuts. The basic cuts available are variations of four styles. The first three are blunt cuts and the fourth one is a layered one (Illustration 8-11). The blunt cuts can range from your chin line on down in length. The differences are: (1) the length is even all around, the sides being the same length as the back; (2) the sides are longer than the back; (3) the back is longer than the sides. Each of these blunt cuts can be with or without bangs, with a side or center part. The fourth cut is a layered one. The layered cut seems to have more body if the layers are blunt cut with scissors rather than a razor. The layers may all be the same length or may be of varying lengths, depending on the style you want.

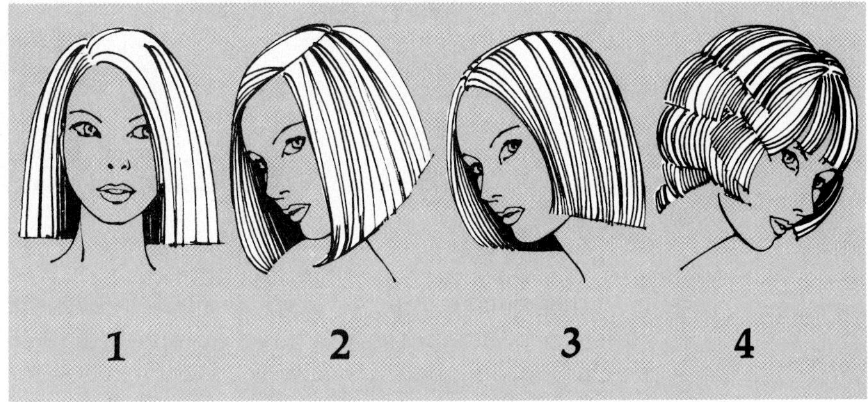

ILLUS. 8-11 *Hair can be blunt cut in three shapes or it can be layered in many lengths.*

Setting. Setting can be accomplished by blow-dry setting, with flat curls clipped or pinned in, and with rollers. Hair can also be wrapped around your head and dried for a very straight look. All setting works better with a setting lotion.

If you use a blow-dry set, you will need a brush or a wide-tooth comb. The hair is usually towel dried — blotted, not rubbed — and setting lotion is combed through. The hand-held hair dryer should be held approximately ten inches away from the head and moved from the scalp to the end of the hair while you comb or brush it in the direction opposite to what it will be when you are through. Move the dryer quickly enough so that not too much hot air is applied for too long a period to the hair. You can burn your hair very quickly. With short hair you can start at the crown or at the front hairline. With long hair you will probably find it easy to start at the hairline, combing forward as you dry it. Dry thin sections of hair at a time. When you use thick sections, the outer hair dries but the under hair remains damp. Blow-dry styles can be shaped with a curling iron; or you can use a few hot rollers at the crown or near the ends to give them shape.

ILLUS. 8-12 *You can set your hair with a hand-held hair dryer and a brush.*

Clairol Progun 1000

When you need just a "bend" around the edges of short hair, flat pin curls can be used. You can also accomplish the bend with hairsetting tape or a curling iron. Usually, you get a longer lasting set if you pin or tape the hair while it is wet with setting lotion. It is also possible to use large, flat pin curls on long hair to achieve a "slight bend" near the ends.

Long hair is more natural looking when it is set dry and allowed to stay in place a few hours before combing.

Plastic curlers are the favorite of most people. They are usually used in hair that is wet with setting lotion and dried under a hair dryer. The longest lasting set is achieved with this procedure. There are some basic hair setting procedures that you can use to achieve several hair styles (Illustration 8-13). To set your hair on rollers, start at the front top and make a row down the center of your head to your neckline. Starting at the top, roll two rows down each side. This basic pattern will comb into many styles. You can angle the top and side rows to achieve different effects. The same pattern can be used with hot rollers on dry hair.

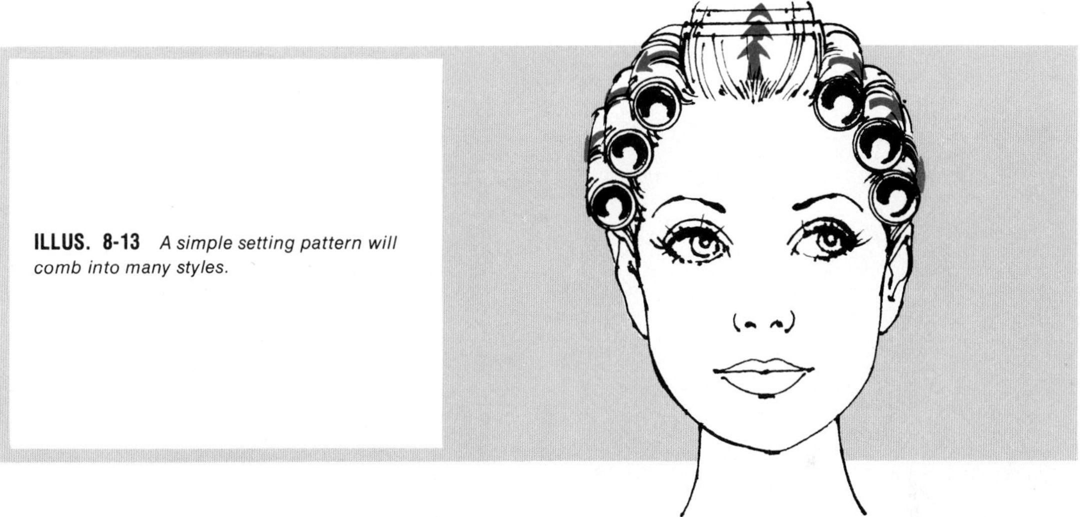

ILLUS. 8-13 *A simple setting pattern will comb into many styles.*

In-between setting can be done with a curling iron. Hot rollers and curling irons with mist give a longer lasting set than those without mist. Be sure to protect your ears and neck from the heat of the rollers with cotton or tissue. Allow hot curlers to cool completely before removing them. The curling iron usually is left in the hair for ten to thirty seconds and gently removed, disturbing the curl as little as possible until it cools. The hot curl can be pinned or clipped in until it is cool, if you like.

Arranging. Keep in mind when you brush and comb your hair that the less wear and tear on your hair, the better its condition will be. Very gentle combing and brushing is recommended. However, the frequency of the handling is important, too. It is better, for example, to do whatever is necessary at one time, even if it requires back-combing gently and use of hairspray. The style should not need rearranging again for several hours. This is far better than giving your hair a few quick "run throughs" with a comb several times a day to keep it well groomed.

Very few people need to brush one hundred strokes a day. The only known benefits are that brushing spreads the scalp oil throughout the hair and it stimulates the scalp. The damage resulting from brushing is worse for most people than the benefit gained.

When you are combing your hair into place after it is set and dried, do so gently. Some back-combing, especially near the crown and near your temples if you need fullness, may be done without harm to your hair if you do so gently. Back-combing, because you are combing the hair against its natural grain, can increase damage to hair that is split by splitting it more. However, back-combing it gently near the scalp where the hair is the healthiest and strongest should not damage your hair, and it can add much to the shape of your hairstyle.

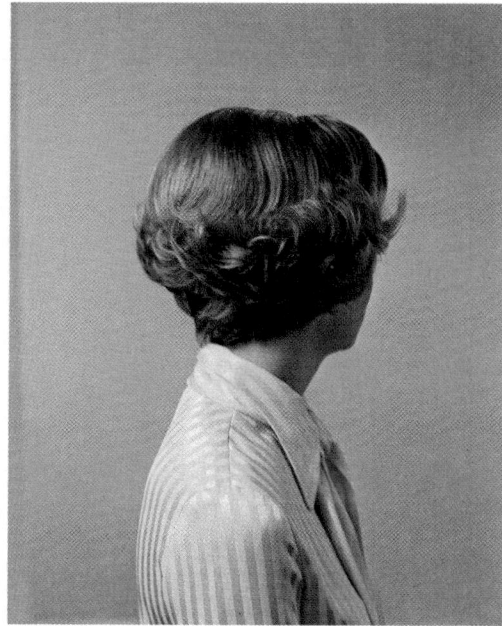

Hairstyles by Travis Johnson *Photography by Terry Webb*

ILLUS. 8-14 *Gentle back-combing to achieve a lift near the crown will not damage your hair.*

Hairspray can be used to hold your hair in place with no damage to the hair. It can prevent tangles by holding your hair in place against onslaughts of wind and other tangling agents. The can should be held away from the hair approximately ten to twelve inches while you are spraying so that the mist will settle evenly on your hair.

Style Selection

To get a style that really suits you, you need to accommodate to the unique characteristics of your hair, your physical features, and your personal habits. Think about what you have to work with. The texture, bulk, oiliness, condition, and curliness of your hair certainly are limiting factors. Your facial features and the relative size of your body are others. Very important is your life style since your hair should be styled appropriately for all your activities. Somewhat flexible are your abilities to style your own hair and the time and effort you wish to spend on it.

ACCOMMODATING YOUR HAIR

Usually hair should be styled according to your physical facial and body features. However, if you have some special problems with hair, you may need to consider these problems when you are selecting a style. Hair that varies far from medium texture, average bulk, oiliness, and curliness, or hair that is in poor condition needs special care in styling.

Fine Hair. Very fine hair will not hold a set for very long. If your hair is fine, it is a good idea to choose a style that does not require intricate setting but that looks good after the set relaxes. While it is true that you can force fine hair into many styles with permanents and spray and constant setting on small rollers, you may end up with fine but brittle, dry, unattractive hair, suffering from too much handling. You will be better off with a style that requires a minimum of setting. A blunt cut that is well shaped so that it looks good when the set relaxes, rather than a layered one, usually is easier to handle with fine hair (Illustration 8-15).

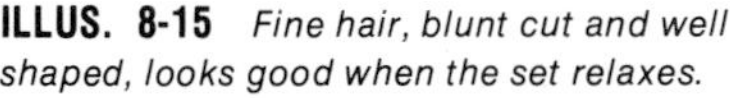

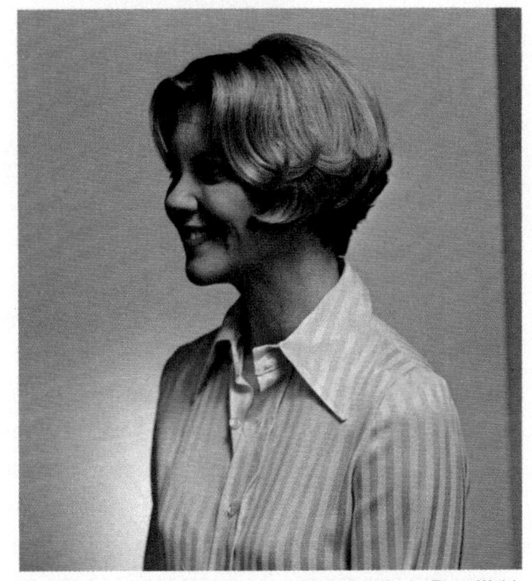

ILLUS. 8-15 *Fine hair, blunt cut and well shaped, looks good when the set relaxes.*

Hairstyles by Travis Johnson *Photography by Terry Webb*

If you do not like a simple blunt cut, consider growing your hair longer and wearing a chignon or hairpiece. When you are setting fine hair, try drying it before you put setting lotion on it. The setting lotion holds better because it is not diluted by the water on the hair. Lotions with body builders or texturizers are good for fine hair, but coloring or streaking it will give more permanent body.

Coarse Hair. If your hair is coarse, use products with a cream base so that they will soften your hair. Coarse hair is not easy to curl although it can be done with a permanent wave. A good idea for very coarse hair is a haircut that turns slightly under on the ends or slightly up on the ends. Don't try for a very curly style if you have coarse hair; you will spend all your time setting it and needing to set it.

ILLUS. 8-16 *Coarse hair may be turned slightly under or upward.*

John and Suzanne Chadwick, Fashion and Technical Directors of Glemby International

Thin Hair. Thin hair should receive your utmost attention. If it is thin naturally, that is one thing; if it is thinning because of some problem, that is quite another. All of us lose up to 50 hairs a day. Don't worry about that. If you are losing more than your share, review your handling techniques and consult a doctor if it seems necessary. Some heads of hair are so thin naturally that the scalp shows through unattractively. Coloring the hair blonde makes the scalp less obvious because the hair becomes approximately the same color as the scalp. However, not every complexion looks good with blonde hair. Very thin hair usually should be short since length tends to pull it very close to your head and makes it look even thinner. Thin hair can be curled or straight. Treat it gently, though, back-combing it very gently and never sleeping in rollers. You don't want to lose a single strand more than is absolutely necessary.

ILLUS. 8-17 *Very thin hair should be short and may be curled or straight.*

Hairstyle by Travis Johnson

Thick Hair. Hair that is very thick usually is a blessing. Thick hair usually needs some layering, though, especially if you wear a curly style (Illustration 8-18). It usually looks good either gently curled or straight with a slight "bend" under or up at the ends.

Hairstyle by Kenneth Battelle

ILLUS. 8-18 *Thick hair usually needs some layering and may be gently curled.*

Oily Hair. Very oily hair should be styled so that you can wash your hair every day if it needs it. A simple, short style will be best for you. Avoid styles that require sitting under hot hair dryers because these seem to stimulate oil production in your scalp. Although a conditioner may be needed occasionally, don't use one routinely since it tends to make your hair oilier. Use a vinegar or lemon rinse and warm-to-cool water when you wash your hair as well as a specially formulated shampoo for oily hair.

ILLUS. 8-19 *Oily hair needs a simple set that does not require a hot hairdryer and that can be washed frequently.*

Hairstyle by Kenneth Battelle

Dry Hair. Dry hair, too, should never be subjected to hot hair dryers. While it is stimulating the scalp, the hot air is drying — really drying — your hair. A quick conditioning treatment each time you shampoo your hair is a good idea. A thirty-minute conditioning treatment approximately every third or fourth shampooing will help. Try to space your shampooings a week apart since dry hair does not attract dirt like oily hair does. Try to protect your hair from dirt in the air and the drying rays of the sun with a head covering when you are outside. Specially formulated cream shampoos are good for dry hair. Avoid hairstyles that require frequent color or chemical treatments since these tend to dry your hair even more. A style for dry hair should be one that requires little in-between hot-roller curling and infrequent under-the-dryer setting or blow-drying (Illustration 8-20).

Curly Hair. If your hair is very curly you can relax and enjoy it, or you can have it straightened. Straightened hair is chemically treated hair and it must be treated carefully. Very curly hair can be worn short and it is better not to thin it. To do so adds bulk to bulk, and those thinned hairs do grow out, causing uneven ends here and there all over your head.

Very curly hair can be worn long only if you plan to pull it back from your face in a chignon. Very curly hair worn loose and long will not be long flowing hair; it will be very bushy. You will be happier if you select a short, soft, curly style that you can manage without straightening (Illustration 8-21).

ILLUS. 8-20 *Dry hair should be styled so that little in-between hot-roller curl or blow-drying is needed.*

John and Suzanne Chadwick, Fashion and Technical Directors of Glemby International

ILLUS. 8-21 *Very curly hair can be cut short and enjoyed.*

Hairstyle by Kenneth Battelle

Hair in Poor Condition. If your hair is currently in poor condition, it probably got that way from abuse. Check the procedures you have used on your hair: Too much coloring? Too much shampooing? Too much sun? Too much chlorine water? Too much permanenting? Whatever the cause of your damaged hair, re-evaluate the practice and your techniques. No hair looks truly good when it has been damaged. It does not heal. You simply must wait for new hair to grow (at the rate of one-half inch per month on the average). In the meantime, damaged hair can look better if you use conditioners, texturizers, and body-building solutions that are fillers and that add some shine and body. A short hairstyle that allows you to cut most of the damaged hair off probably will be the most attractive way to wear your hair until new healthy hair grows in. Avoid styles that require chemical curling or coloring.

ACCOMMODATING YOURSELF

When you have learned to care for your hair and to accommodate any pecularities it may have, you have the opportunity to style your hair so that it suits your physical and personal characteristics exactly.

Physical Features. Consider your face and head shape and the relative size of your body in height and width. Be careful to examine any style you may be considering in light of how you will look in a full-length mirror, front, side, and back. The front should frame your face according to its best features, camouflaging your weaker ones. The side view should balance a high forehead, protruding nose, and any irregularities in your chin line. The back should reflect a hairstyle that is in proportion to the size of the remainder of your body, balancing irregular width or height of your frame.

The idea in selecting a hairstyle to complement your facial features is to balance any irregularity in breadth or width in your forehead by not repeating a bad line in your face. The style should also provide a clear view of your strongest features, such as high cheekbones or lovely eyes. If, for example, your chin line is wider than your forehead, select a style that is wide at your forehead and temples and that falls on your face just a bit at your chin line to conceal its width (Illustration 8-22). If you have a broad forehead and a pointed chin, select a hairstyle that covers part of your forehead on each side and is full at your chin. This hairstyle will draw the eye in a horizontal line and give the illusion of widening the chin (Illustration 8-23). If your forehead is very wide in proportion to the length of the rest of your face, select a hairstyle that has some kind of bangs so that you can conceal at least part of your forehead, giving your face better overall proportion. If your eyes are close-set, choose a hair-

ILLUS. 8-22 *To conceal a wide chin, use a hairstyle that falls on your face at the chinline.*

Hairstyle by Kenneth Battelle

ILLUS. 8-23 *A broad forehead can be concealed by your hair.*

Hairstyle by Kenneth Battelle

style that is full and widened at the temples. This will draw the eye in a horizontal line, widening the illusion of your eyes (Illustration 8-24, next page). If you have high cheekbones, select a hairstyle that shows the profile of your beautiful bone structure — never one that covers it (Illustration 8-25).

Your profile may be the least important consideration in your hairstyle. If you must fudge on any point, do it on this one. The idea in

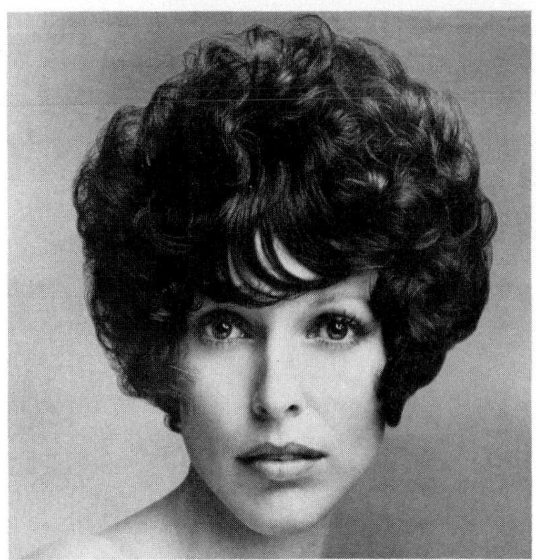

Hairstyle by Kenneth Battelle

ILLUS. 8-24 *For close-set eyes, choose a hairstyle wide at the temples to draw the eyes apart in a horizontal line.*

ILLUS. 8-25 *Beautiful eyes should be accented with a complementing hairstyle.*

Hairstyle by Travis Johnson

Photography by Terry Webb

selecting the right style for your profile is to consider the size and shape of your nose and chin. If either has an extreme shape, you should be extra careful that your hair does not contribute to the irregularity. A long nose under hair that is rather flat on top slanting upward to the crown will increase the illusion of length of the nose. A little height and softness on the top with a rounded profile will de-emphasize the length of the nose (Illustration 8-26). A receding chin requires slightly longer than chin-length hair, curling and slanting to the front on the ends to "bring the chin out." Never pull the hair back at the chin line if the chin is receding. To do so, emphasizes the receding line by repeating it.

Hairstyles by Travis Johnson

Photography by Terry Webb

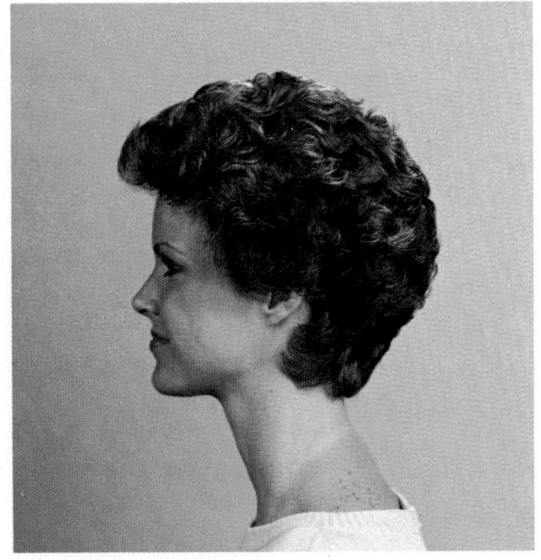

ILLUS. 8-26 *The shape and height of the crown of your hairstyle will affect the profile of your face.*

The relative size of your body should be balanced by your hairstyle. If your body is petite, choose a "small" hairstyle, not too long, not too full (Illustration 8-27, next page). If your body is wide, choose a style that is "tall" and of medium width so that your head will contribute to the illusion of height but will balance your width. The width in your hairstyle, however, should be above your earlobes. Width in your hairstyle near your shoulders tends to widen your body. If you are tall, don't wear your hair too short or too "tall." A longer, flatter-on-top style will balance your frame size better.

Hairstyle by Kenneth Battelle

ILLUS. 8-27 *A small hairstyle fits a small person better than a large hairstyle does.*

Personal Characteristics. How willing are you to learn the techniques needed to keep the style you select? How much time are you willing to spend daily on it to keep it attractive? How appropriate is the style for your lifestyle? This may be the place where you will have to compromise between not wanting to learn how to fix your hair and needing to learn so that you can look well-groomed every day. Remember that the reason you are developing these dimensions of yourself is that you want to attain certain goals. Well-groomed persons always are preferred in business and public life over those who are not. Actually learning to care for your hairstyle is not difficult, and it becomes habit after about a week of practice. A few minutes at night and each morning spent in caring for your hair can make learning easy and can make a tremendous difference in your all-day confidence in your appearance.

Select a hairstyle that fits your activities. You wouldn't wear a formal dress to work in an office, and you wouldn't wear your hair in a formal, upswept style there either. Too casual a style that swings free and has loose flowing strands is inappropriate for the tailored appearance needed in the office. Variations of a single style, though, can be versatile enough for any need. If you select a chignon for daytime tailored wear, you could let it flow loosely for casual wear and put it up for formal, special occasion wear. Very short styles are less versatile but frequently can be adapted easily with hairpieces (Illustrations 8-28 and 8-29).

Take into consideration the climate in which you live. Wet climates tend to wilt elaborate hairstyles and to make naturally curly styles unruly. Dry ones tend to aggravate thin, fly-away hair that is short, and

Hairstyle by Kenneth Battelle

Hairstyle by Travis Johnson Photography by Terry Webb

ILLUS. 8-28 *Hair that is too elaborate is not good for daytime activities. Daytime styles, though, can usually be worn easily with special-occasion clothes.*

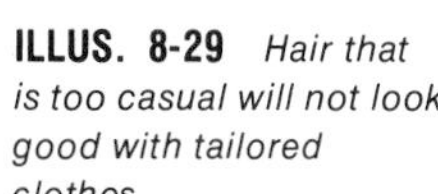

ILLUS. 8-29 *Hair that is too casual will not look good with tailored clothes.*

Hairstyle by Kenneth Battelle

windy ones tend to destroy free-swinging styles of little body. Consider also your personality. Do you need to change your hair somewhat to be happy with it? Can you wear the same style several months without becoming bored with it? Chin- to shoulder-length hair tends to be more versatile than short hair.

Make a thoughtful inventory of ways you have worn your hair in the past, ways you would like to wear it, and what your hair actually will and will not do without excessive use of chemicals and handling. For example, if you have very fine, curly hair, it will never be coarse and straight without chemically damaging it. Be realistic about your inventory items. Cross out styles that you have worn in the past that were too difficult to make your hair conform to or that you felt uneasy with. Disregard the styles that did not look good on you or that were faddish and are now out of date. When thinking of the ways you would like to wear your hair, consider its texture, bulk, oiliness, condition, and curliness. Then eliminate styles that are not suitable because your hair is too fine or coarse or too thin or thick. Forget about styles that would not allow you to wash frequently or that would require too frequent washings. You should not consider a style that would require straightening or permanent waving hair that is in poor condition or a style that would not suit the natural curliness or lack of it in your hair.

USING HAIRPIECES AND WIGS

Hairpieces can be used to cover your hair or to supplement it. The key to using them successfully usually depends upon your getting a color that exactly matches that of your own hair and upon your getting one of approximately the same bulk as your own. The most common mistake of people who desire hairpieces is that they select those of too much bulk, and the hairpiece looks "wiggy."

A wig which covers all of your own hair can be a lifesaver when you are subjected to weather, summer sports, and illness. It is very easy to maintain and frequently is as attractive as your own hair. When you wear a wig, wear it with ease. If you have put it on correctly, everyone won't be staring at you, commenting about your wig (Illustration 8-30).

Gently section your own hair, and using flat pin curls and pins, pin it flat against your head. Place the front of your wig on your forehead near your hairline and pull the remainder of the wig gently down over your head. Use the end of a rat-tail comb to push stray hair under your wig at the back. Some wigs need to be anchored to your pin-curled hair. Do so with pins that match the color of the hair. Gently arrange the wig hair until it fits around your face and neck comfortably. Check your profile and neckline in the back to see that the wig is shaped properly, not too far forward, not too far back, and that all your own hair is neatly

Hairstyle by Travis Johnson *Photography by Terry Webb*

Hairstyle by Kenneth Battelle

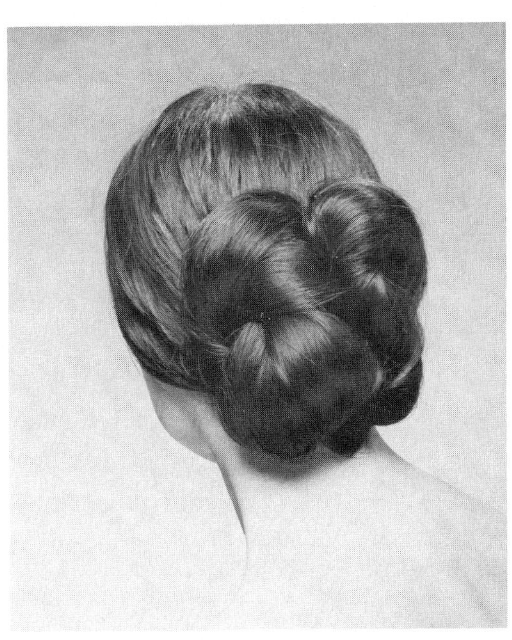

Hairstyle by Travis Johnson

ILLUS. 8-30 *Wigs and hairpieces can provide versatility to your hairstyle.*

tucked away. Now act as if the hair on your head is your own. It it needs attention, take care of it privately; don't pull or tug on it in public.

A hairpiece that covers part of your hair or supplements either the crown or the length of your hair is usually attached to a large flat pincurl near the crown of your head. It is important not to attach supplemental hair to the same spot too often. The weight of the hairpiece tugging at the roots of the same hair all the time, will eventually pull out your hair. Vary the place at which you attach supplemental hair if you use it very often.

SUMMARY

Caring for your hair must become a matter-of-fact procedure if you are to be well groomed. When hair is neglected, little else is noticed about a person's grooming. Resolve to master the use of hair grooming aids and to know your hair and its capabilities well. Pretty hair all day every day is just a step away. Take that step.

Understanding Hair Halos

1. Describe the procedure for effectively shampooing your hair.
2. Describe corrective procedures for less-than-manageable hair.
3. What is basic to good hair handling procedures?
4. Describe the different ways to set your hair and what to expect with each method.
5. What kind of style would be good for fine, thick hair?
6. What kind of style would be good for curly, oily hair?
7. How can you balance physical features of your face with your hairstyle?
8. What personal characteristics do you consider when selecting a hairstyle?

Chapter 9

Radiant Touches

Care of your body concludes with radiant touches to your hands and feet and with your fragrance. It is easy to concentrate on larger areas, such as your skin, face, and hair; but often it is easy to overlook those vital smaller areas that enhance your radiance. Your hands contribute much to your appearance if they are manicured and your skin is soft. Your feet affect your disposition more than your appearance but require much the same kind of care as your hands. The aura of your presence is influenced by the fragrance you use. It should be carefully chosen and artfully worn.

Fingernail and Hand Care

Your hands are practically always in view. Their grooming or lack of it are almost as often noticed as your face and hair. The procedures for grooming lovely hands are simple and can easily become habit if you conscientiously work at them.

THE NAIL ITSELF

Your fingernails and your success in having attractive ones are the result of many factors. Your inherited characteristics certainly have an impact on your nails just as they do on other personal physical characteristics. Beyond dealing with what you were born with, other factors you can control are the effects that your personal habits and practices have on your nails.

The characteristics of the nail itself are important for you to understand. The hard epidermal cells that form the nail are called the nail plate. The chemical makeup of the nail plate is very much like the chemistry of your skin and hair. Nails are influenced by your overall health as your skin and hair are. Just as well-cared-for hair and skin contribute to your overall appearance, so do well-cared-for fingernails improve your appearance. A graceful hand requires well-cared-for nails.

There are variations among people's nails as there are among their other physical characteristics. There are even variations among the different nails on a person's hand. Some differences are inherited; some are the result of injury to the nail bed — that area beneath the cuticle where the nail plate is formed. Just as some hair will be thicker and coarser, some nails will be thicker and stronger for no reason other than simple differences in people. Just as you adjust your hair care procedures to accommodate the kind of hair you have, you adjust your nail care procedures to accommodate the kind of nails you have.

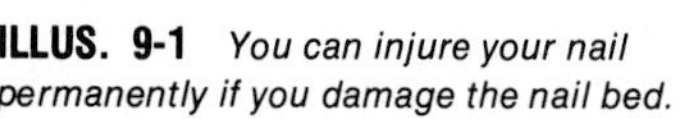

ILLUS. 9-1 *You can injure your nail permanently if you damage the nail bed.*

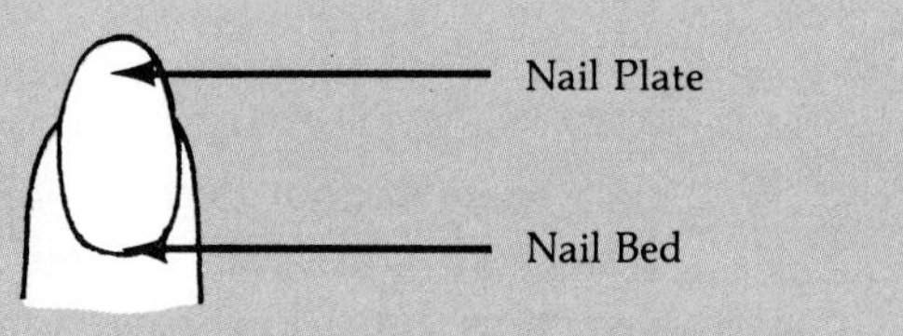

Environment has a definite effect on the nature of the nails. Skin subjected to harsh detergents day after day becomes dry and flaky. Nails subjected to the same abuse suffer injury also. Very cold weather, chemical solvents, wax, and hard blows all affect the skin; they affect the nails also. The difference between caring for your skin and your nails lies mainly in the time it takes to effect improvement or to correct damage that has been done.

Skin is constantly flaking off and replacing itself, resulting in a shedding of abused skin on the outermost layer every twenty-six days. Therefore, it you have chapped, burned, or just flaky skin, lotions applied for about a month seem to correct your problem, provided, of course, your skin is not repeatedly subjected to the same abuse. Nails, however, do not completely replace themselves so quickly. It takes about six months for the part of the nail closest to your cuticle to grow to the end of your nail and to be filed, clipped, or, unfortunately, broken off. This means that when a nail is abused, you must live with it much longer.

Even more important is abuse of the nail bed. Excessive pressure due to a blow to the finger, such as shutting it accidentally in a drawer or squeezing a pencil constantly too hard against the side of the nail bed, can permanently damage the area where the nail is formed. This damage results in ridges, thickening, and weakened areas of the nail and cannot be cured. You can learn to live with it, though, by developing techniques to groom it.

Because, from beginning to end, the nail is on the tip of your finger for approximately six months, it has much greater potential for abuse than your skin does. During their six-month lifetime, consider how many times nails are exposed to soap and water, which are drying agents, and how often they are subjected to chemicals, such as household cleaners, or to hair preparations, such as permanent solutions and coloring agents. Then, wonder how they survive as well as they do; and decide to take better care of your nails before you complain again of brittleness, flaking, peeling, chipping, or just plain "poor nails."

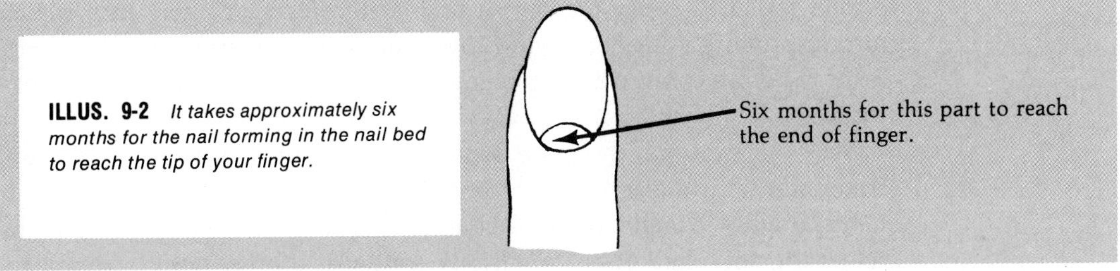

ILLUS. 9-2 *It takes approximately six months for the nail forming in the nail bed to reach the tip of your finger.*

PROBLEM NAILS

There are bodily impairments that affect your nails. Skin diseases such as psoriasis and fungus can affect your nails and should be treated by a physician. Diseases such as anemia and insufficient thyroid secretions can contribute to nail problems. Certainly, these kinds of complications must be treated by a qualified physician before you can hope to achieve healthy, well-groomed nails.

Some stopgap measures are available to help you have presentable hands while you are seeking more permanent solutions. It is important to keep in mind that good, strong nails are developed in the nail bed of each finger. Other means of achieving satisfactory results are temporary and offer no lasting results.

It has been commonly believed by many that increased intake of protein improves nails, because they, like hair and skin, are dependent upon protein for replacement of dead cells that are continuously shed. The common practice has been to consume amounts of gelatin daily, either in capusle form or mixed in fruit juice. The truth of the effectiveness of this kind of treatment depends upon the reason for your nail problems. If you have weak nails because your diet is low in protein, increasing the intake of protein should, of course, effect an improvement in your nails (and incidentally, in your skin and hair). Check back in the nutrition section of your personal development plan. Analyze your intake of daily protein and the suggested daily allowance to determine if protein deficiency could be the cause of nail problems before you decide to prescribe increased intake for yourself in the form of gelatin.

If, in fact, your diet is not low in protein and you add protein in the form of gelatin to your diet, you may well effect only a weight gain. Excess protein, like excess fat and carbohydrate, is stored by the body as fat if it is not burned as energy. If you are low in protein and choose to correct the condition by consuming gelatin or any other protein-rich food, do not expect immediate results. Remember that good nails are formed in the nail bed and that it takes six months for the nail being formed today to cover the entire nail plate of your finger. Any benefit from improving your health and diet will take approximately six months to show before completely replacing the entire nail plate with a healthier surface.

In the meantime, there are some chemical substances you can use to strengthen your nail plate. Two basic kinds are available. One is a substance, mainly formaldehyde, that actually acts to harden the protein surface of the nail plate upon contact. The other is a preparation, containing fibers such as nylon in a clear, thick liquid, that, when dry, supports the nail with a strong film.

Formaldehyde has the tendency to cause allergic skin reactions and is not made available by cosmetic companies in nail preparations because of numerous such complaints. Many drug stores, however, have such preparations, and you may be able to obtain them by prescription from your dermatologist.

The fiber-type hardeners sometimes leave a rough, unattractive surface on your nails. Frequently, however, colored nail enamel can be used over the hardener to achieve a better appearance. Nail enamel applied over any of the hardeners may not wear well, though.

There are other hardeners that are said to work because they contain protein substances that strengthen the nail upon contact. It is doubtful that protein applied to the surface of either the nail or the hair has any beneficial effect on the strength or quality of either one. Studies are not conclusive in this area, and you should beware of spending resources and time on a process that may be worthless.

Soft nails that do not respond to good diet, precautionary care, and temporary help may be best groomed by keeping them short so that they are less vulnerable to tearing, and snagging. It is better, by far, to have short, well-groomed nails than long, ragged ones.

PREVENTIVE CARE

Some protective practices you can cultivate to protect precious nails are easy to develop. Unlike hair that has been neglected for weeks and can be spectacularly conditioned and groomed within two or three hours, nails require constant, continuous, habitual care if they are to look good for special occasions as well as every day.

Begin your route to lovely nails by reviewing how you treat them daily. If your nervous times are relieved by picking at your cuticle or by biting your nail plate, you must concentrate on some other release of tension — one that is not destructive to your physical structure.

Some of the things that you do daily can wear down the nail plate without your even being aware of it. A rough surface in your handbag can catch your nail as you reach for something near the bottom. The zipper tab on the back of your dress may "notch" your nail as you grasp it to zip your dress. Dialing a telephone with your finger wears the nail down; and simply picking things up like paper, coins, pins, or paper clips can wear your nails down.

Try to develop new habits like dialing the telephone with the rubber end of a pencil; picking up a piece of paper by using the straightened fingers to gently pinch an uncreased fold in it to lift it; and sweeping coins, clips, and pins off with the side of one hand into the palm of the other.

ILLUS. 9-3 *Learn to pick up items in a way that does not damage your nail.*

Obtain a letter opener or other device to force stubborn latches open. Switch lights on and off with your knuckle or the side of your thumb instead of your fingertip. Avoid handbags and jewelry with clasps that snag your nails when you attempt to operate them.

Use cleaning brushes with handles that allow you to keep your hands out of the water and cleaning solvents. Wear rubber gloves when you must put your hands in water. If you have strong, long nails, keep them a length that is practical for the tasks you are expected to perform with your hands. You can, for example, wear down too-long nails with simple typing or writing.

During periods of extreme exposure, such as to cold weather or to harsh solvents, conscientiously keep your nails well lubricated with creams.

If you find that you must perform a very messy job and for some reason you cannot wear protective gloves, scrape your nails across a bar of soap to deposit soap under your nails and apply a heavy coat of lubricating cream before you start. That will prevent ugly stains from discoloring the skin beneath the tip of your nail and will make it much easier to clean that area when you are through with the messy job.

MANICURING

A weekly manicure is an excellent preventive care practice as well as a grooming technique for your nails. There seems to be more incentive to preserve the beauty of a lovely nail than to protect a ragged, stubby one. There is a set routine to follow in manicuring your nails.

It is necessary to start with clean nails. This is best achieved with gentle washing with soap and water and a soft fingernail brush. Avoid using pointed, sharp objects beneath the nail to clean it. You can separate the nail plate from your skin before it is ready and damage the nail. Gentle brushing removes the dirt and debris without damaging the area where the nail is joined to your skin. Next, clean any buffing wax or nail enamel off the surface of the nail plate.

Nail enamel remover is specially formulated to dissolve and remove chemicals applied to the nail, but it must be used carefully. It is never wise to dip your nail into the remover. Use, instead, a cotton ball saturated with remover, applied to the surface of the nail only. Usually enamel and wax are effectively and gently removed if you allow the saturated cotton ball to rest for a few seconds on the nail plate to dissolve the chemicals. Then, with only very light pressure, wipe the surface clean. The area near the cuticle should be cleaned very gently and can be most effectively cleaned with a cotton-tipped stick or an orange stick that is wrapped in cotton and saturated with remover. The more effectively you keep the remover away from the cuticle and your skin, the better. It is the strong solvent in remover that is not good for your skin. Because the solvent is very drying, the shorter the time the remover is allowed to stay on the nail plate itself, the better (Illustration 9-4).

Some enamel removers have oil in them that keeps the dissolved enamel from smearing and staining your cuticle and the surrounding skin. If you have smudging problems, it is worthwhile to try these non-

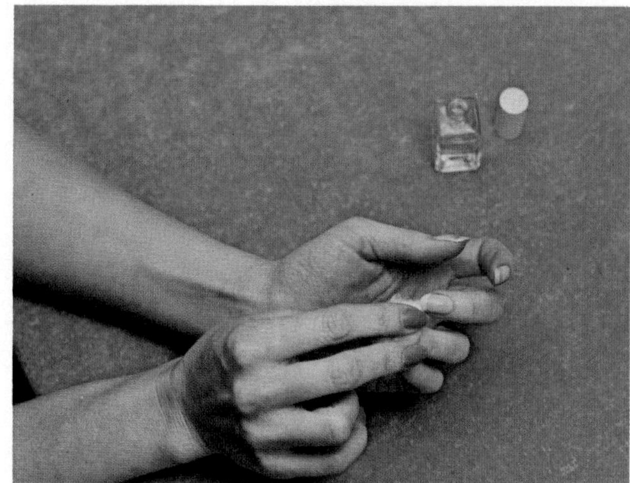

ILLUS. 9-4 *The first step in a manicure is removal of the old enamel.*

Photography by Terry Webb

smudge kinds of enamel removers. After you have wiped the enamel and buffing wax from the surface of the nail, rinse your nails quickly to remove any remover that may have been deposited on your skin.

Dry your nails carefully but gently, and you are ready to shape them. Shaping can be done with either an emery board or a metal file. Many people feel that a metal file is destructive to the nail plate. If you seem to have more trouble with your nails when you use the metal file, switch to the fiber emery one, which generally is gentler to your nails.

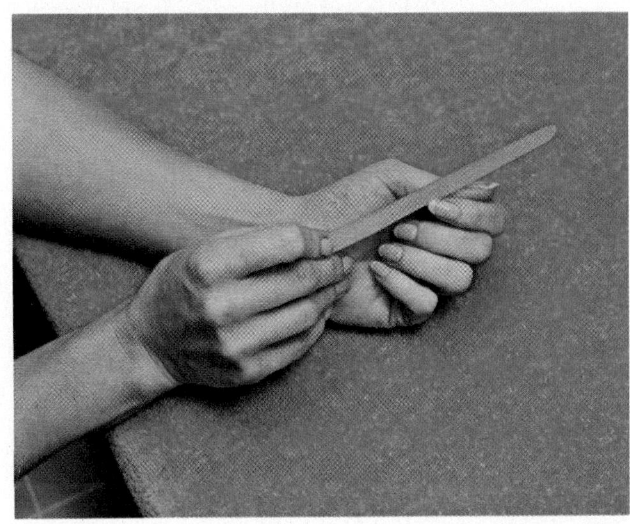

ILLUS. 9-5 *After removing enamel, shape your nails.*

Photography by Terry Webb

Filing is done in one direction only — from the side to the center of the nail. The file is held at a slight angle so that it files the underside of the end of the nail first. A back-and-forth sawing action tears the fingernail by pulling it against the grain near the outer corners.

The shape of your nail is very important to its strength. The sides of the nail must be allowed to grow to the top of your finger. That means that you should not file down into the corners of the nail since to do so severely weakens it.

ILLUS. 9-6 *Angle the file or emery board so that you do not file into the corners of your nail.*

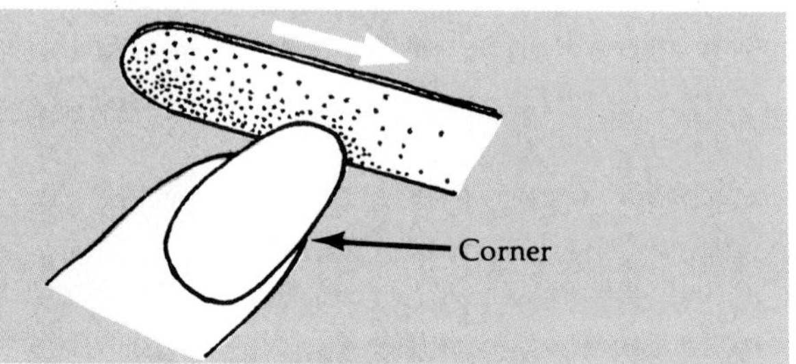

Everyone would like to have oval-shaped nails because these present the most graceful line for your fingers. However, it is far more important to maintain the strength of the nail that you do have than to strive for an oval before you have enough length to effect it. If your nails are short and barely reach the end of your finger, it will not be possible to have the sought-after oval. Depending upon the length you do achieve, you should first strive for a smooth finish on the end of the nail and as nearly an oval as possible without filing into the corner of the nail.

It is generally considered very hard on nails to clip or cut them. The layers forming the nail plate tend to split and separate when they are subjected to cutting or clipping, thus weakening the tip of the nail, making it vulnerable to snags and splits.

Nails are shaped before they are soaked because the plate itself becomes somewhat pliable when it is soaked, making a smooth surface difficult to achieve with a file or emery board.

After shaping has been effected, though, it is an excellent procedure to soak your nails in warm water, to which you can add mild soap or a cuticle softening agent made especially for soaking nails. The purpose of the soaking is to loosen cuticle from the nail plate so that the cuticle can be pushed back with a minimum of effort. Very gentle handling of the cuticle is vital because the nail bed can be permanently damaged if you use too much pressure or force the cuticle away from the plate before the nail is fully developed.

If you do not have time to soak your nails, use instead a cuticle cream or cuticle remover that you apply directly to the nail plate around the cuticle. These substances will soften the cuticle somewhat but generally are not as gentle or effective as the soaking agent.

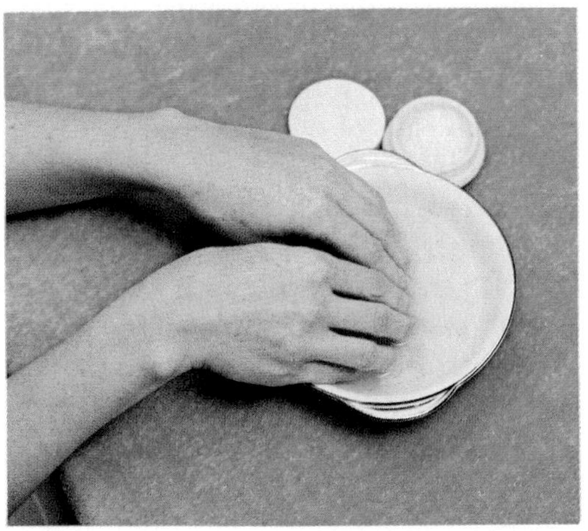

Photography by Terry Webb

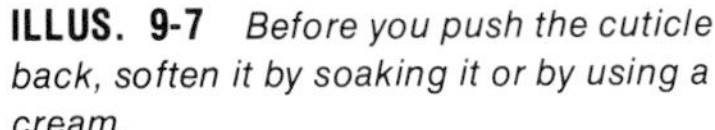

ILLUS. 9-7 *Before you push the cuticle back, soften it by soaking it or by using a cream.*

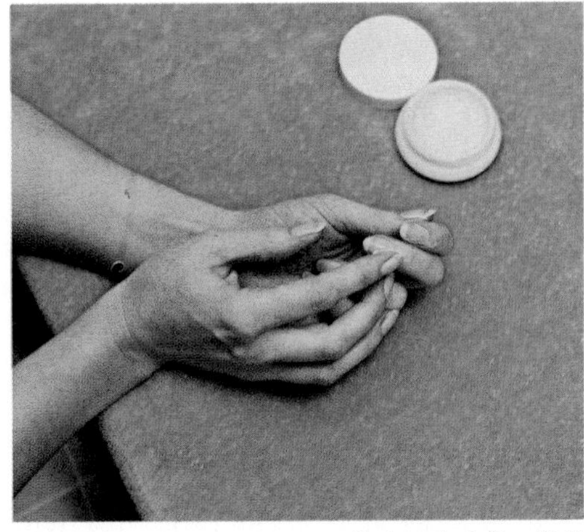

Photography by Terry Webb

Allow the softening agent to work about five minutes; then wash and dry your nails. With an orange stick, gently push the cuticle back away from the nail. Cuticle never should be cut or torn. It is part of the protective area that contributes to the formation of new nail plate. Abusing it leads to weakened nail plates. It is far better not to push enough cuticle back than to push too much. Your goal is simply to allow the nail plate that is matured to be exposed.

ILLUS. 9-8 *Treat the cuticle carefully by pushing very gently with an orange stick.*

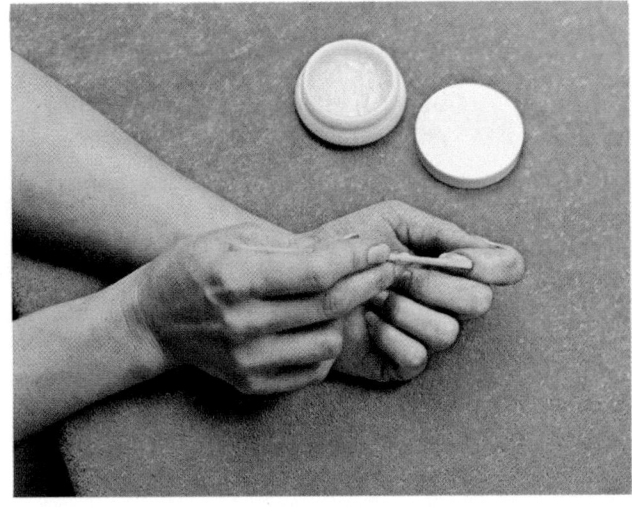

Photography by Terry Webb

When you have followed the regular practice of softening and pushing your cuticle back with an orange stick for a few months, it probably will not be necessary to continue to do it weekly. After you have achieved a rounded "moon" area at the base of the nail plate that complements the oval shape of the nail, simply pushing the cuticle back with the towel on which you dry your nails each day will be enough to contain the growth of cuticle on the nail plate.

Cuticle sheds itself regularly just as the surface of all your skin does. Occasionally, due to dryness or harsh treatment, the shedding may produce a jagged area that snags your clothing. If that happens, carefully clip the snag, but do not attempt to cut the semicircle of the entire cuticle off the nail. Your nails have a far better chance of growing strong with the protective band of cuticle intact than without it.

After nails are cleaned and shaped and the cuticle has been pushed back from the nail plate, you are ready either to apply nail enamel or to buff the nails.

The procedure which produces the longest-wearing enamel follows certain methods. First, be sure that the nail-plate surface is clean and free from oil or debris. If you have used cream or oil to remove the cuticle, it will be necessary to cleanse the nail plate of the substance. Soap and water with your soft fingernail brush are effective. Some people find nail enamel remover useful for this cleaning. However, the enamel remover is very hard on the nail plate, and the less time you allow it to stay on the nail surface, the better.

The nail plate should be completely dry. Be especially careful to dry the area around the cuticle where water may deposit itself. A base coat usually is applied first to the clean nail plate. Its purpose is to provide a smooth surface for the enamel and in many cases to provide a buffer for the nail plate from the enamel, which may be formulated with chemicals that are hard on the nail itself. The base coat usually enhances the wearability of the enamel if it is applied not only to the upper surface of the nail plate but also to the under edge of the tip of the nail.

The correct procedure for applying base coat, enamel, and top coat to the nail is first to dip the brush in the fluid, wiping one side of the brush against the bottle top edge. Then apply the full side of the brush to the base of the center of the nail and lightly brush to the tip of the center of the nail. Quickly follow with one sweep from the base of the nail plate to the tip on each side. Those three sweeps should cover the nail entirely with a very thin layer of liquid. Additional strokes should not be used at this point. Redip the brush anew for each nail. Additional coats after the first one has dried thoroughly will fill in any gaps that may be left. Very thin applications that are allowed to dry thoroughly before the next application provide a more durable surface than thick coats do.

ILLUS. 9-9 *The nail should be dry and free of debris before enamel is applied.*

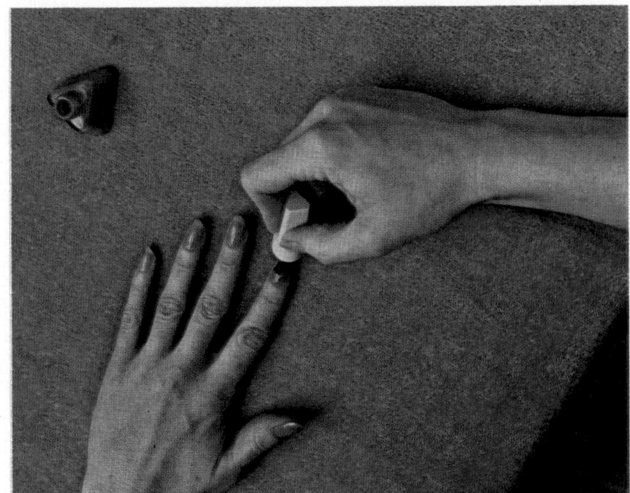

Photography by Terry Webb

ILLUS. 9-10 *Apply one stroke down the center of the nail and one stroke down each side. Allow the enamel to dry between coats.*

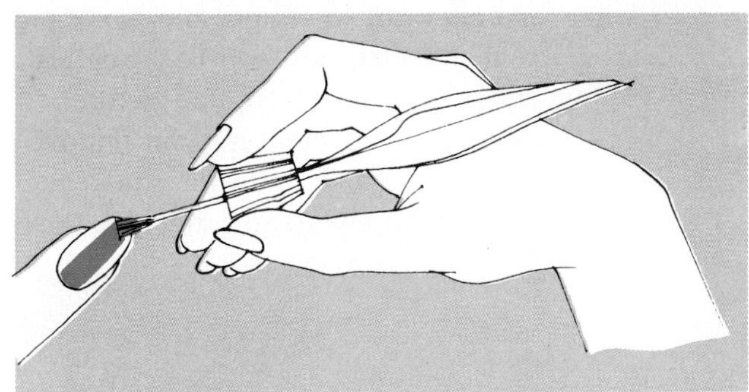

The first application is a base coat. The next application is an enamel of the color you desire. Nail enamel colors change with the dictates of fashion. It is always in fashion and always presents a well-groomed hand, though, if you select enamel according to the way it looks with the color of your skin. Usually a light tint of either muted pink, beige, brownish orange, or one of the infinite mixtures of these will take you through numerous changes of wardrobe without clashing. Bright, pure colors generally are eye-catching but are very limiting as to the clothes with which they mix well. Subdued enamel colors are far more practical. It is, of course, not necessary to use color at all. Clear enamel is never out of style and can present a very well-groomed hand, in good taste for any occasion.

The number of coats of the enamel depends upon the color of the enamel. Very light colors usually require three very thin coats for maximum shine and durability. Darker colors may be satisfactory with only two coats.

When the enamel has dried completely, a top coat is applied. It is a clear coat, the purpose of which is to take the abuse of wear without showing chips that would appear if the color were exposed to abuse. The top coat is best applied in very thin layers from the base of the nail to the tip and under the tip just as the base coat was. Two top coats are usually sufficient for protection. Many people apply one coat of top coat daily to provide protection for the enamel.

A good quality, fresh product is essential to a successful manicure. Base coat, enamel, or top coat that has thickened will never be satisfactory. Any of the three that are not fresh can reduce the wearability of the manicure. Nail enamel solvents are available but usually do not produce very good results. It is better to buy one versatile color in the smallest bottle you can find, use it regularly as long as you wish, and plan to destroy whatever may be left when it becomes thick.

An alternate to using enamel on your nails is to buff them. Buffing is especially useful if your manicure does not last a full week. Generally, it is better not to subject the nail plate to fresh nail enamel remover, base coat, enamel, and top coat applications more than once a week. If the enamel becomes chipped before it is time to manicure the nail and to apply new enamel, you can remove the old enamel and maintain attractively groomed nails for the remainder of the week by buffing them rather than enameling them again so soon.

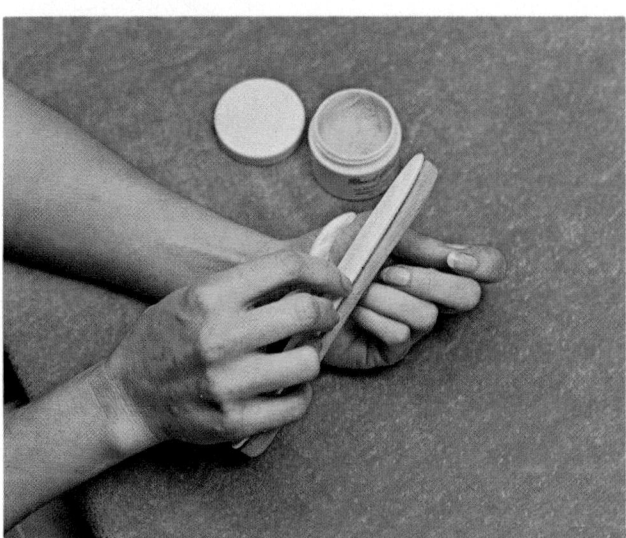

Photography by Terry Webb

ILLUS. 9-11 *Nails may be buffed to a high gloss.*

Buffing is done with a soft chamois and buffing wax. After you have cleaned and shaped your nails and have pushed back the cuticle, buffing wax is applied sparingly to the nail plate and allowed to dry. Some wax may be applied to the buffing chamois also and allowed to dry. The buffer is drawn across the nail plate in one direction only. Lift the buffer for each stroke and avoid roughing the cuticle or placing pressure on the unsupported tip of the nail. A few strokes are usually all that is needed to achieve a lovely shine on the nail that lasts for several days. Using a sawing motion with the buffer creates too much heat on the nail plate and can damage it. Be careful not to buff with too much pressure or too much vigor since either may damage the nail plate.

When the nail plate is as shiny as you desire, clean the surface of the buffer with an orange stick and wash and dry your nails. After buffing and nail enamel applications is an excellent time for applying rich lubricants to dry, rough surfaces that may appear around your nails.

EMERGENCY CARE

Practically everyone has a problem sometime with a nail plate. It will either peel, snag, chip, or be broken off. When disaster hits, there are some remedies that are available to you.

If your nail begins to peel, there are two ways to treat it. If you wish to preserve the length of the nail even though one layer is beginning to peel, you can apply base coat to the surface of the nail plate and under the tip of the nail and follow it with top coat, reapplying the top coat every day to "seal" the separating edge of the nail so that the layer does not snag and peel off. If you are willing to lose the length of the nail, you can simply file the nail down past the peeling part. If you choose to file the nail, do so gently. You can aggravate the situation with pressure, causing the layer separation to spread deeper into the nail. If you do file the nail down, file your other nails to approximately the same length so that your hands will remain gracefully groomed and your problem nail won't be a glaring misfit.

If you have a crack or snag, you can either patch your nail plate or you can file the nail down past the snag. To patch a nail plate, the snag or cracked area must occur near the tip of the nail so that you can patch both the upper and underside of the crack. Prepare the nail plate just as you would for a manicure, removing all old enamel and debris. Take a small piece of facial tissue or shredded cotton and saturate it with clear nail enamel or base coat. Fold the saturated tissue or cotton over the nail at the split or snag so that it covers both the top and underside of the nail. Smooth the paper before it dries. Proceed with your regular manicure, using three or four coats of base coat before you apply colored nail enamel so that the ridge of the patch will be somewhat obscured. Each time you manicure the nail, the patch must be carefully replaced until the split or snag is filed off (Illustration 9-12, next page).

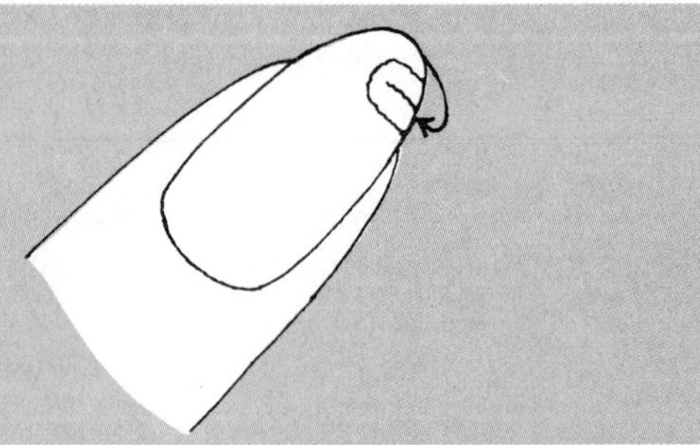

ILLUS. 9-12 *A nail may be saved from breaking off after it has been snagged if you apply a patch.*

If your nails seem so brittle that they are easily broken or nicked, they may simply be very dry. Try massaging cream into them every night for a few nights to improve the brittleness. Cuticle cream is excellent for this procedure since it also allows you to push the cuticle back in the morning after you wash your hands. Other creams, such as hand or face cream or simply petroleum jelly, may also be used.

Nails that are so soft that they seem to shred or tear unusually easily should be kept somewhat drier than normal. Protective rubber gloves worn while you are exposing your hands to water will help. Nail enamel can add strength to such nails.

Artificial nails have long been of interest to people with less-than-perfect nails. Artificial nails seem to be the answer to short, unhealthy nails; however, none have been developed as yet that are satisfactory for the long term. They have two main disadvantages. Natural nails that have ridges in them rarely present a surface to which artificial nails will adhere for a satisfactory length of time. Also, applying artifical nails properly takes a considerable length of time, and then they do not last for more than two or three days. Any kind of trauma to the nail will loosen the artificial nail. Simple moisture from washing your hands, vibration from typing or drumming your fingers, and other ordinary uses of your hands loosen the artificial nail. There is often allergic reaction to the prolonged exposure of the nail plate to the adhesive used to apply artificial nails. This may damage the natural nail surface somewhat.

It is far better to work with the nails that grow on your fingertips than to try to depend upon artificial ones. The best you can hope for is to satisfactorily use one or two artificial nails for a special occasion to even out the length of a hand. Presently, they simply are not satisfactory for everyday, routine wear.

HAND CARE

Well-cared-for nails are the beginning of graceful, lovely hands. Most hands are naturally graceful but become unattractive sometimes because of dry skin and abuse. The procedures for caring for your hands are simple and easy to learn.

The skin on your hands is the most abused skin area of your body. It is exposed to more soap, water, weather, and offending substances than any other area. It is small wonder that hands dry out and age so easily. They need special care in moisturizing, and you should be aware that they will be the first part of your body to reflect unattractive signs of aging.

Some precautions and remedies that you can take to protect your hard-working hands are to keep hand lotion in several places at your home and in your place of work. Try to keep a bottle of hand lotion near every sink where you wash your hands — kitchen, bathroom, utility room, and garage. Try to keep a bottle or tube of hand lotion in desk drawers, bedside table drawers, and in your handbag. Use it every time you wet your hands, handle papers excessively, or expose your hands to extreme temperatures.

ILLUS. 9-13 *Apply hand lotion frequently throughout the day.*

Photography by Terry Webb

If you notice dryness, apply a heavy coat of lotion or petroleum jelly on your hands before you go to bed. Wear some old fabric gloves to keep the lotion on the hands and off the bed clothes, and allow the lotion to work overnight. The morning should bring a much improved situation for the skin on your hands.

Hardened skin surfaces on your hands, both in the palm and on your fingers, can be treated so that your hands stay soft and lovely. Use a fine emery board to file the hardened surface in one direction only. You can see the direction in which the skin grows, as it will be smoother when you file in one direction than in the other. File in the direction that smoothes the skin. Often the hardened skin occurs alongside the nail on your thumb and first finger. Carefully emery-file those areas while they are dry; then apply cream to soften the newly exposed skin. Be careful when you are filing away the hardened, dead skin not to file into the nail along the side because you may weaken it.

Warts on your hands usually are believed to be caused by viruses. Although there are many old wives' tales about how to remove them, the most reliable process is to have a dermatologist perform the job. It is a painless, relatively inexpensive procedure to be rid of the unsightly imperfection, and well worth the week or two you are required to wear a small bandage. Picking at a wart yourself or trying to cut it off with a razor or other sharp instrument is definitely not recommended. It is possible to spread the virus to other parts of your skin as well as to subject the area to an infection. Such risks are not justified since it is a very simple matter to have the job done by a dermatologist once and for all.

As some women age, small brown spots appear on the hands. These spots can be bleached if they are offensive or make you feel self-conscious. Creams designed especially for lightening these spots are available, but the creams are designed to be used daily. Actually the spots are harmless and usually are not noticeable. Unless they are serious enough to make you feel uncomfortable about the appearance of your hands, you may simply and safely ignore them.

Toenail and Foot Care

Caring for your feet often is the last thing you think about in grooming yourself. Actually it may have the greatest impact on that elusive quality of warmth and glow that shines in your face; for if your feet hurt, it shows on the face, allowing little else to be reflected.

FOOT CARE

Care for your feet is simple and can be incorporated easily into your bath and hand-care routines. Protection of your feet includes wearing shoes that allow movement within the shoe and arranging your activities so that your feet are not suffering from restricted circulation for hours at a time.

The ordinary pull of gravity is simply unjust to your feet because of the difficulty incurred in pumping blood that carries waste from them, against the pull of gravity, to organs in the upper part of your body that rid your body of such waste. Therefore, you need to be aware of promoting such flow of waste-carrying blood from your feet to the upper part of your body by sitting so that there is no pressure at any point along the leg. Do not tightly cross your knees, hang knees over a ridge at the edge of a chair, or tightly cross your ankles. Also, whenever you can, in the privacy of your home, you should elevate your feet somewhat as you are sitting. A small foot stool beneath your desk also can provide some relief during the day if it is not noticeable and if it can be used so that the remainder of your body alignment is not distorted. You can select shoes that allow enough room for your toes to move and for your arch to slide in and out without pinching. Changing the position of your feet often as you sit seems to provide relief to restricted blood flow.

Poor circulation in your feet leads to numerous problems. Besides pain and numbness resulting in the blood-starved, waste-harboring muscles, the skin on the feet is starved of nutrients carried by blood. You may notice hardened areas of the skin, and general dry skin resulting from abuse to the feet. The hardened areas are destructive to nylon stockings and can be smoothed with a pumice stone, an emery board, or a specially designed rough-skin remover. Corns and calluses can be smoothed on the surface with the same appliances, but they should not be trimmed with a razor or other sharp instrument. Corns and calluses generally are caused by pressure on a particular area of the foot and will never be cured as long as the pressure exists. It they become painful, a podiatrist or dermatologist may surgically remove them, but you may expect them to reappear if the pressure is not corrected.

Another surface problem that may occur on your feet is warts. They are called plantar warts when they occur on the soles of your feet, but they are believed to be caused by the same virus as warts on your hands. The difference is that they grow inward because of pressure on your feet instead of outward as they do on the hands. These warts may be extremely painful, and the only known successful treatment is to have them removed surgically.

If the circulation is poor in your feet, it probably is poor in your legs. The skin on the lower part of the leg may become scaly and develop a rash if it does not receive enough nourishment. The best treatment, of course, is to promote good circulation by elevating the feet and avoiding sitting and standing positions that deter good circulation. Treatment of the affected skin can be undertaken by using good creams and lotions each night and morning on the scaly areas of skin.

Some good practices in caring for your feet are to buy shoes that are large enough, to wash your feet thoroughly and often, to dry them carefully, and to purchase hosiery that is properly sized.

Shoes should be bought late in the day so that you can fit your feet when they are at their largest. Most feet tend to swell somewhat during the day. If shoes are bought to fit your "morning" size rather than your "afternoon" size, they will pinch all afternoon, severely restricting the circulation of the blood and affecting your disposition. Most people's feet vary somewhat in size from foot to foot. Learn which of your feet is larger, and be sure the shoes you buy are comfortable for both the larger and smaller foot. Stand in shoes and walk in them before you buy them. If you are in doubt about whether or not they fit, put off buying them at the moment. Come back later and try them again until you are satisfied that they fit well. A poorly fitting shoe at any price is a very bad bargain. Try to change the heel height of your shoes during your day. When you get up in the morning, wear one heel height until you are ready to walk out the door; wear another heel height while you are away from home; and change to another heel height once you get home. This procedure allows the muscles in your legs and feet some stretching and contracting to accommodate the different walking postures required by the varying heel heights, thus keeping the muscles from becoming inflexible.

When you wash your feet, carefully wash the area around your toes. Most fungus, athlete's foot, and other debris collect in that area and are most apt to flourish if the area is not clean and dry. Powder may be lightly sprinkled between your toes if you have a tendency to perspire in this area. Moisture is a prime breeding ground for diseases of the skin on your feet. Be careful, however, not to cake the powder on your feet. Caked powder may absorb moisture, stay wet, and breed its own bacteria.

Be sure your socks and nylon stockings are long enough to allow your toes unrestricted movement. Because hosiery seems so flexible, you may think it cannot cramp your toes. It can, and it will if you wear a size too small for you.

Because of poor circulation, the skin on your feet may be very dry. If you notice such a problem, treat it somewhat as you treat dry skin on your hands. Apply a heavy coat of cream, lotion, petroleum jelly, and wear fabric socks to bed over the lotion overnight. In the morning, you should notice considerably improved skin on your feet. This procedure may be repeated as often as you wish to improve the skin on your feet.

After your bath, you may find it helpful, also, to rub baby or mineral oil over the skin on your feet and legs and rinse lightly before you dry. The very thin coating of oil is somewhat protective, but it is not heavy enough to soil your clothing.

TOENAIL GROOMING

Toenails are treated somewhat like fingernails. Instead of a graceful oval, however, the desirable shape of the toenail is one that is squared across the end, extending no further than the fleshy part of your toe.

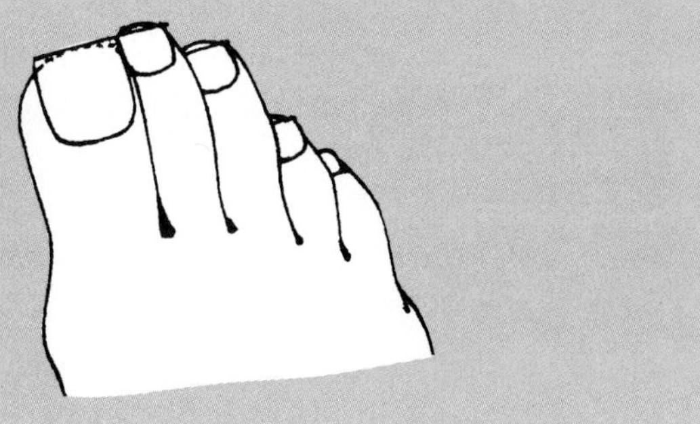

ILLUS. 9-14 *Toenails should be squared off at the end of your toes.*

It is especially important in shaping the toenail, as it is in shaping the fingernail, not to file or cut into the side of the nail. Although you need not worry about weakening the toenail when the sides are cut, you will suffer the risk of painful ingrown nails as the nail replaces itself during regular growth. As long as there is a straight surface along the side of the nail that replaces itself with regular growth, there is little possibility of the nail cutting into your toe, developing the ingrown nail. However, if there is a corner where the side has been cut, that pointed edge may easily penetrate the skin and cause you much pain before you are able to correct the situation.

Toenails may be filed or clipped. Clipping may promote separation of the layers of the nail, as it does with more fragile fingernails. Often however, toenails are so tough that they do not succumb to filing and must be clipped. Try to find clippers or scissors that enable you to get a straight edge across the end of your toe. Curved clippers may invite ingrown nails. Gently filing your toenails often gives the most satisfactory surface since there is little chance of a rough edge resulting in torn stockings or catching other surfaces and tearing the nail. Even if you do choose to clip your toenails, it is a good idea to smooth them with an emery board to avoid snags.

The surface of the nail plate is treated exactly like the surface of your fingernails. You may manicure the toenails with the same procedures, including pushing back the cuticle and applying enamel. The skin around your toenails is very tender, however, and you should use very gentle touches in manicuring them if you are to avoid soreness. Enamel is more easily applied if the toes are separated with cotton balls or laced with a folded tissue, to expose the entire surface of each nail.

Fragrances

Fragrances applied to your person are designed to enhance your grooming. It is possible to detract from your grooming with indiscriminate use of fragrance. Omitting it entirely deprives you of a little extra that can be a very enjoyable part of your grooming.

Fragrances are available in three main forms: perfume, cologne, and eau de toilette. They vary in strength and should be used in different amounts to achieve the same degree of fragrance.

Perfume is the most concentrated of the forms. Incidentally it, too, is the most costly. A very small amount of perfume is required to impart a lasting fragrance.

Cologne is less concentrated and less expensive, but it takes more of it to achieve the same lasting fragrance as perfume. Cologne can be splashed or sprayed on large areas of your shoulders without overdoing the fragrance.

Eau de toilette is less concentrated than cologne and usually is applied over your body after your bath, sometimes before you towel, so that the surface water spreads the fragrance over the entire surface of your skin. Neither cologne nor eau de toilette will last as long as perfume, but they may last as long as you need or desire before you bathe and change your fragrance for a different activity of your day.

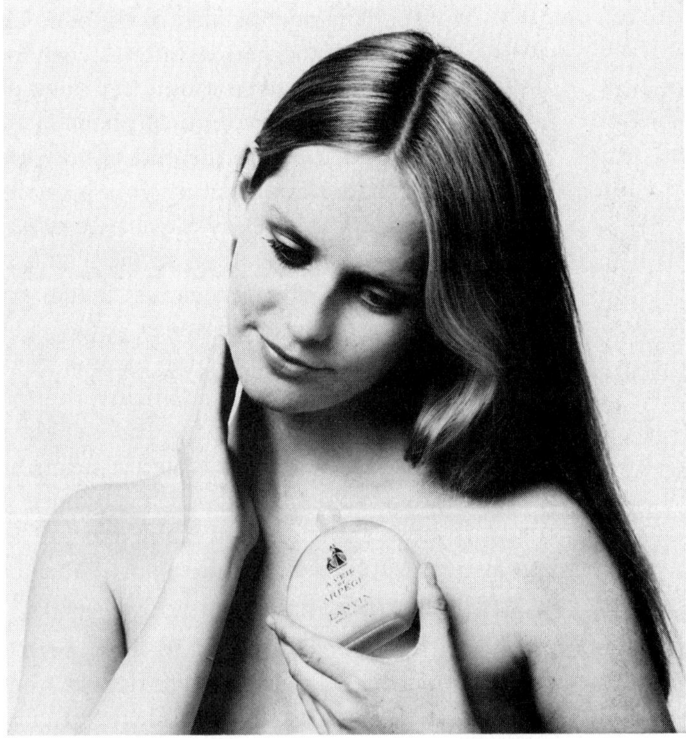

Lanvin

Photography by Peter Kenner

ILLUS. 9-15 *Use a fragrance to enhance your clean, unscented body.*

A very important point to remember about fragrances is that they are not designed to cover unpleasant body odors. Body odors are caused by bacteria which decompose debris on the surface of your skin. These odors cannot be covered by anything. They must be removed by washing to eliminate them. Use your fragrances to enhance your clean, unscented body, never to cover an undesirable odor.

SELECTING A FRAGRANCE

Almost everything you buy in cosmetic lines is scented with some fragrance. Fortunately, these scents are specifically designed to evaporate rapidly so that they do not compete with the one you select and apply in the form of a perfume, cologne, or eau de toilette. If you find a scented product, such as a hairspray, lotion, or cream, that does seem to compete with the fragrance you select for yourself, look around for an unscented substitute. Frequently, unscented products are the same as the scented ones except for the added fragrance. Be prepared to distinguish any natural scent of the chemical makeup of the product, if it is unscented, since the fragrance that is normally added serves to disguise less appealing odors of the natural substances of the product.

Perfumes, colognes, and eau de toilette products are formulated for long-lasting emission of the fragrance with which they are scented. They are available in an infinite variety of mixtures including flowers, fruits, woods, and foods. There are heavy, light, smooth, sharp, gentle, and strong scents. Each person will find that a scent will be a little different when mixed with her own natural body oils and body scent. The care that must be taken when you select a fragrance for yourself is to suit it to yourself, the occasions for which you plan to wear it, and, of course, to your budget.

At the fragrance counter, try only one or two fragrances at a time. Spray each lightly on your hand or arm and allow it to evaporate. It is a good idea to walk around the store and shop for a while before you decide for sure that you want to purchase the fragrance. The scent may change somewhat with exposure to your body chemistry.

You can actually find scents that suit your personality — there are some fragrances that seem to complement a bright, loquacious person, while others enhance a subdued, thoughtful personality. Most people have many moods and find that a fragrance contributes to the enjoyment of a particular mood if it seems to fit. You might want a quiet, dramatic scent for evening wear and a light, airy one for daytime wear. One thing you should be aware of is that when your are indoors, working closely with people, strong fragrances are offensive. Stick to the very subtle, light fragrances when you are working closely with people in offices or other enclosed areas. Save the strong, pronounced ones for outdoors or when you are in a large area, such as a large ballroom. Too strong a fragrance is as offensive as a strong body odor.

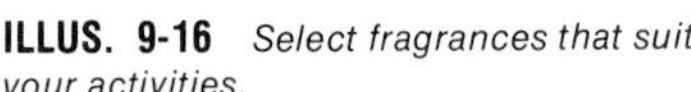

ILLUS. 9-16 *Select fragrances that suit your activities.*

Photograph Courtesy of Cotton Incorporated

USING FRAGRANCES

The warmth of your body enhances the strength of the fragrance that you use. If you place the scent in an area that is very warm, such as the bend of the elbow, near your neck, or between your breasts, the warmth will promote emission of the fragrance. There is, however, no validity to the claim that pulse points of the body are the best spots for fragrance. Because of the alcohol and other chemicals used in fragrances, it is not a good idea to saturate cotton balls and place them near your body inside your clothing. Unpleasant rashes can result from constant exposure to such strong solutions.

Fragrances can be used in many ways if they are used lightly. You want a hint of fragrance noticeable only to those very close to you, not a screaming announcement of your latest discovery.

A drop of fragrance in the last rinse water of your shampoo can enhance the scent of your hair every time you shake your head. You can add a small amount to some baby oil to use in your bath or to spray on your body after a shower and achieve the same results as a scented bath oil. A light spray on your ironing board will impart a light scent to your clothes as you press them. Cotton balls that are saturated and placed in loosely tied plastic bags will impart a fragrance to your lingerie drawer, as will a bar of scented soap. A few slivers of scented soap placed in a container in your handbag emits its fragrance every time you open your handbag. A loosely covered bar of scented soap placed in your desk drawer makes your work area smell good for a long time. When the fragrance is gone, use the soap like a regular unscented bar.

SUMMARY

The radiant touches of hand and foot care as well as use of fragrances are those special areas that complete the grooming of your body. If you concentrate on skin, face, and hair but neglect those areas, you will be only half-groomed. Well-groomed hands, healthy feet, and just a hint of a suitable fragrance show that you have grasped the entire concept of grooming your body and that you are willing to do the job — the whole job.

Understanding Radiant Touches

1. What part does the nail bed play in the quality of the nail?
2. Why can't nails be rejuvenated in a day as hair can?
3. What causes adverse effects on the nail-plate surface?
4. Does gelatin help grow healthy nails? If so, how?
5. What equipment and products do you need for a manicure?
6. What are some emergency care procedures you can practice for grooming your nails?
7. What can you do about dry skin and hardened surfaces on your hands?
8. What effect does foot care have on your appearance?
9. What are some good foot care procedures?
10. What are the considerations in choosing among perfume, cologne, and eau de toilette?
11. How do you decide on a fragrance for yourself?
12. What are some special ways to use fragrance?

Projects for Part 2

1. Make a weekly program for caring for your particular kind of skin. Describe the daily routines, morning and night; weekly routines; and the products you plan to use for each one.
2. Rough-sketch the shape of your face. Draw and describe the kind and color of cosmetics you should use for enhancing your best features. Draw in the appropriate shape for your brows and any shading or highlighting you need for contouring.
3. Describe a hair cut for your own hair in terms of length: blunt or layered cut; short front—long back; long front—short back; or all one length; etc. Explain your choices in each case. Diagram the setting pattern or blow-dry procedure, including any conditioner, appliances, or setting lotion you need for such a set. Describe carefully at least one variation you can use, either for evening wear or for casual wear, with the same cut. You may include the use of artificial hair pieces and wigs for the variation.
4. Outline a six-month plan for improving your nails and hands. Include changes you plan for your diet, the way you use your hands, your weekly care routine, and emergency measures for the interim. Include any special plans for special occasions you may be planning and state whether or not purchases must be made to implement your six-month plan.

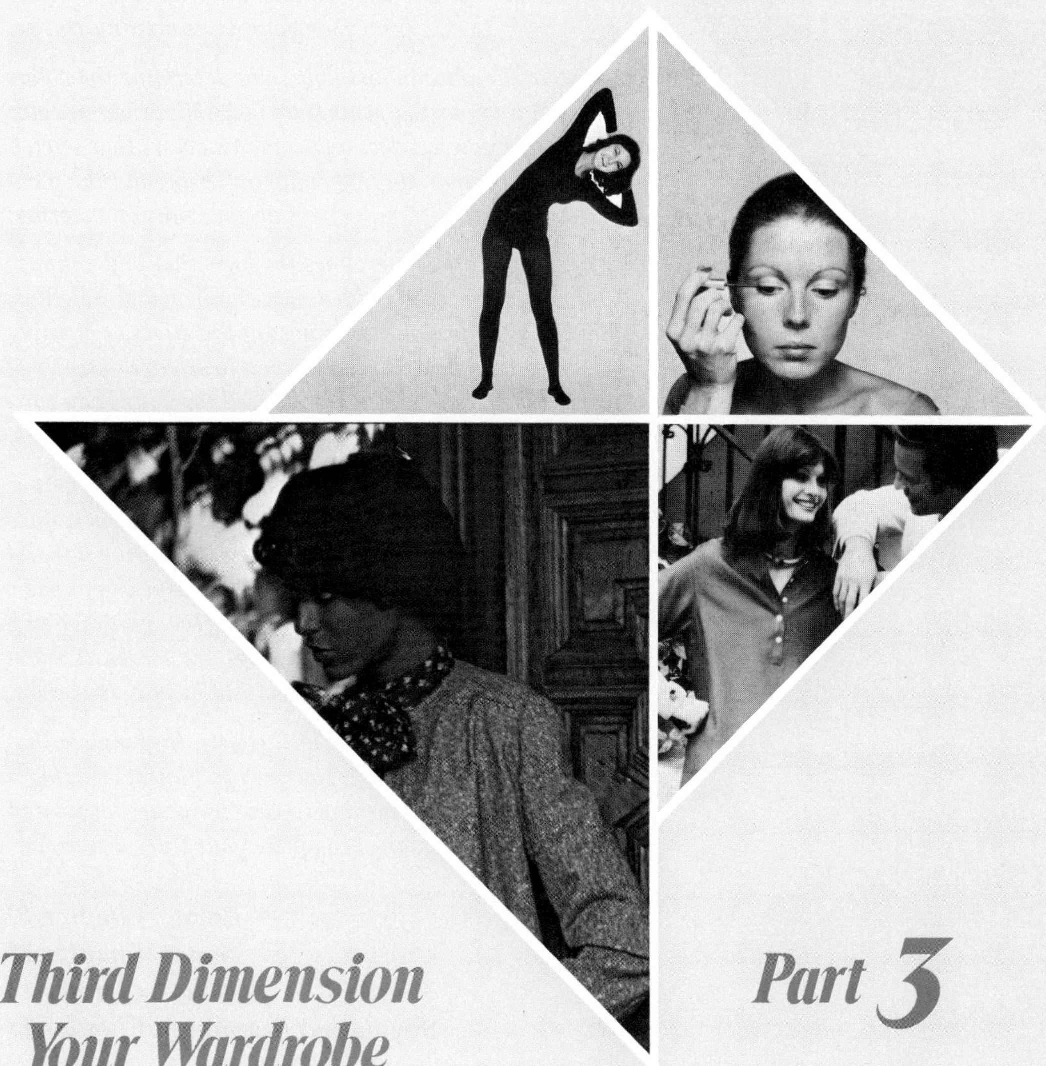

Third Dimension Your Wardrobe

Part 3

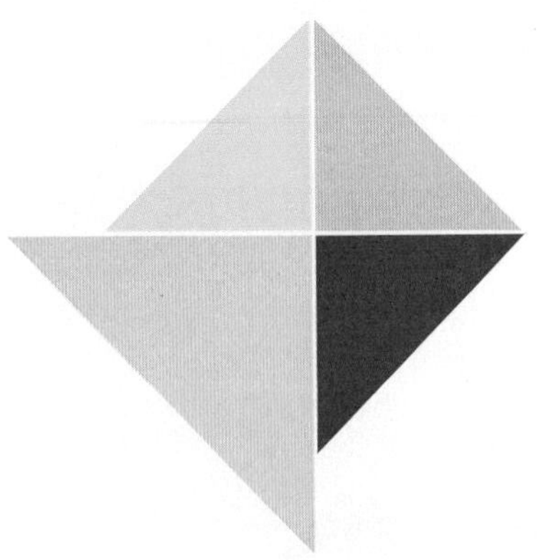

You have nurtured, exercised, and enhanced your body. Now, you are ready to clothe it. Appropriate and functional clothes are necessary for your comfort and confidence. Learn to make your selections thoughtfully, and you will find how easy getting dressed every morning for your day's activity can be.

Your complexion and hair color determine the colors you will find most appealing on you. The study of color will enable you to select and combine colors that stretch your clothing dollar and bring out the glow of your natural coloring.

Your body type determines the lines that will enhance your appearance and balance any irregular height or width in your frame. Awareness of the effect of clothing lines will make it easy for you to select the styles of clothing that hang well and move well for your body type and personal activities.

That persistent problem of what to wear where is solvable by planning your purchases with your activities in mind. A basic wardrobe is your key to wearing apparel that serves all your needs. The descriptions of basic designs provide for coordinating such a wardrobe at a minimum cost. Shoes and handbags are accessories you will learn to fit into your plan.

Other accessories must be well chosen to complete that well-dressed appearance you wish to project. Having a shopping plan and learning to care for your clothes and accessories complete your third dimension.

Chapter 10

Color

The importance of color today is apparent everywhere. From the beauty of the landscape, a sunset, or a field of flowers, to the warnings and signals of danger it provides, color influences the feelings and actions of people everywhere. Color in clothing is important, too, for it can influence a mood, the illusion of a shape and size, the way others perceive a personality, the suitability of an ensemble for an occasion, and the flexibility of a wardrobe.

You can use color in your wardrobe to make you appear thinner, fatter, warmer, cooler, aggressive, or subdued. You can define your shape or obscure it with color. You can achieve harmonic combinations that are flexible and flattering and that give the illusion of balance to your figure. Since your wardrobe is one of the most expensive investments you make in your personal development, it is very important that it contributes to your success and self-confidence. Wise use of color is one way to improve it.

Principles of Color

To make good choices of color for your wardrobe, you will need to understand principles of color. Color is usually discussed in terms of color, hue, intensity (saturation), and value (lightness). These words must be understood precisely if you are to use color wisely for your wardrobe.

DEFINING THE PARTS

Color has been a part of your everyday life for so long that you may be surprised to learn that there are many ways to describe a particular color. It is not practical to use terms developed by dye and paint manufacturers, such as "moss," "teal," or "apricot" to designate colors because these are not standardized and are, therefore, hard to organize in your thinking. The terms and relationships that follow will be easy to understand since color organization employing them will be introduced in a logical pattern of primary, secondary, intermediate, tinting, toning, and shading designations.

Color. *Color* is the term used for a phenomenon of light or visual perception that enables you to differentiate otherwise identical objects. Colors are thought of as primary, secondary, and intermediate and as pure pigment, tints, tones, and shades. An example of these relationships is shown in a hue chart (Illustration 10-1). The primary colors are blue, yellow, and red. The secondary colors, which are formed by mixing two primary colors, are violet, green, and orange. The intermediates, formed by mixing a secondary with a primary, are blue-violet, blue-green, yellow-green, yellow-orange, red-orange, and red-violet. Some of the tints of each of these colors are shown in Rows 1 through 4 of the chart. The tones and shades are Rows 6–9. The pure pigment color is Row 5. Each square on the hue chart is a different color.

Hue. *Hue* is a term used to classify gradations of a color. On the hue chart, the first square in the violet column is a tint of violet. Although manufacturers of dye or paint may give it various names, it is a gradation of violet, therefore, a hue of violet. In fact, each square in the violet column is a hue of violet. Number 9, which is recognizable as purple, is obviously a hue of violet. However, Number 9s under yellow, yellow-orange, and orange (the browns) are not so obvious as hues of those colors.

The hues of the primary, secondary, and intermediate colors are formed by adding white, gray, or black to the pure pigment. When white is added, the resulting hue is a *tint*. Gray added makes a *tone*. Black added makes a *shade*.

Intensity. The amount of pure pigment visible in a color is referred to as its intensity or saturation. Row 5 shows the most intense or most saturated of each of the colors. Tints, tones, and shades each dilute the intensity of the pure pigment that is visible.

Value. Value describes the amount of light that is reflected by a color. The lightest of all colors is yellow. In any row across the chart, the yellow column will show the color reflecting the most light (highest

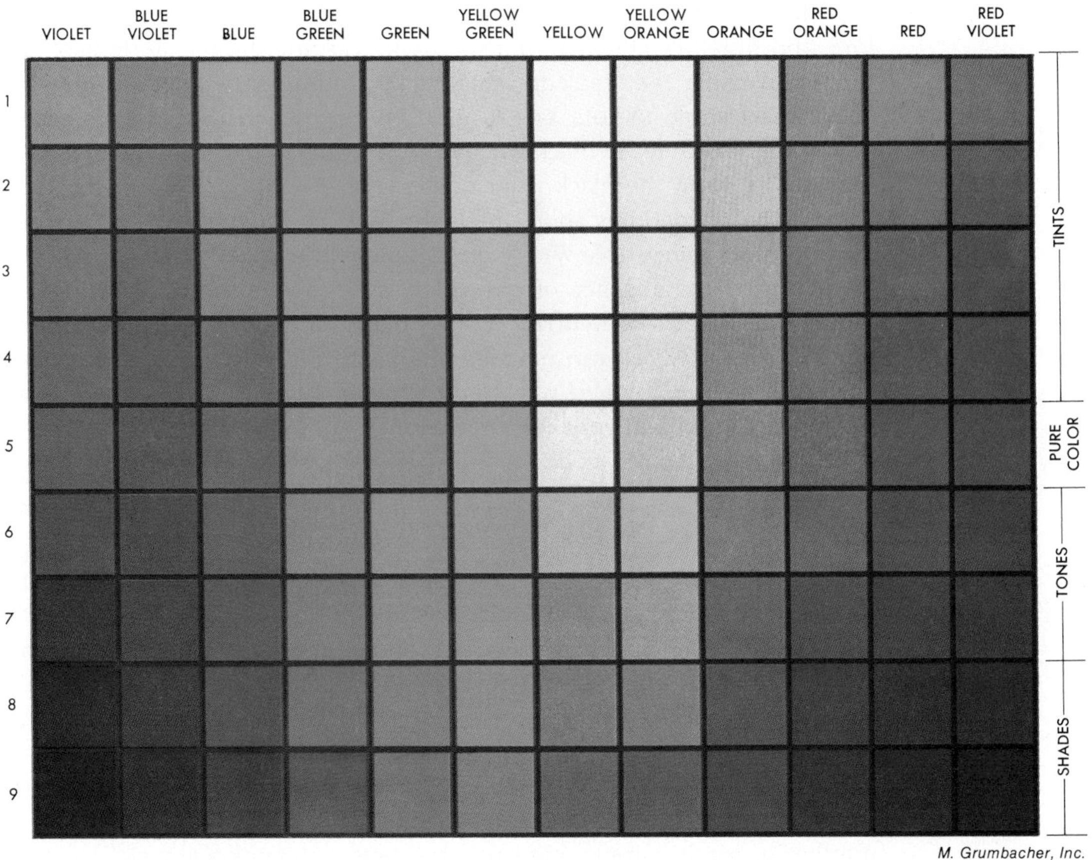

M. Grumbacher, Inc.

ILLUS. 10-1 *Row 5 is pure color. Rows 1 through 4 are tints (pure color plus white). Rows 6 through 9 are tones and shades (pure color plus gray and pure color plus black).*

value). As you move away from yellow in both directions, the lightness decreases. Violet is regarded as the color of lowest value.

Tints, Tones, and Shades. Tinting, toning, and shading may occur in many degrees. All such modifications, however, are not pleasing to the eye. An orange, for example, with a very small amount of black added looks dirty; with more black, it becomes a more appealing brown. A small amount of white added to red may make it faded and weak; but more white will make it pink and very pleasing to the eye.

The pigments of any of the primary colors (blue, red, and yellow) plus black and white, can be combined in varying proportions, yielding an infinite variety of secondary and intermediate colors. All colors, however, can be broken down finally to the primary pigments (of red, blue, or yellow), black, and white.

The Neutrals. The presence of all three primary pigments (red, yellow, and blue) in equal amounts is black. Varying the proportions of the three and using the result for shading or toning gives another range of colors discernible to your eye. If you see a brown with a greenish cast, you will know that the black was not pure but had more yellow and blue than red to form the black used to shade the orange. These unexpected "casts" that sometimes show in shades will be important to you in selecting colors compatible with your complexion.

White is the absence of any color, and gray is the combination of white and black. The neutrals (white, black, and gray) will be useful in your wardrobe. Black can be used similar to the way you will use dark shades of color. Gray and white will be used similar to the way you use the tones and tints in your color selections.

The Color Wheel. A color wheel is frequently used to show how colors are related so that you can use them in harmony. The three primary colors of pigment that are used as the basis of all other colors appear equal distances apart on the color wheel (Illustration 10-2) usually with the yellow at the 12 o'clock position, blue at the 4, red at the 8. Between the primaries are green at 2, violet at 6, and orange at 10. The colors formed by mixing the primaries and secondaries — the intermediate colors — appear yellow-green at 1, blue-green at 3, blue-violet at 5, red-violet at 7, red-orange at 9, yellow-orange at 11. The nearer a color is to a primary or secondary, the more of that color it takes on. However, some of the less dominant color is still visible. There are an infinite number of combinations that could be shown on such a wheel. The ones that this color wheel shows supply a frame of reference into which you can fit any color you encounter.

The relationship of one color to another is classified according to its placement on the wheel. Colors directly across the wheel (12 and 6; 1 and 7; 2 and 8; 3 and 9; 4 and 10; 5 and 11) are called complementary colors. Any five adjacent numbers are called analogous colors. These terms will be used later in planning harmonizing combinations for your wardrobe.

CHARACTERIZING COLOR

There are emotional responses you experience consciously and unconsciously when you are exposed to color. Some of these responses have been proved scientifically; some have not. All of them occur often enough for you to know about and to consider when you select your wardrobe colors.

Warm and Cool Colors. The colors on the color wheel usually are classified as warm or cool in feeling. A line through the center of the circle intersecting 1 and 7 makes this division. All colors from 1 through

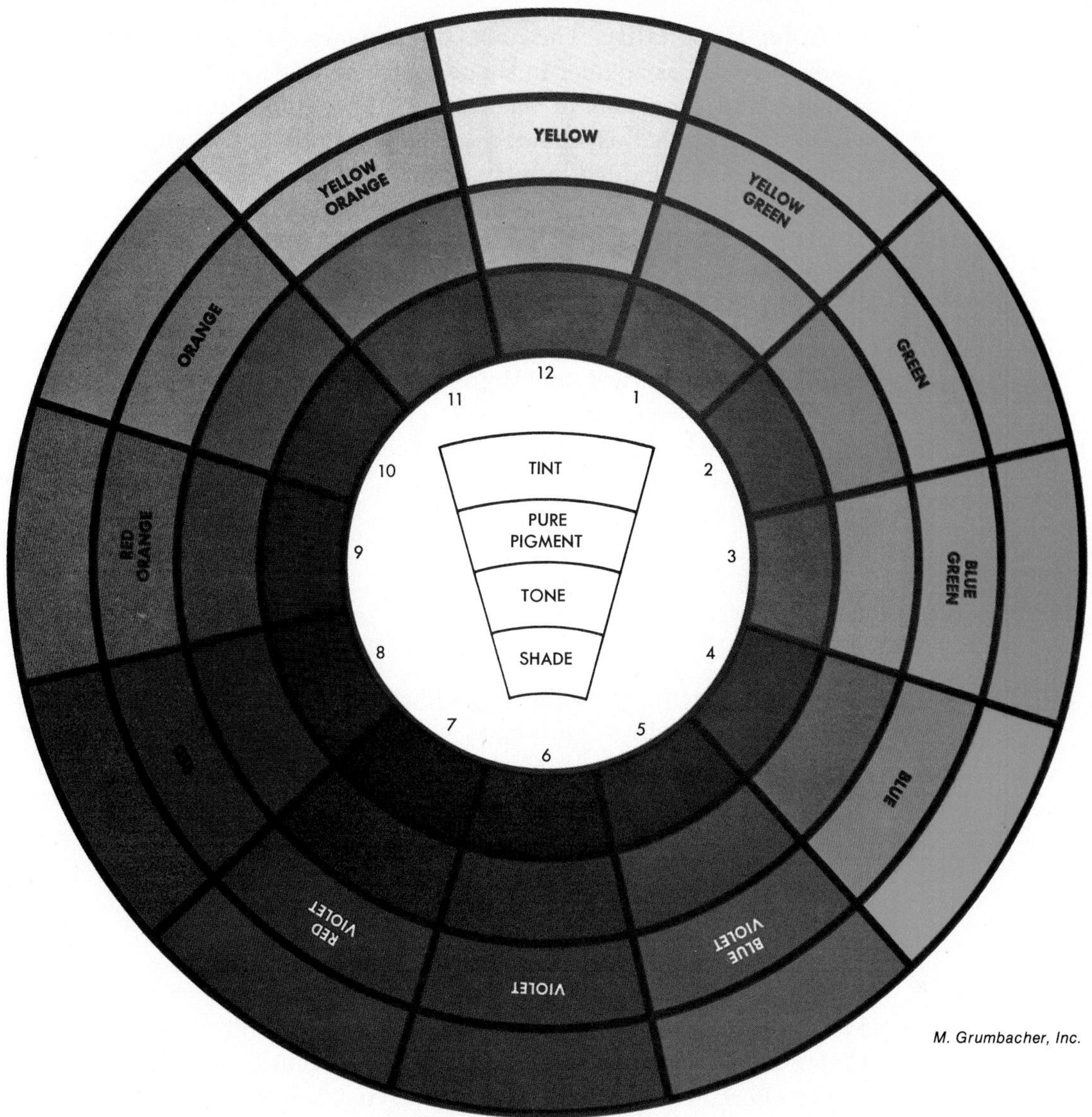

ILLUS. 10-2 *The three primary colors are blue, yellow, and red. All other colors are mixtures of the primaries.*

7 clockwise on the color wheel (greens, blues, violets) are classified as cool. All colors from 7 through 1 (reds, oranges, yellows) are warm colors. Red-violet and yellow-green are considered neutral in temperature, giving neither a cool nor warm feeling. These classifications are easy to remember if you think of cool blue water and green shade trees or warm red fire and yellow sunlight, from which they derive their cool and warm classifications.

Color Personality. The colors on the warm side of the wheel usually are perceived as angular in shape, aggressive in movement, definite in attitude, and dominant in relationship. Those on the cool side of the wheel are perceived as rounded in shape, gentle in movement, blurred in attitude, and subdued in relationship. The generally accepted descriptions of the color personalities are:

(1) Red is described as hot, dry, solid, and substantial.
(2) Orange is warm, dry, and compelling.
(3) Yellow is crisp and lofty.
(4) Green is cool, fresh, and soft.
(5) Blue is cold, wet, and dignified.
(6) Violet is soft, filmy, majestic, and refined.

Red is known to increase muscular tension and blue to relax it in the observer. Red tends to relate to excitment, green to tranquility, and blue-violet to subduing. All of these responses can be modified by shading, tinting, and toning the pure pigments. The less intense the color, the less intense the response to it.

Your Colors

It is important to find the colors that look good on you. Make up your face as you normally do, arrange your hair as you normally do, and place yourself before a mirror large enough to view your shoulders and head in good light, preferably some daylight. Drape fabric of each of the twelve colors of the color wheel around your neck and across your shoulders and observe the effects each has on your complexion.

COMPLEXION COMPATIBILITY

Colors suited to your complexion should brighten and warm your face. Begin with a color you believe looks good with your complexion. Observe the effect it has on your face, and use it as a point of comparison to the effect of the other colors. Colors not suited to your complexion probably will seem to drain your face of its glow or distort your complexion color unattractively. They may cast dark shadows around your mouth and eyes, emphasizing any lines in your face.

Distortions. Complexions may have any of the primary and secondary color undertones. Few, though, show well-defined color because of the tinting, shading, and toning pigments that are present in the skin. A person, for example, may have red, yellow, orange, green, blue, or violet undertones that are not recognizable until various other colors are placed near the face. Even then, the true undertone may be distorted because of the ways adjacent placement of colors are perceived by the eye.

Colors appearing adjacently on the color wheel, when combined, cause each color to "move" farther away from the adjacent color and assume some of the properties of the next color on the wheel. Red, for example, worn by a person with yellow undertones, makes the yellow undertones appear greenish. Red, worn by a person with orange undertones, makes the orange look yellowish.

Colors appearing across the color wheel (complementary colors) brighten the undertone present. Violet, for example, worn by a person of yellow undertone, brightens the complexion. All these distortions are shown in Illustration 10-3. They occur also when fabrics of the two colors are combined. In fabrics, though, you can select a hue that compensates for the distortion. For your complexion, you will learn to avoid certain colors or to use them in areas not near your face.

DISTORTIONS RESULTING FROM COLOR COMBINATIONS

Color Causing Distortion	Color Showing Distortion*					
	Red	**Orange**	**Yellow**	**Green**	**Blue**	**Violet**
Red	Intensify	Yellow	Green	Brighter	Green	Blue
Orange	Violet	Intensify	Green	Blue	Brighter	Blue
Yellow	Violet	Red	Intensify	Blue	Violet	Brighter
Green	Brighter	Red	Orange	Intensify	Violet	Red
Blue	Orange	Brighter	Orange	Yellow	Intensify	Red
Violet	Orange	Yellow	Brighter	Yellow	Green	Intensify

**Use this chart to determine slight distortions of color that may be expected when certain colors are combined. For example, when red is combined with orange, the orange will take on more of the yellow cast; when red is combined with yellow, the yellow will take on more of a green cast.*

ILLUS. 10-3 Distortions Resulting from Color Combinations

The distortions of natural undertones will play a major role in the selection of colors for your wardrobe. If, for example, you have yellow undertones in your complexion, red close to your face may make you turn greenish. However, if the yellow is not too strong, you may find that red shades (black added) may be used moderately and that blue-reds may be attractive with your complexion. Red in all its tints, shades, and tones will not necessarily be excluded from your wardrobe — just the clear, bright ones near your face that turn you "green."

The amount of undertone pigment varies from person to person and varies in your complexion according to your age and to your exposure to sun. Complexion undertones tend to fade as you age. Therefore, it is not possible to say that all yellow undertone complexions will benefit from the brightening effect of violet. A slightly yellow undertone may be brightened, but a strong one may become much too strong when violet is worn.

Hues. When you have determined which colors look good with your complexion, rank them according to the effect each has on your complexion. Next, shade each color with a film of black, placing the combination near your face to see if the shaded color may be worn. While this procedure does not simulate exactly all the shades of each color, it will give you an idea of each color shade you may be able to pursue for your wardrobe. Do the same with a white film and a gray one to check the tints and tones.

It is important to remember that there are infinite combinations of shading, tinting, and toning available in fabrics. The ones you have observed are just a few; but they will give you guidelines around which to select your main wardrobe colors. If you really like a particular color that doesn't seem to work with your complexion, try it in several shades, tints, and tones at a fabric store, observing the effect in a mirror. You may find a few hues that will complement your complexion. If that fails, you still have the opportunity to accessorize with the color and to use it away from your face.

HAIR-EYE-COLOR COMPATIBILITY

Often the colors that complement your complexion will also complement your eye and hair color. You can add drama to your eyes and hair, though, with careful selection of colors. Using the exact color of your eyes or hair, for example, presents a dramatic effect. Generally, however, a contrast color near the face will be needed to provide a single point of interest and relief from the drama.

Care should be exercised in trying to match the colors exactly. A brighter or higher value hue of the same color should be avoided since it will dull your eyes or hair. A bright brown dress with greyed brown hair, for example, will make the hair look drab; a bright yellow dress with slightly yellow blonde hair will make the hair color look drab.

Avoid combining colors that are only slightly tinted, shaded, or toned to a different intensity. Gray eyes with a dress of only slightly grayer color will be unappealing, whereas, a dress with a considerable amount of additional gray toning may be very harmonious. If you wish to emphasize your hair with wardrobe color, use light colors to make dark hair look richer and dark colors to make light hair look brighter. Complementary colors may be used to increase the vividness of the eye color. Orange and orange hues, for example, worn by a person with blue eyes, intensifies the blue.

Color Combinations

Your mastery of the principles of color will enable you to combine colors to your best advantage. Expertise in combining color for your wardrobe will provide for a variety and flexibility that allows you full use of each item of apparel you possess. Good color combinations result from careful consideration of harmony, value, intensity, and the number of colors to be used in one ensemble.

KINDS OF HARMONY

Appealing combinations of color are referred to as color harmony. Several kinds of harmony are available for your wardrobe. With each one there are strengths and weaknesses for you to consider.

Monochromatic Harmony. Monochromatic harmony is achieved by using one color of various values (amount of light reflected) and intensities (amount of pigment visible). Too much of one hue of a color, however, can be monotonous and should be carefully avoided. Combinations of hues of only slightly differing intensity are not appealing. Monochromatic schemes that are most successful are those that combine varying hues and fabric textures (Illustration 10-4) and those that are relieved by a print or plaid blend of the hues of the color (Illustration 10-5, next page).

ILLUS. 10-4 *The most successful monochromatic harmony is one that combines varying hues and fabric textures.*

Vogue Pattern Service

ILLUS. 10-5 *Monochromatic color schemes that are relieved by a print or plaid blend of the hues are appealing.*

Vogue Pattern Service

Analogous Harmony. Analogous harmony is achieved by combining colors that are close to each other on the color wheel (any five adjacent numbers), blues with greens, beiges with reds, browns with yellows, greens with yellows, etc. The analogous combinations that are most pleasing are those that lie between two primary colors rather than those between two secondary colors. There is great flexibility in analogous harmony, and the success of the harmony depends upon good choices in tints, tones, and shades. These combinations are probably the most familiar to you and the easiest of the harmonies to assemble and wear comfortably. The key in assembling analogous harmony is to skip a color on the wheel. If you have a violet, for example, do not go to a red-violet for the accent. Skip it and use a shade of red as in Illustration 10-6.

Complementary Harmony. Complementary harmony is achieved by combining colors that are directly across the wheel from each other — blue with orange, red with green, yellow with violet. These combinations are usually most pleasing if one color is a tint, tone, or shade, and the other is pure. Complementary colors used together intensify each other. For example, in a red and green combination, each color will seem

Vogue Pattern Service

ILLUS. 10-6 *The secret to assembling analogous harmony is to skip a color on the wheel. Instead of using a red-violet hue with a violet one, skip the red-violet and use a shade of red.*

redder and greener. Complementary harmony works best with a large amount of one subdued color and an accent with the other (Illustration 10-7). Shading the color used in the larger amount frequently improves complementary harmony.

Vogue Pattern Service

ILLUS. 10-7 *Complementary harmony works best with a large amount of one color subdued and an accent of the complementary color.*

Other Contrasting Harmonies. Double complementary harmony is achieved by combining two complementary combinations. Split complementary is achieved when colors on each side of the complement are used instead of the complement — red with blue-green and yellow-green instead of with green. A triad is achieved when three colors touched by the points of a triangle are combined. Until you have developed a very refined sense of color, these combinations may not be easy for you to assemble or wear comfortably.

Unappealing Combinations. By definition of the harmonies, there are no colors that cannot be combined. However, you are aware that some combinations, be they monochromatic, analogous, or complementary, are unappealing. The usual reasons these are unappealing are:

(1) In monochromatic color schemes, a slight amount of shading, toning, or tinting combined with pure pigment is not appealing. Beware of combining fabrics of only slight gradations of hue.

(2) In analogous combinations of color, use of colors side by side on the color wheel usually is not appealing. Better combinations are colors separated by an intermediate or secondary color.

(3) In complementary harmony, intensity is usually the problem. Because the combination of complementary colors automatically increases the intensity of both colors, the shades, tones, and tints are preferred over pure pigment for this harmony. Equal amounts of the two colors are usually overpowering and uninteresting.

All harmony can be improved if one primary is combined with two secondary colors rather than one secondary combined with two primary colors. Some harmony can be improved by a white or black outline for separation, such as a belt or piping around a contrast collar.

VALUE IN HARMONY

Combinations of tints, shades, and tones are improved if the light and dark properties are observed. Colors of low value (blue, violet, red, and shades) tend to harmonize better with black. Colors with high value (yellow, orange, green, and tints) harmonize better with white (Illustration 10-8). When these properties are observed, the colors high in light value appear lighter and colors low in light value appear darker. If the reverse combinations are made (yellow combined with black), the color will be somewhat distorted from its true value. Used in very small amounts, however, for accents, dark with light may be dramatic. Use it sparingly if at all. Too much drama, like too much of anything, is boring.

ILLUS. 10-8 *Colors with high value harmonize better with white than with gray or black.*

Vogue Pattern Service

When you combine two colors of differing value, the one having a higher value should be used in the lighter hue and the one having a lower value should be used in a shade or tone (Illustration 10-9, next page). Examples are:

(1) Dark blue looks better with pale green than dark green looks with pale blue.
(2) Light orange (beige) looks better with dark purple than light violet looks with brown.
(3) Light red looks better with dark blue than dark red looks with light blue.
(4) Pale yellow looks better with any dark color than olive drab (dark yellow) looks with any lighter color.

In combining colors of different values, an appealing combination frequently can be achieved by using one shade, one tint, and one pure color.

INTENSITY IN HARMONY

Various combinations may be used to emphasize or to dull the intensity of a color. Complementary colors, when used together, will intensify each other. A color also will seem to be intensified if it is repeated in the

Vogue Pattern Service

ILLUS. 10-9 *In combining colors of differing value, use a lighter hue of the one of the higher value and a shade or tone of the one of lower value. A tint of yellow combines well with a shade of violet.*

ensemble (Illustration 10-10). The intensity of a color is enhanced if a less intense hue of the color in a larger amount is included in the ensemble (Illustration 10-11).

To dull the intensity of a color, combine it with a color of low intensity of a slightly different color. Analogous colors used together affect the intensity, giving the illusion of distorting the two colors by causing each to appear to take on more of another primary or secondary color. The red turns orangey and the violet turns bluer in Illustration 10-12.

NUMBER OF COLORS IN HARMONY

Too many contrasting colors can make an ensemble overpowering, attracting more attention to the ensemble than to the person wearing it. A good rule is to stick to a maximum of two contrasting colors in complementary harmony and a maximum of three in analogous harmony, using a great deal more of one than of the others. In a monochromatic color scheme, it is possible to have more colors in an ensemble than in complementary or analogous schemes without overpowering the wearer. The triad and double complementary color harmonies combine three and four contrasting colors and should be used with great care.

Prints frequently have more colors than are desirable. Avoid them if they appear too strong. Study the colors in a print fabric carefully before

Vogue Pattern Service

ILLUS. 10-10 *To intensify a color, repeat it in the ensemble. The red seems redder because it is repeated.*

ILLUS. 10-11 *The intensity of the collar and hat color is increased because of the orange tint in the pants.*

Vogue Pattern Service

Vogue Pattern Service

ILLUS. 10-12 *Red takes on orange and violet turns blue when these analogous colors are used together.*

you select one for your wardrobe. Used in a monochromatic scheme, the colors in a print tend to give the impression of one unit even though they are various shades, tints, and tones of the same color. Frequently prints are at their best and improve this harmony when they are used as accents in small amounts.

Color Applications

Judicious application of the principles of color and harmony can influence the appearance of your figure and the suitability of your clothes for the occasion for which you choose them.

REPROPORTIONING YOURSELF

The most effective way to reproportion yourself is with diet and exercise. You can enhance your figure and improve the balance of your proportions, however, to some degree with color. Warm and cool colors, intense colors, high value colors, and the placement of each of these influence the appearance of your shape and size.

Value. One of the most important considerations in altering the illusion of your size is the value of the color utilized. The colors high in value (yellow, green, orange) will appear to enlarge the areas they cover, (Illustration 10-13). (Green, because of its cool feeling, tends to recede and appear somewhat smaller than yellow or orange.) Those low in value (blue, violet, red) will appear to diminish except for red, which, because of its warmth, appears closer to the viewer — therefore larger. The value of these colors refers to the amount of light reflected by the pure pigment. It is always possible to use shades of any of the colors to achieve a lower value and modify the illusion of enlarging.

A low intensity yellow, though, will be lighter and tend to enlarge more than the same intensity blue or violet. Using a tint of any of the colors will emphasize its capacity to enlarge. A tint of blue, because of its low value, however, will closely equal a shade of yellow in its capacity to enlarge.

If you are overweight, colors of low light value and only dark shades of those of high value will be best for you. If you are underweight, colors high in light value and tints of those low in light value will compensate for your underweight. If parts of your figure are proportionately larger than they should be, you can balance them with color. These irregularities will appear more balanced if you will wear enlarging colors in the normal areas and diminishing colors in the large areas. If your hips are disproportionately larger than your bust line, for example, you can better achieve a sense of balance by wearing enlarging colors for blouses and dress bodices and diminishing colors for skirts.

ILLUS. 10-13 *Yellow, because of its high value, tends to enlarge the area it covers.*

Vogue Pattern Service

Warm and Cool Colors. Another consideration in size illusions is the fact that warm colors tend to advance and cool ones to recede. Red, orange, and yellow will advance toward the observer and appear larger. Green, blue, and violet will recede, appearing to be farther away and, as a result, smaller to the observer.

Warm colors define shapes more accurately, whereas cool ones tend to blur shapes. If you want an area of your figure to recede and its shape to be slightly obscured, stay with the cool colors for that area. To further create the illusion, use a warm color in an area that is well-proportioned, and to which you want to draw attention. The warm color will further push the area of the cool color into obscurity because warm colors tend to cause cool colors to recede into the background.

Intensity. In a monochromatic color scheme, it is possible to achieve a balancing effect by using pure color in place of the warm color and by using shades in place of the cool color because pure color will overpower grayed ones, pushing them into the background.

Detail and Plainness. Another way to give an illusion of the size and proportion you desire is to use detail (prints, intricate seaming, plaids) and plainness (solid colors and uncluttered lines). Detail will appear nearer and command more notice. It should be used in areas to be enlarged and places that you want to emphasize. Plainness should be used for receding and diminishing. Plaids and prints tend to enlarge regardless of the color (Illustration 10-14). The larger the pattern, the more the detail tends to enlarge.

ILLUS. 10-14 *Prints tend to add bulk to the figure and to enlarge the area they cover. The larger the pattern, the more the print tends to enlarge.*

Vogue Pattern Service

For a large figure it is best to use plaids and prints only for very small areas, such as in a blouse under a solid color jacket or in a scarf. This arrangement, incidentally, also allows for more versatility than a plaid jacket would since a completely new ensemble can be achieved by varying the accents used with the solid jacket — a difficult feat with the plaid jacket. Versatility with accessories will be studied in a later section.

A solid color especially a dark one, will give an illusion of less bulk and should be used if you wish to appear smaller. The solid color ensemble, because of the unbroken line it makes, will make you appear taller than mixed colors will. Lines will be discussed in detail later.

Placement. Various placements of color can give balance to an ensemble and create illusions as well as complement your natural coloring.

Black, used close to the face, often "absorbs" the face colors, whereas white close to the face will reflect the colors of the face. A black dress or one with black near the neck, therefore, will need relief near the face to prevent the face from appearing drained of its glow. (See Illustration 10-4, page 211.)

Light colors attract the eye and can draw the eye away from undesirable figure flaws. Too many eye-attracting points, though, will destroy the continuity of an ensemble, making the eye dart from one to another of the points. A dress with a white collar will draw the eye to the face. White cuffs on a long sleeved dress, though, will draw the eye to the hip line, a line many people do not wish to emphasize (Illustration 10-15). A row of light-colored buttons down a dress will draw the eye to the straight line and obscure any undesirable curves in the dress (Illustration 10-16, next page). However, the top-stitching around the sleeve in Illustration 10-16 draws attention the the bust line, enlarging it.

ILLUS. 10-15 *A white collar reflects the color of the face. White cuffs draw the eye to the hip line.*

Vogue Pattern Service

Placing a high-value, enlarging color in any area tends to enlarge that area. Illustration 10-17, next page, shows a dress that, on a figure of too

Vogue Pattern Service

ILLUS. 10-16 *A row of contrasting buttons or of contrasting stitching may draw the eye away from undesirable curves in your silhouette.*

Vogue Pattern Service

ILLUS. 10-17 *White, because of its high value, tends to widen the figure.*

much width, would be wrong because it would enlarge and emphasize the width. An underweight person, however, might wear such a dress with much success because of the widening effect. The large person would do better with a solid, low-value color dress with an eye-catching, light fabric at the neck to draw attention away from the disproportionate width.

Waists are another area of concern. A high-value color belt will "enlarge" a waist, whereas, a dark one will diminish it. Compare the waists in Illustration 10-18. High-value colors draw attention to those areas you wish to emphasize and enlarge. Placing color at the wrist (cuffs of a bright print blouse), waist (a belt of a light or intense color), or hem of an ensemble will draw the eye to those areas, emphasizing that part of your body. If your hands, waist, or legs are not your most attractive features, you may want to direct the eye to other points.

ILLUS. 10-18 *A black belt tends to diminish the waist; a white belt tends to enlarge it.*

Vogue Pattern Service

The placement of dark colors above light ones gives a feeling of the dark colors resting uneasily on light ones. Blue worn above yellow, for example, is less appealing than yellow worn above blue. Orange worn above violet is more appealing than violet worn above orange.

When you are emphasizing a color, such as the color of your eyes, by repeating it somewhere in your ensemble, do not place a higher value color near the one you wish to emphasize because higher value colors tend to overpower lower value ones.

The emphasis of an ensemble should be on one color. The larger the space to be covered, the more subdued the color should be. The smaller the space, the more intense the color may be, as in the dark green dress with the red accent (Illustration 10-7 page 213). If the one color that is emphasized is bright, as in a yellow dress, be sure that the design is simple, or the dress will appear to be wearing you rather than you wearing the dress.

SUITING THE OCCASION

Because color elicits certain emotional responses in the observer and the wearer, and because of customs and traditions, it is wise to consider the occasion for which an ensemble is intended before you decide on the color you want.

City and Country. Throughout the United States, it has always been considered appropriate to wear a darker color in the cities than in suburbs and the country. The main reason for darker colors has been their capacity for showing less of the inevitable dirt, smog, and pollution found in the air of a typical city. These city darks and country lights are not hard and fast rules; but if it is the custom in the area where you live, you will probably be more comfortable observing the customs than not.

Indoors and Outdoors. Bright, light-reflecting colors in large amounts are tiring to the eye, as are the warm colors in pure pigment, and are, therefore, less desirable for business than pastels (tints), darker shades, and cooler colors. The warm, bright colors are good for casual wear, however, because they are stimulating and generally give the wearer a happy, warm feeling.

Seasons. The season of the year is less important now than it once was in dictating color choices. Nevertheless, many of the ideas made sense. Dark colors, traditionally designated for winter, absorb warmth from the sun and buildings, actually making the wearer warmer. Light colors reflect heat and light, making the wearer cooler.

Solemn and Serious Occasions. The cooler and darker colors traditionally present a more dignified, refined image, appropriate for serious and solemn occasions, than bright, warm colors that are identified with excitement and gaiety. If the impression you wish to make is a calm, cool, collected one of seriousness and refinement, a cool or dark color will be your ally. Save the warm colors for accents and for ensembles for casual wear, or wear them in less intense hues (Illustration 10-19). Hues of orange, green, and yellow, for example, can be found that are suitable for business wear.

Vogue Pattern Service

Vogue Pattern Service

ILLUS. 10-19 *Warm colors in low intensity hues are suitable for office and career wear.*

Your Clothes

The value of knowing how color affects your wardrobe, appearance, and comfort is in applying your knowledge both to the clothes you presently have as well as to those clothes that you will add to your wardrobe in the future.

ANALYZING THE COLOR OF YOUR CLOTHES

Analyzing the clothes you currently own not only will help you in wearing them more effectively but will give you practice in viewing wardrobe colors critically so that your clothes shopping will be simplified as you add items. A chart shown in Illustration 10-20, page 229, may be helpful to you in your analysis.

Occasion. A careful analysis of what you have now should be made first. It will be easier to analyze what you have if you group items by the occasion to which they are suited. The analysis might follow these categories: career clothes, casual clothes, and special occasion clothes. Designate other classifications if you need them. You may have items that are suitable for all three; for example, a blouse that combines with a jacket and skirt for career wear, with slacks for casual wear, and with a long evening skirt for formal wear. Since part of your analysis will be in determining what color combinations are suitable, you should list an item like the blouse under each category. The combinations needed for each category will be different. For example, your career-wear jacket and skirt will be of a color that suits the surroundings of your work and that is not tiring to your eyes. The slacks for casual wear, on the other hand, may be of the warm, bright colors that suggest excitement and fun. The evening skirt may be of the refined and dignified colors.

Color. Next, designate the color of the item. You may find it easy to use the numbers on the color wheel and designate whether the color is a tint, tone, shade, or pure color. The numbers will make it easy for you later to make the harmonizing combinations desired.

Complexion Compatibility. Note whether or not the item is of a color compatible with your complexion. If it is, you may want to consider a monochromatic or complementary harmony combination to emphasize and intensify the color. If it isn't, you may want to consider analogous harmony, which enables you to include colors that are more compatible with your complexion.

Eye-Hair-Color Compatibility. Decide whether or not your eye and hair colors will be enhanced by the color of the item; but consider them secondary to your complexion. Your appearance will suffer less from a poor eye-hair color combination than from a poor complexion color combination.

Enlarging-Diminishing. The designation of a color as enlarging or diminishing is the next classification. The warm, high-value colors will appear closer and larger, therefore enlarging the area they cover. Shades of those colors, however, may not be as enlarging as the pure pigment or tints. The cool, low-value colors will appear farther away, obscure, and smaller, thus diminishing.

Detail-Plainness. The detail or plainness of the item influences the harmonizing choices you will make in combining items. Detail seems closer and is eye-catching, drawing attention to areas where it is worn. Plainness, on the other hand, will not draw the eye to any particular point and usually does not by itself either enlarge or diminish. If the item is detailed, designate whether the detail is seaming, top stitching, print, etc. When you later decide on appealing combinations, you will find this full description helpful.

Figure Compatibility. After the other designations are determined, consider the part of your figure this clothing item is for. Decide if it is suited proportionally for the enlarging-diminishing property of the color and for the detail or plainness of the item. Figure compatibility will be very important to you if you are overweight or underweight or if your figure is out of proportion. If the item is a blouse, for example, and your bodice size is disproportionally smaller than your skirt size, you will want your blouses to be of enlarging colors. The enlarging colors of the blouses, combined with diminishing skirt colors, will give the illusion of balance to your figure.

COMBINING YOUR COLORS

After you have analyzed what you have in your wardrobe, study your classifications and make color combinations of items that are appealing and suitable for you.

Harmony. In the planned combination section, designate whether the item falls in the monochromatic, analogous, or complementary harmony group. Remember that monochromatic color schemes require different hues and textures to be interesting; analogous colors too close on the color wheel are unappealing; and complementary colors may appear too intense. Also, there should be a great deal more of one of the complementary colors than of the other, and the complementary color used in the larger amount should be in a shaded hue.

Balancing. Make the decision about whether the item to be combined will be of an enlarging color or of a diminishing one. Take into consideration the idea of balancing your figure if it is out of proportion. The planned combination item may be plain or detailed, depending upon the relative plainness of the matching item and the effect you wish to achieve. Remember that detail appears bulkier and more eye-attracting than plainness.

Subduing and Intensifying. If you feel that an item is of a color that is too intense, combine it with one of just a slightly different color (analogous color) in a deep shade. If you have a color that needs brightening or intensifying, combine it with a complementary color.

Evaluating. The evaluation of the combination should be made carefully. Does it suit the same occasion as the item with which it is combined? A blouse, on first evaluation, may be considered a career item, but when combined with a skirt of a bright, warm color in your current wardrobe, it may look too casual. A more suitable skirt or jumper for career wear may be needed if you are to fit the blouse into your career-wear category of clothes.

Evaluate the harmony of the colors taking into consideration whether:

(1) The high value color appears at the top.

(2) The fabrics and textures are varied in a monochromatic color scheme.

(3) The colors are far enough apart to be appealing if it is an analogous color scheme.

(4) One color is prominent and subdued and the other is pure or nearly so in complementary harmony.

Harmonies may be slightly improved with an outline of white or black, such as a belt. If you are not entirely satisfied with the combination you have planned, try such an outline.

WARDROBE ANALYSIS

								Combination Item Planned					
								Harmony					
Item	Color	Complexion Compatibility	Hair-Eye Compatibility	Enlarging-Diminishing	Detail or Plainness	Figure Compatibility		Complementary	Analogous	Monochromatic	Detail or Plain	Enlarging Diminishing	Planned Combination Item

ILLUS. 10-20 Wardrobe Analysis

Evaluate the complexion compatibility of the entire ensemble. Examine your face color carefully when you try on a garment. Your face color should be enhanced and preferably brightened and warmed by the combination of colors. Avoid combinations that appear to drain the glow from your face, create shadows on it, or distort your complexion color unattractively.

Evaluate the effect the coordinated outfit has on your hair and eyes. Although compatibility here is less important than with your complexion, an outfit can be planned to complement and enhance all your features if you work at it.

Examining. Continue to examine the ensemble in a full-length mirror. Step back far enough so that you are able to see your figure in relation to other objects in the room. That will give you a perspective in determining figure-color compatibility. See if your figure is complemented with the colors and placement you have assembled. It should appear balanced and in proportion to the relative size of the other items in the room.

If you have used prints, plaids, or detailed seaming, check to see that the effect of enlarging or diminishing appears where it is desirable. Make sure high-value and warm colors give the proper balance to cool, low-value colors in correct placement for any figure irregularities.

SUMMARY

The color in your wardrobe can be your ally or enemy. You can enhance your appearance or detract from it. Give your wardrobe colors the consideration they deserve in relation to the important part they play in your overall appearance.

Understanding Color

1. What are the relationships between primary, secondary, and intermediate colors?
2. How do you achieve tints, tones, and shades of color?
3. Is a color of high intensity also necessarily of high value? Why or why not?
4. What characterizes the "personality" of warm colors? of cool colors?
5. Why is it necessary to coordinate color to your complexion?
6. What are key elements in monochromatic harmony? Analogous harmony? Complementary harmony?
7. Why are some combinations unappealing?
8. What is the importance of value in harmony? Of intensity?
9. How can color be used to reproportion your figure?

Chapter 11

Line

An object is defined by two characteristics: (1) color and (2) structure or line. The way you are perceived by others is defined by the same two characteristics. You know about color and how to enhance your figure with it. Now, you can add the principles of good line utilization to your considerations of wardrobe selection.

Learning about lines includes the illusions lines create when they appear singularly, in multiples, horizontally, and vertically. It includes the influence of fabric texture, the construction, and also the trim of a garment.

The combination of knowing your own figure well, selecting the proper undergarments, and applying the principles of line can yield an exciting dimension to your personal development. Just knowing how to emphasize your best features and obscure your poor ones nurtures a measure of confidence that is reflected in your everyday poise.

Principles of Line

One way to describe an object is to discuss its shape and markings. In clothing, the shape and markings are known as the lines of the garment. The effect of a singular line on a garment is amazing. By changing the direction in which the eye is drawn, the size, balance, and proportion can be altered.

NATURE OF LINES

A line can create an optical illusion. The line can lead the eye in a certain direction. It can contrast one area against another. It can divide areas into equal or unequal spaces, yielding illusions of size, emphasis, and balance.

Widening, Narrowing, Heightening, and Shortening. Straight lines themselves, by leading the eye, make figures seem taller if the lines are vertical and shorter if the lines are horizontal (Illustration 11-1). A diagonal straight line does not add height; but by adding width, it makes a figure seem shorter. Parallel diagonal lines make a figure seem shorter than parallel vertical lines but taller than parallel horizontal ones (Illustration 11-2). Adding accents to the ends of straight lines changes the illusion. A V at the end of a line seems to extend the figure; whereas an inverted V or a — (bar) seems to diminish the figure (Illustration 11-3). Multiple straight lines in any direction tend to widen a figure because the eye travels from side to side (Illustration 11-4). Any line that leads the eye to the perimeter of the figure tends to widen, and a line that keeps the eye attracted to the center of a figure tends to narrow the figure. In V-lines, for example, the point of the V narrows the figure wherever it appears, and the stems that lead the eye to the perimeter of the figure widen it wherever they appear.

ILLUS. 11-1 *Vertical lines lengthen the figure. Horizontal lines widen the figure.*

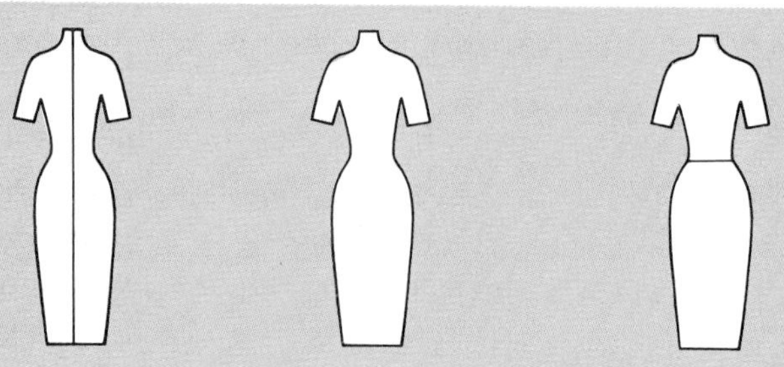

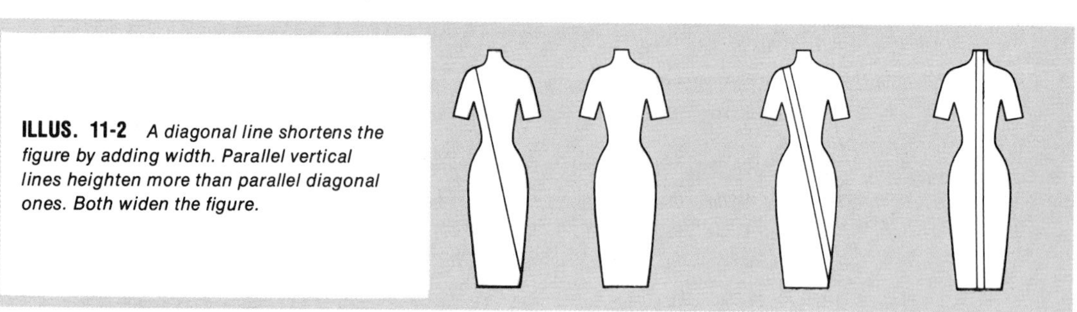

ILLUS. 11-2 *A diagonal line shortens the figure by adding width. Parallel vertical lines heighten more than parallel diagonal ones. Both widen the figure.*

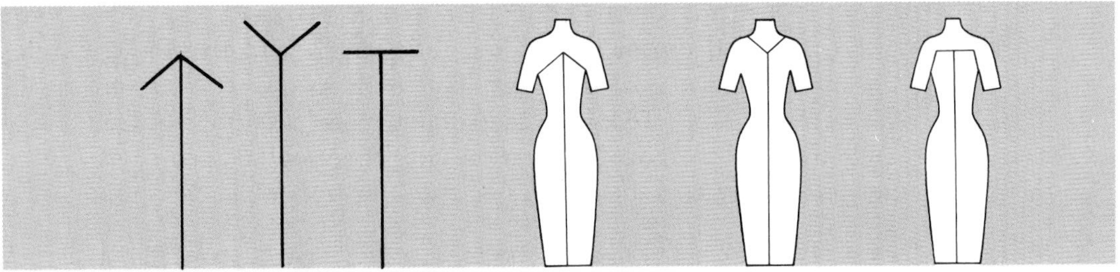

ILLUS. 11-3 *Accents at the ends of straight lines seem to alter the lengths of the lines. An inverted V shortens; a V lengthens; a bar shortens.*

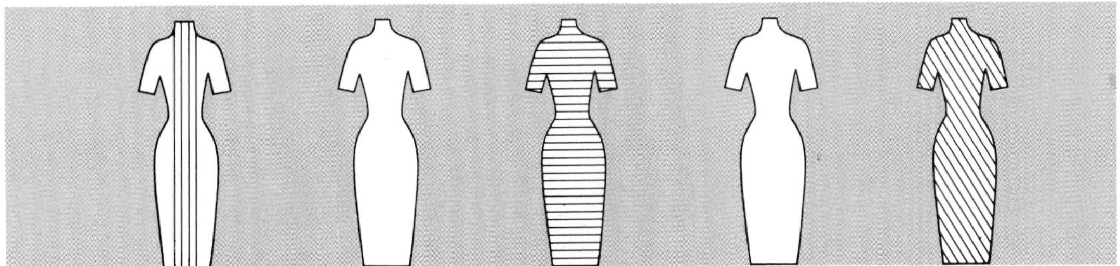

ILLUS. 11-4 *Multiple straight lines in any direction tend to widen the figure.*

Defining, Softening, Accenting and Obscuring. The shape of a line, if it isn't straight, makes a definite difference in the way a figure is perceived. An angular line defines sharply the area it surrounds, whereas a curved one tends to soften the shape of the area it surrounds. Angular lines give an emotional feeling of stateliness, sophistication, dignity, and calmness. Curved lines that are full are graceful and luxurious. Controlled curves are spritely and somewhat nervous in feeling (Illustration 11-5, next page).

The direction of a curve is important. A downward curve is droopy, but a diagonal or upward one is especially lovely when formed by soft folds of fabrics. A full circle is usually monotonous and requires some relief with a contrast or accent. The points to which the eye is led by a line are accented, and the areas away from which the eye is led are are obscured (Illustration 11-6).

Proportional Balance. Lines in clothing form boundaries of spaces, the sizes of which determine the proportion perceived by the eye. The placement of a line, then, becomes vital to achieving good proportion to a figure. The nearer a horizontal line is to the center of the figure the more it shortens the figure. The nearer to the center a vertical line is, the more it heightens the figure. (Illustration 11-7). A very close border makes a figure appear larger. A slightly larger border tends to maintain the true proportion of the figure but tends to give it a slightly smaller appearance. A very large border draws more attention to itself and its bulk than to the figure (Illustration 11-8). The contrast of a short line to a longer one extends the longer one and diminishes the shorter one (Illustration 11-9).

ILLUS. 11-5 *Controlled curved lines are spritely and "nervous" in feeling.*

Vogue Pattern Service

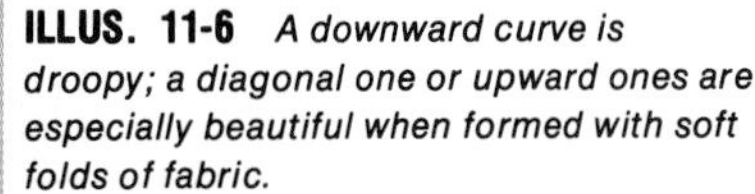

ILLUS. 11-6 *A downward curve is droopy; a diagonal one or upward ones are especially beautiful when formed with soft folds of fabric.*

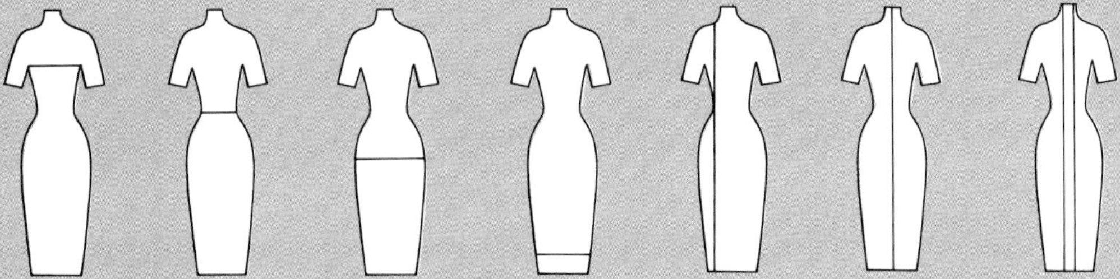

ILLUS. 11-7 *The placement of a line alters the proportion of the figure. The nearer the center of the figure a horizontal line is, the more it shortens the figure. The nearer the center of the figure a vertical line is, the more it heightens the figure.*

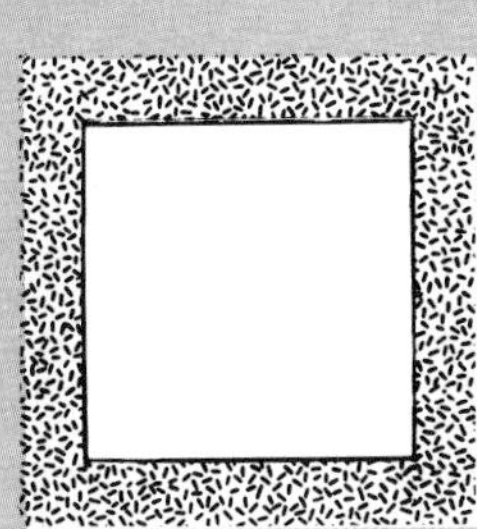

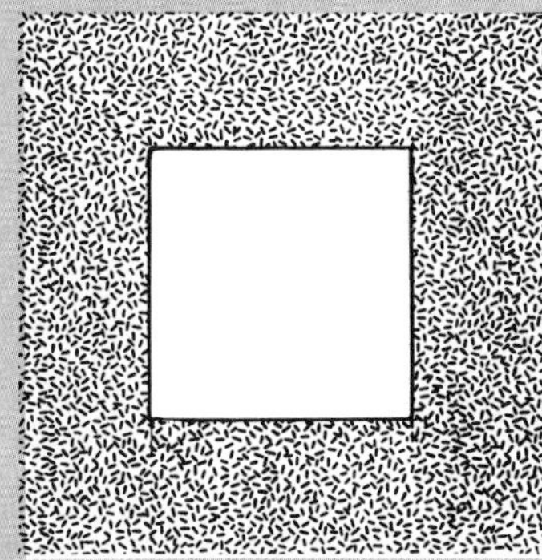

ILLUS. 11-8 *The very close border makes the inner figure seem larger than the figure inside the larger border. The inner squares are exactly the same size.*

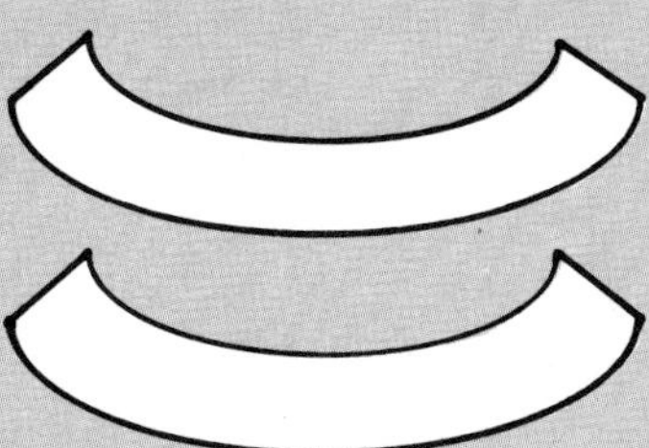

ILLUS. 11-9 *A short line contrasted to a longer one makes each seem more extreme. The long, straight lines are all the same length. The one sandwiched between the two shorter ones seems longer than the others. The upper, curved figure seems larger than the lower one, even though they are the same size, because the longer, lower line of the upper figure is contrasted to the shorter, upper line of the lower figure.*

LINES IN CLOTHES

The principles of lines are easy to apply and play an important part in making a figure more attractive. There are several ways to influence the appearance of the figure with lines. Fabric texture, silhouette shape, and seaming most commonly influence the lines of a garment. The trim on an ensemble can accent areas and draw the eye away from or attract it to the desired line.

Fabric Texture. Although your figure itself forms the basic lines in your clothes, the texture of the fabric contributes to the effect of the line you wear. Fabric textures range from soft to stiff. The softer the fabric, the more revealing of the silhouette it will be; the stiffer the fabric, the less revealing. Soft fabrics that cling to the lines of the body tend to give the illusion of increasing the size, just as a small border on a figure makes it look larger. Stiff fabrics tend to obscure the shape of the figure and reflect more of the silhouette of the garment than of the figure.

Shiny and dull textures affect the illusion of size and line. Dull fabrics minimize the size of the figure, while shiny ones enlarge it. A shiny fabric that clings is suitable for a thin figure but should be avoided by the plump figure. Medium figures with no bulges may wear shiny, clinging fabrics but should select carefully the fit and style of such garments.

The weight of a fabric ranges from light to heavy. Lightweight ones are revealing, and heavy ones, though they add bulk, obscure the lines of the figure. A dull-surfaced, medium-weight texture will be suitable for many figures and especially for stout figures, since the dull surface diminishes the size and the medium weight will not be too revealing. Heavy-weight fabrics may be worn by tall, thin figures since they add inches to the figure and give a massive appearance to the ensemble.

The texture of the fabric should be suited to the style of the dress. Medium- and heavy-weight fabrics are best suited for straight and shaped lines; while thin, lightweight fabrics are used in eased, fluid styles. A straight-line dress of lightweight, thin fabric will be unsuitable since the fabric will not provide enough body to hang properly; however, a full-skirted dress of lightweight, thin fabric will flow beautifully and hang more evenly than one of medium- or heavy-weight fabric. Fortunately, the style that is appropriate to each figure size is compatible to the texture that is suitable for each figure size. If you select the proper texture for your figure, the correct style for that fabric will probably be suitable for your figure size also.

Patterned textures also affect the lines of the clothes you wear. The larger the pattern, the more bulk it adds to the line. Small designs are suitable for thin and average figures, but large designs should be confined to tall, thin figures. The design of the texture influences the appearance of the size of the figure. Any design with horizontal or near horizontal lines adds width to a figure. Vertical designs will add height. All designs add more bulk than a plain fabric does.

Fabrics are available today that do not wrinkle. Insist on nonwrinkle or wrinkle-resistant fabrics when selecting the woven variety. Knitted fabrics rarely wrinkle and are very well suited for almost any kind of clothing and for any occasion. Be sure to select one of proper weight for your figure size and the style of the ensemble you are wearing.

Construction. Although your figure itself forms the basic lines in your clothes and the fabric texture contributes to the bulk of the apparel, most lines in clothes are formed by the overall shape of the silhouette and the interior seaming of the garment. The shape of a garment is determined by whether the cut and construction have been bloused, eased, tapered, tunneled, or flared. Bloused and eased construction generally adds bulk to the figure. Tapered and tunneled construction generally diminishes the width of the figure. Flared construction diminishes the small part of the flare and widens the wide part of the flare.

Fashion at any given time revolves around certain silhouette shapes. They are usually straight, A-line, or bouffant (Illustrations 11-10, 11, and 12, next page). Each of these may be modified or extreme and thus suited for any figure type. The hardest to modify for a plump figure is the bouffant. The hardest to modify for the very thin figure is the straight. The A-line in its many versions can be adapted to almost any figure.

Interior seam lines vary with fashion. They may be curved, straight, or angular. Curved lines generally give a soft, rounded feel to the line of an ensemble. Angular lines generally provide a contrast of smallness to largeness in the line of an ensemble and give a feeling of definition to line instead of a softness.

Horizontal line seaming adds width to the figure where the eye follows the line across the figure. The placement of such seaming is emphasized when it occurs where a sleeve ends, which further extends the line that the eye follows, or where the seaming is repeated in the sleeve at the same level. A contrast belt always provides a horizontal line and should be avoided by those who do not wish to emphasize or increase the size of the waist. Wide, horizontal lines tend to shorten the figure and to widen it (Illustration 11-13, page 239). Short figures should carefully avoid horizontal lines, especially the wide ones.

Plaids, which are a combination of horizontal and vertical lines, add bulk to the figure and widen it slightly (Illustration 11-14, page 239). If

ILLUS. 11-10 *Straight silhouettes and tunneled construction are fashion favorites because they add height to the figure and slenderize it.*

Vogue Pattern Service

Vogue Pattern Service

ILLUS. 11-11 *The A-line silhouette of tapered lines is easily adapted to most figure sizes and shapes.*

Vogue Pattern Service

ILLUS. 11-12 *The bouffant silhouette of bloused construction adds bulk to the figure and shortens it.*

Vogue Pattern Service

ILLUS. 11-13 *Horizontal lines on the bodice and skirt shorten the height of the figure and widen it.*

Vogue Pattern Service

ILLUS. 11-14 *The plaid design has lines that lengthen and widen the figure. Plaids, like most designs, add bulk to the figure.*

the plaid appears on the bias, it forms a series of V's, which, if they are wide, will widen the figure. A series of wide V's also shortens the figure by drawing the eye in a horizontal line across the figure.

Modifying a dress line for a tall figure can be done easily in some cases. A vertical line with a V at the top normally heightens a figure (Illustration 11-15, next page). A black belt at the waist, though, breaks the lengthening line, making the dress more suitable for a taller figure. With a self-belt or no belt at all, the eye would follow the line down the dress from the V, making the dress suitable for a short figure.

A single vertical line usually lengthens the figure (Illustration 11-16). Multiple vertical lines, whether they are placed wide apart or close together widen the figure because the eye is drawn across the figure (Illustration 11-17).

ILLUS. 11-15 *The vertical line, vertical pockets, and V at the neckline give this figure height. The contrast belt, however, widens the waist.*

Vogue Pattern Service

Vogue Pattern Service

ILLUS. 11-16 *A single vertical line in the center of the ensemble lengthens the figure.*

Vogue Pattern Service

ILLUS. 11-17 *Multiple vertical lines add width. Even narrowly placed vertical lines draw the eye across the figure, widening it.*

Single and multiple V's are popular seam line trims. A repeated V gives the feel of width because it is repeated and because it draws the eye to the perimeter of the figure (Illustration 11-18). The width of a V, as well as the placement of the widest part of it, gives the skirt of a dress a more flared look than it would have without the V-seaming (Illustration 11-19). The placement of the V so that the tips end at the hips tends to widen the hips. If your hips are wide enough, avoid placing any line at the hips that would further widen this line. A longer V not only controls the amount of flare a skirt seems to have but also lengthens the lines and adds height to the figure — something the wide V's will not do (Illustration 11-20, next page). The placement of the point of an inverted V makes the top of a dress more narrow than it would seem without the V point. The wide-shouldered person would find that the use of this inverted V placement would "narrow" her shoulders. A very narrow V may be ineffective in influencing the shape of the figure. It provides more of an interest point that obscures the shape of the skirt than a line that determines the shape of the figure in the ensemble.

Vogue Pattern Service

ILLUS. 11-18 *Multiple inverted V's draw the eye to the perimeter of the silhouette, making it seem larger.*

Vogue Pattern Service

ILLUS. 11-19 *The inverted V gives a narrow look to the bodice and a wide look to the hips, where the eye is drawn outward.*

ILLUS. 11-20 *An elongated V may add height to a figure.*

Vogue Pattern Service

Trims. Trim on a dress draws the eye in various directions on the garment, giving the feeling of lines. Buttons down the front of a dress, either centered or off-center, form a vertical line. When combined with contrast trim, the effect is more pronounced.

By drawing attention to itself, contrast trim draws the eye away from other areas. Badly placed, attention-getting trims cause the eye to jump from one to the other and may destroy the rhythm of the line of the dress. Short horizontal or vertical lines of contrast trim, randomly placed, usually are not rhythmical. Well-placed, related trim can create lines that give an otherwise plain dress new interest (Illustration 11-21).

Contrast trim can be used like internal seaming to widen and to heighten. The placement of pockets at the hip line tends to widen it. When cuffs on a long-sleeve dress repeat the pocket trim, the hip line is widened further (Illustration 11-22).

Diagonal lines created by trims have the same effect as internal seaming. The figure is shortened and widened slightly (Illustration 11-23).

Vogue Pattern Service

ILLUS. 11-21 *An otherwise plain dress can achieve distinction with well-chosen trim.*

Vogue Pattern Service

ILLUS. 11-22 *Diagonal lines at the neck and hips and horizontal ones at the cuffs draw the attention of the eye to the outer perimeters of the figure, widening it at the shoulder line and hip line.*

Vogue Pattern Service

ILLUS. 11-23 *The V made with contrast trim tends to widen the shoulder and narrow the waist. The parallel diagonal line on the skirt shortens and widens.*

Your Lines

Next to your facial expression, the most noticeable parts of your person are your clothes and the image of your figure they present. Your figure may have flaws; but well-chosen undergarments and wardrobe lines can camouflage its flaws and enhance its overall appearance.

YOUR FIGURE

Have you ever tried on a dress you saw on someone else and found that it didn't look the same on you as it did on the other person? That's because each figure is different. By now, you probably have attained the proper weight for your height and size. In your proper weight range, though, you may have slight figure imperfections, perhaps in the length of your arms, neck, bodice area, or legs. Or, you may have hips or a bust line that are too large or too small for ideal proportion.

If you are outside your proper weight range, the most important undertaking for you is to diet and exercise until you reach it. Wardrobe lines can camouflage some irregularities in your figure, but bulges caused from overweight will be obvious even when the best lines are selected. The lines in your wardrobe should be chosen according to your figure, and your figure analysis must be brutal. Ignoring imperfections or making excuses for them will only delay your improvement.

You can analyze yourself in front of a full-length mirror, nude or wearing a tight-fitting swim suit. Use a hand mirror with your full-length mirror to view your back and sides. Perhaps you could have a friend take your picture in a tight-fitting swim suit. You will need a front, side, and back view. The imperfections recorded in such pictures are particularly effective because you can refer to them for comparisons later.

Comparing Your Figure. One way to analyze your figure is to compare it to an "average" figure. Americans today consider an average figure desirable, and most manufacturers recognize it as a standard for sizing clothes. The "average" height range of today's woman is 5 feet 4 inches to 5 feet 7 inches tall. You may find that you are shorter than average or taller than average if your height falls outside that range.

The "average" weight is related to height (page 23), and is distributed so that the bust is ten inches larger than the waist and the hips at the fullest part are 10 or 11 inches larger than the waist. If your measurements are not in proportion, you can select lines in clothes that give the illusion of that proportion. A too-small bust can be filled out with horizontal lines and blousing. A too-large waist can be obscured with tapered dress lines. Hips that are too wide can be "narrowed" by drawing attention to the center of the dress and away from the perimeter.

Proportion. Observe whether your height is well proportioned or whether you have a long or short neck, bodice area, torso, legs, or arms. Make a note of these pecularities so that you can camouflage them when you select your wardrobe lines. Look at your shoulders, waist, and hips from front and back. Decide if they are in proportion, with your hips small enough that your arms hang straight from your shoulders without touching your hips. Make a note if either your shoulders or waist seems too wide or too narrow. Note if your hips seem too wide or too narrow in relation to your waist and shoulders.

Check your face shape; it will be important in determining necklines you select. Note the proportion of your hands and feet to the rest of your body and whether or not your legs are well shaped. The lines in your wardrobe will be based on all the observations you have made about your figure. Decide what you wish to emphasize, de-emphasize, enlarge, diminish, and obscure. Keep these in mind as you select lines for your clothes.

UNDERGARMENTS

Undergarments include your bra, girdle, and lingerie. You can make your clothes fit more beautifully and make your figure appear to be in better proportion than it really is by selecting undergarments carefully.

Foundations. Your bra and girdle are the foundation garments and the foundation of the lines in your clothes. Most figures require both a bra and girdle under some fashions and some figures require both under all fashions. If you are considering omitting either your bra or girdle, be sure the muscles are firm and smooth and that you have not one ounce of excess fat. Carefully check your image front, back and profile in the garment you are considering wearing without foundation garments. If your lines are not smooth and the tone of the muscles that support your breasts and hips is not firm, wear your foundation garments. If your undergarments are obviously missing, you are not well dressed.

The purpose of your bra is to support your breasts and shape your bodice so that hips that are too wide or too narrow are better balanced. The fashion looks that fade into and out of popularity are a soft natural look, a flattened look, and a voluptuous look. Rather than trying to copy the latest dictate of fashion, decide whether you need (1) to increase the size of your bust with a padded bra, (2) simply to support a well-formed bust, or (3) to de-emphasize a too-well-endowed figure. Your purpose will dictate which kind of bra you need.

Whatever your needs, carefully measure your bust line to determine the size you need. Two measurements must be made; one is of your rib cage just under your breasts, the other over the fullest part of your breasts. Be sure that your tape measure makes an even horizontal line around your body. Take the measurement of your rib cage and add five or six inches to arrive at the closest even number, i.e., to a measurement of 28, add 6; the size is 34. To a measurement of 29, add 5; the size is 34. Take the measurement of your fullest part to determine the cup size. If the reading is the same as you arrived at for your bra size, you wear an A cup; if it is one inch more, a B cup; two inches more, a C cup; three inches more, a D cup. (If your rib cage measures more than 38 inches, add only 3 or 4 inches, since you are harboring some excess fat that may or may not be reflected in your cup size.)

Always try on a bra before you buy it. Observe the shape of the cup and the naturalness of the curve. Be sure that the neckline is what you need for the clothes you intend to wear. Check the straps to see if they are placed for comfort over your neck bones and that you can swing your arms unrestrictedly.

Girdles are designed to provide a smooth line under skirts and pants and to control any bounce in the hips as you walk. To determine your girdle size, measure the fullest part of your buttocks. That is your girdle size. Sometimes girdles are sized simply petite, small, medium, and large. The measurements in inches for those designations are: 34 inches or under, petite; 34 to 37, small; 37 to 40, medium; and 40 to 44, large. Try on your girdle before you buy it. Walk, sit, and bend in it. Note that the legs fit comfortably as well as the crotch and waist. Be sure that the waist and legs do not roll.

If you are exercising regularly and keeping your muscles firm, you may be able to wear the control-top panty hose instead of a girdle. When you try such control, observe whether or not you have bulges that show up under your clothes. Also ask someone to observe you from the back as you walk. If any bouncing is evident, stick to a girdle until you have toned your muscles sufficiently for a firm, smooth line under your clothes.

If you have bulges at any particular spot, you can select a girdle made to control specific areas. Side panels are available for figures that have bulges on the sides just under the waist or at the top of the legs. Front and back panels are also available in girdles for protruding stomachs and flabby buttocks. It is far better to keep your muscles in shape and to diet off your bulges of fat than to depend upon a girdle to control them. However, a girdle can be of help while you are reshaping yourself and for ensembles that cling to your figure.

Bras and girdles come in different lengths and styles. A bandeau bra has a one- or two-inch band around the rib cage and can be worn by most figures. A long-line bra will have wider bands, ranging from three to six inches, to control midriff bulges. Girdles may have a wide waist band, ranging down to no waist band, and the length of the legs is varied so that you can get a girdle that exactly meets your requirements for any bulges or control you need in the thigh area.

Bras are available with underwiring that provides for additional support for heavy breasts, mainly C and D cup sizes. Try on an underwired bra before you purchase it. Be sure that you are comfortable where the wires rest against your rib cage underneath your breasts and under your arms.

Lingerie. Panties, slips, and petticoats are not considered foundation garments but are important in the lines of your clothes. Your main concern is to select lingerie that promotes a smooth line under your clothes. Bikini style panties stretched over a less-than-firm stomach may make unslightly bulges that show up under your clothes. A slip or petticoat that is too full for the dress you are wearing may look bundlesome under it. Anti-cling fabrics are available in slips and petticoats to keep them from clinging to your legs as you walk.

Special items that are available for smooth lines under knit ensembles and pants are all-in-one garments that combine the long-line bra with the girdle and pant underliners that are girdles with legs that reach to just below your calves.

LINES FOR YOUR FIGURE

When you know what your figure strengths and weaknesses are, you can select just the right lines to emphasize the well-proportioned parts and obscure the slightly unbalanced areas. Silhouettes, of course, govern the overall effect of the size of the figure; but a less-than-oval-shaped face can be made more attractive with a good selection of collars and necklines. A large hip area can have attention directed away from it to a more balanced area of the figure with the right length jacket. Legs that are less than perfect can show their best side in skirts of well-chosen lengths.

In selecting lines for yourself, decide what shapes of your figure you wish to emphasize and obscure. Remember that you do not repeat any line in your clothing that you do not wish to emphasize in your figure. For example, if your chin line is square and you do not want to emphasize its squareness, you will not select square necklines or square seaming on your bodice. If your chin line is pointed, you will avoid V-shaped necklines and V seaming on your bodice.

Silhouettes. For your own figure select the silhouettes that flatter your relative size. A tall figure can wear the bouffant and A-line styles easily. The tall, thin figure should allow for as much fullness in the skirt as is in good proportion. A tall, plump figure, however, should scale down the amount of fullness so that the image presented will not appear massive or bulky. If the tubular or straight silhouette is worn by a tall figure, wide horizontal lines should be used to "shorten" the illusion of height.

The average figure can wear any of the silhouettes and needs only to compensate for figure irregularities with interior lines in the ensemble.

A short figure can wear the tubular and A-line silhouettes but will appear juvenile and shorter in a bouffant style. If the bouffant silhouette is desired for this figure, select a soft fabric that hangs very straight and select eased construction rather than gathered, to cut down on the fullness that widens and shortens a figure. The less flare in the skirt of either the bouffant or A-line dress, the taller the figure will appear.

Necklines. Necklines and collars tend to be rounded, angular, and irregular (Illustration 11-24). Rounded necklines are easily worn by most face shapes. Very round faces, however, should carefully avoid repeating the roundness of the chin line in the neckline of an ensemble. Some of the rounded necklines that may be worn by those with round faces are the jewel, the moderate turtle, and the mandarin. Other round necklines that could be worn by other face shapes are the scoop and the U-shapes. The length of the neck should be considered when a turtle neck is selected. Very long necks may wear the large turtle. Short necks should wear only the moderate turtle. Pointed, square, and oval face shapes will find the round neckline attractive and probably flattering. The rounded neckline can be especially effective in softening the angularity of a square chin line and in softening the point on thin, pointed chins.

Angular necklines include the sabrena (boat), slit, V, square, and halter. The angular necklines will not be especially effective on faces that are angular since they will do nothing to soften the facial features. They are effective, however, on round and oval faces. A square face will find

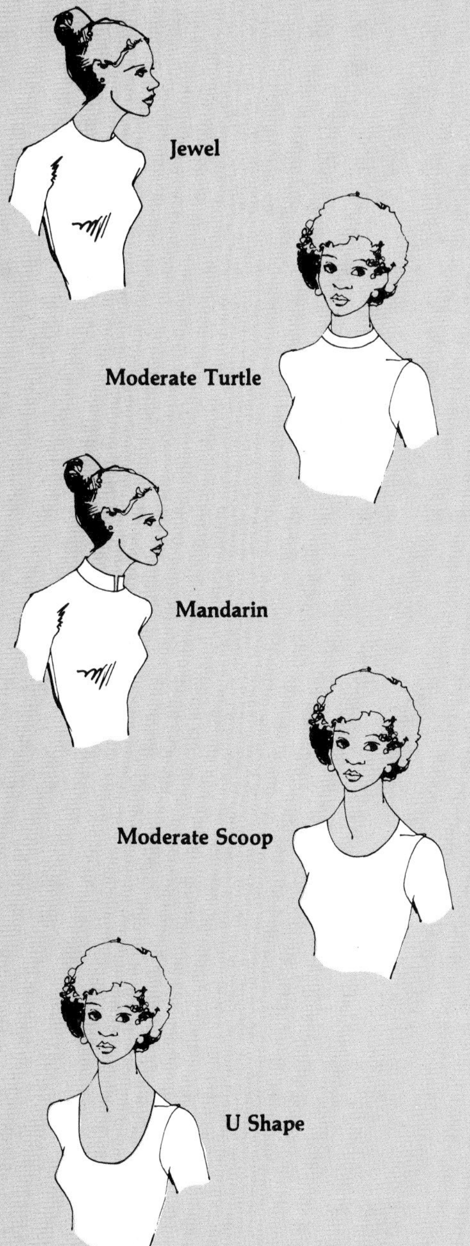

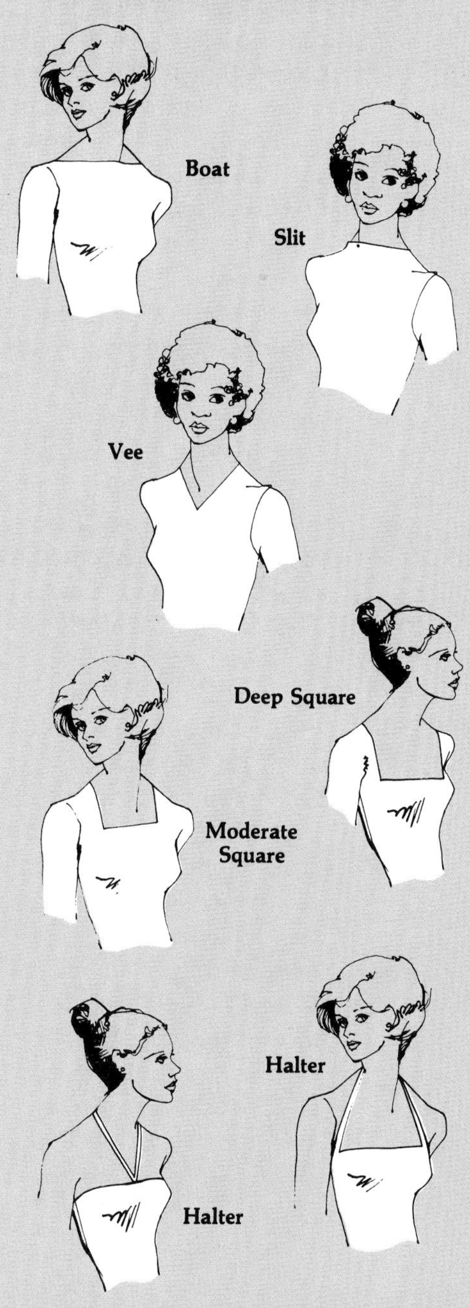

ILLUS. 11-24 *Consider the shape of your face and the length of your neck when you select a neckline.*

the V neckline helpful in reshaping the illusion of the squareness of the chin line. Care should be taken that the lines of the V neckline do not end at the outer corners of the square jaw. Select V's that end either inside or outside the corners of the jawline.

The irregular necklines include the sweetheart, portrait, cuff, cowl, and combination necklines. The placement of these as well as the line that each forms will determine whether or not they are attractive with your face shape and figure. The cuff collar, for example, makes a horizontal line and will broaden the face and shoulders. The sweetheart will accent a pointed chin as well as round a rounded face. Cowl and draped necklines are softening to angular faces but if they are too high on the neck, they will "choke" a person with a short neck.

Sleeves. The shoulder line can be broadened or narrowed by the construction of the sleeve. The arm can be slenderized or fattened according to the style of sleeve selected. The bust line, waistline, and hip line can be accented by the length of the sleeve. Wherever the sleeve ends, a horizontal line is formed, giving a broadening effect (Illustration 11-25).

Sleeveless dresses are more acceptable now than in the past, especially in warm climates. They are particularly revealing of any bulges in the upper arm and should be avoided by people who have flabby upper arms or who have excess accumulations of fat in the upper arm area. Only well-formed, firm upper arms are attractive with sleeveless clothing. A cap sleeve is one with the shoulder line extended slightly over the arm. It has a broadening effect and can give the feel of a slightly more covered look to the upper arm than a sleeveless dress. Short sleeves may end anywhere from the cap sleeve line to the elbow. The style of the dress and the shape of the arm determine the length of a short sleeve that is best for you. Decide if you wish to give a fuller look to the bust line or to the neckline when you select a sleeve length. Cuffs on short sleeves further add to the widening effect and make the arm seem larger than it is. Elbow-length sleeves end at the bend of the arm and tend to emphasize the elbow and to broaden the waistline. Three-quarter-length sleeves end anywhere between the elbow and approximately an inch above the wrist bone. They tend to form a horizontal line that is broadening to the stomach area. Bracelet-length sleeves end just above the wrist bone. This length sleeve fades in and out of fashion and frequently requires a glove that covers the wrist bone to give a completed look. Long sleeves that cover the wrist bone are usually preferred. The hip line is accented with long sleeves, especially those that are cuffed in accenting colors.

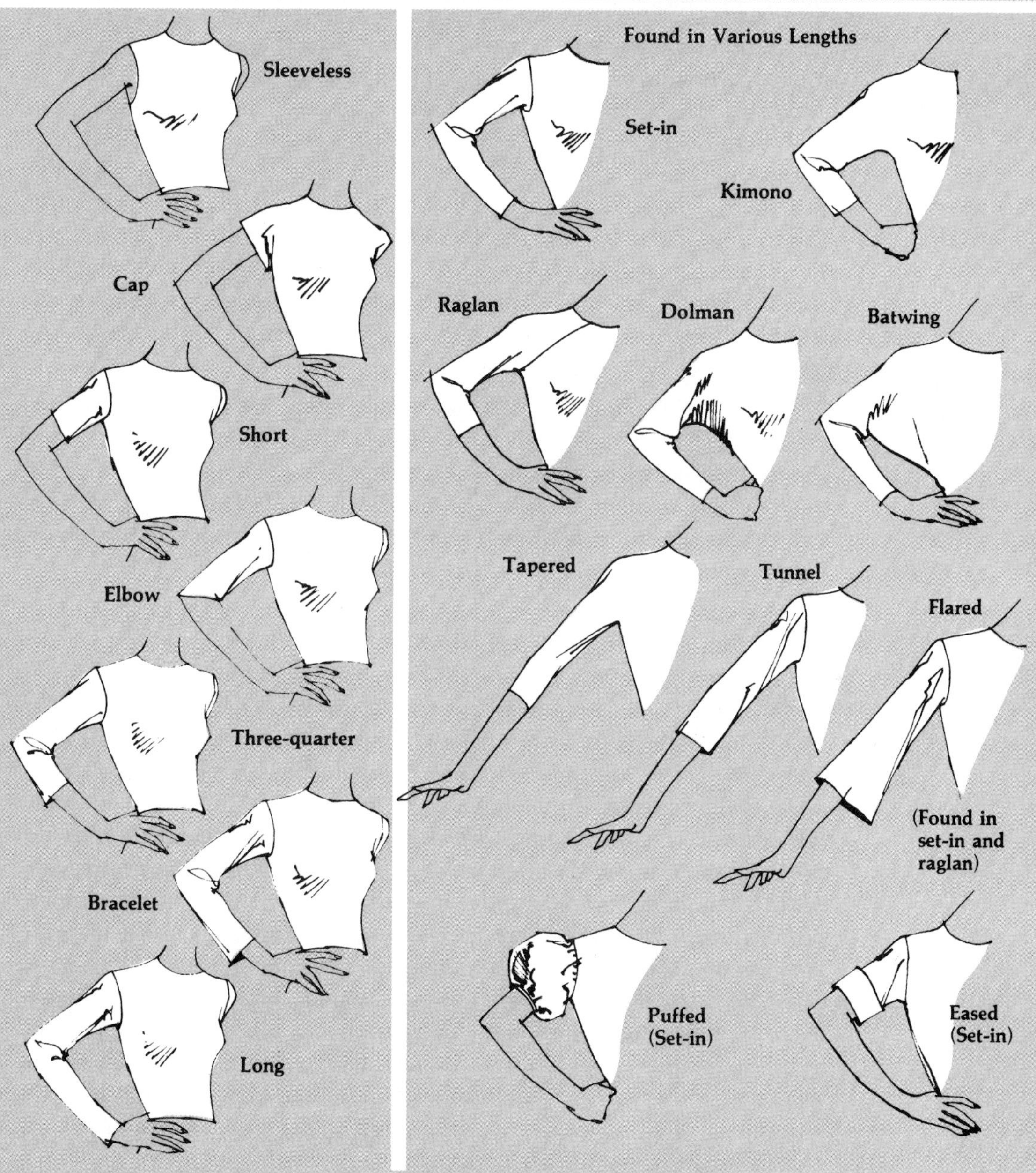

ILLUS. 11-25 *The style of sleeve you select influences the appearance of your shoulders, arms, bust line, waist, and hips.*

The construction of the sleeve includes the way it is cut and sewn into the dress and the shape of the sleeve. Sleeves may be set in or raglan if they are cut separately from the bodice. Those that form part of the bodice are kimono, dolman, and batwing.

The set-in and raglan sleeves, because they are sewn in, form lines where the seaming takes place. Set in sleeves may be eased in, giving the smoothest finish, or they may be puffed (gathered into the armhole), giving a broadening, fluffy look. Raglan sleeves are sewn in from the neckline to the underarm line and form a downward line from the neck that may give a droopy effect but can be offset by other lines. The raglan sleeve will tend to narrow the shoulder if it is fitted closely at the tip of the shoulder. Set-in sleeves can be fitted closely at the tip of the shoulder or they can be dropped. The dropped shoulder tends to broaden the shoulder line because it extends the distance from the neck to the armhole sleeve seam.

Those sleeves that are cut as part of the bodice may narrow the bodice and bust lines if they are fitted closely, as the kimono, or they may widen them if they are loosely fitted, such as the dolman or batwing. The shoulder line tends to remain true to its size in this kind of sleeve, since most of the attention is drawn to the bust line and waist. Heavy upper arms may be concealed in dolman and batwing sleeves.

The shape of the sleeve may be tapered, tunnel, flared, puffed, or eased. The tapered sleeve forms a contrast of widening the upper arm and narrowing the lower arm — the opposite effect of the flared sleeve. The tapered sleeve usually is not cuffed, and the flared sleeve may or may not be cuffed. Cuffing the flared sleeve minimizes the widening effect of the lower arm and frequently makes the wrist seem smaller because of the contrast of the blousing to the control of the cuff. The tunnel sleeve forms a straight line from shoulder to wrist and usually is not cuffed. It may be closely fitted or loose. If closely fitted, it minimizes the width of the arm and silhouette. If loosely fitted, it widens the arm and silhouette. Puffed sleeves are gathered at the armhole and at the cuff. They occur in any length and are always controlled either with a small band or a normal size cuff. These sleeves broaden the silhouette and give the ensemble a light, airy look. The eased sleeve is smooth at the armhole but gathered onto a cuff. It has slight shaping from the elbow to the wrist and usually is very flattering to the silhouette. The width of the lower part of this sleeve may be varied to suit the ensemble. If the gathers are only slight, this sleeve gives a narrowing effect to the silhouette; if the sleeve at the cuff is very full and the gathers are full, it can widen the silhouette.

Jacket Shapes. Jackets may be fitted, flared, straight, or tapered, and they may be any length from just below the bust line to just above the hemline. The jacket styles that complement your silhouette are determined by your height and the balance of your shoulders to your hips. It is important to remember that a small waist that is accented will seem to broaden the hips. The contrast in line makes each seem more extreme than it really is.

ILLUS. 11-26 *Consider your height and the balance of your hips and shoulders when you select a jacket.*

The fitted jacket has a shaped waistline and frequently is called the classic or dressmaker jacket. This kind of jacket enjoys continuing popularity, with the amount of shaping at the waistline varying from fashion year to fashion year. You will want to adjust the amount of shaping you desire according to the relative width of your shoulders and hips. Too much shaping at the waist will broaden those widths and should be avoided. A hint of shaping may obscure a pretty waistline. Usually an easy fitted look with two to three inches of ease at the waistline is attractive for most silhouettes.

The flared jacket gets fuller from the underarm to its hem. It gives the shoulders a narrow look and the hemline a wide look. If the flare is considerably more than the width of the silhouette at the hemline, the contrast of the hemline to the relative narrowness of the silhouette can exaggerate each one. When this style jacket is worn, the length of the jacket is critical. If it ends at or above the broadest point in the silhouette, it widens unmercifully. If it ends below the widest part and is not flared too much, it may obscure any excess width and be very flattering.

The tapered jacket tends to be wide at the shoulder or bust line, usually with a dolman or batwing sleeve, and tapers to a narrow line at the hem of the jacket. It tends to widen the shoulder and slenderize the hip line. If your hips are too wide, however, this jacket will seem to add bulk to your entire silhouette and should be avoided.

A straight jacket forms a vertical line of the silhouette and can be slenderizing as well as heightening the figure. If the hips are disproportionately large, and form a flare of the straight jacket, however, the inverted V occurring at the front of the jacket because of the pull of the hips gives an even more widening effect to the hip line and the figure.

Lengths. Remember that the hemline of a jacket makes a horizontal line that widens the figure wherever it falls. The placement of that horizontal line also will shorten the figure and should be placed very carefully on a short person. A long jacket on a short figure further shortens the figure. Shorter jackets allow a longer skirt line that tends to add height to the short figure. Street-length coats, because of the unbroken vertical line, do not shorten the figure — only jackets that form a horizontal line in the costume create the shortening effect.

Skirt lengths should be determined by the shape of the legs and the overall height of the figure. A very tall figure should avoid very short (mid-thigh) skirts, and a very short figure should avoid very long (mid-calf) skirts since they exaggerate the extremes of the figure. Fashion frequently changes dress hem lengths. Each person should carefully consider her own figure and the shape of her legs before adopting a new fashion length.

It is usually a better dressed person who considers her own needs before those of the fashion picture. When mid-calf skirts are being worn by high-fashion models, the short-figured woman can lengthen her skirts perhaps to mid-knee from the former above-the-knee level and present the overall look of a longer hemline without distorting the proportion of her entire figure. When hemlines are raised, the tall-figured woman can raise her hemline to the top of the knee instead of that length dictated by high fashion, without distorting her entire proportion, and still consider herself fashionable. It is a rare figure that can easily adopt every high-fashion dictate to the nth degree without sacrificing personal proportions in the process.

Bodice lengths range from just under the bust line to below the hip line. The principles that apply to jacket lengths apply equally to bodice lines. However, since bodices frequently are more fitted than jackets, they can be more definitive of the figure. The woman with midriff bulge may find that the horizontal line of a raised waistline only emphasizes her problem. A protruding stomach can sometimes be obscured with a slightly raised waistline since the fabric is eased at the bulge instead of forming a horizontal line just above it. Waistlines that fall below the normal waistline add height to the figure but cannot be worn if you have excess girth below the waist because the horizontal line of a lowered waistline draws attention to that girth.

Pant lengths are often dictated by fashion. However, the short figure needs to wear slacks as long as possible without allowing them to touch the floor, as the added length will tend to give her figure height. A tall figure, on the other hand, may wear pants that end at the bend of the foot, with or without a cuff. The shape of the pant leg influences the look of height of the figure. A flared leg shortens the figure, whereas a straight, stove-pipe one heightens the figure. Cuffs on pant legs tend to shorten the figure.

Proportion is important in line selection. A small figure should avoid large hats, prints, plaids, and trims (such as very large buttons), since they will destroy the overall balance of her appearance. A large figure, including the tall and heavy, should avoid small hats, very small prints, plaids, and trims because of the unbalancing effect on the figure. Heavy, bulky items should be confined to the tall, thin figure. Only dainty items can be suited to the small figure.

SUMMARY

Your confidence is related to the image you have of yourself. The clothes you wear and the lines they reflect can enhance that image and bolster your confidence.

Examine the lines in the clothes you own. Determine which textures, constructions, and trims look best on your figure. Examine your figure and undergarments to make sure the foundations on which your lines depend are what they should be.

Lines can work for you to project your prettiest image. Take advantage of the lines that suit you and start "lining up" your best image.

Understanding Lines

1. What effects do straight vertical lines have on a figure? What effects do straight horizontal ones have on a figure?
2. How does placement of lines affect proportional balance?
3. What effect does fabric texture have on the illusion of figure size?
4. How can a short person use construction to make the figure seem taller?
5. Why and when are foundation garments needed?
6. In selecting lines for a figure, what do you consider?
7. How do you decide on a good dress length for yourself?

Chapter 12

Plans

Line and color are very basic to your wardrobe. Application of those principles opens the way for you to begin to plan exactly what you want to wear. These plans should reflect you — your activities, needs, preferences, complexion color, and figure. Various lines, colors, and fabrics make clothes suitable for various occasions. A good wardrobe plan will provide appropriate kinds and amounts of clothing for all occasions.

Your Plan Calls for Clothes

Clothes are what your wardrobe is all about. You want them to fit your figure, of course, but you want them to fit your life also. Some clothes are easily classified as casual or tailored, but there are some specific characteristics about clothes and some other classifications that you will find helpful in assembling your wardrobe. Some clothes of classic design are useful as the core for every wardrobe. They are basics. You will not survive forever on basics alone (although you probably could), and you will add the nonbasics as your budget allows.

CLOTHES THAT FIT YOUR LIFE

Your activities, occasions, community, and climate determine what you will need in your wardrobe. A few of the considerations that will help you start your analysis of what you need are the nature of your occupation, where you live, the local customs, your leisure-time activities, and the standards of dress prevalent in the community where you live and work.

Occupation. Think about your occupation because it requires certain kinds of clothing. A student does not need the same clothes that a business employee needs. A homemaker needs different clothes than a lawyer needs. Generally, the lawyer and business employee need tailored clothes while the student and homemaker need clothes with a casual look. If you are changing roles and making wardrobe plans for your new occupation, it will be helpful for you to evaluate what you have in terms of whether or not it is tailored or casual. "Tailored" and "casual" are words used interchangeably with the words "city" and "country" to describe clothes. Tailored clothes are usually of a classic design and fabric, without frills and trims. They are accessorized with varieties of jewelry and scarves and are usually very versatile. Casual clothes frequently reflect more of the current trends in fashion and even fads. They easily bear the latest trims, colors, and designs and are usually suitable for the easy going style of country and surburban living.

Community. The community where you live influences your wardrobe. The southern climates of the United States are, of course, warmer than the northern ones. The fabric content and weight of your clothes, especially your coats, are dependent upon the kind of weather you face. Also, the size of the city will play a part in your selections. Large cities tend to be more "tailored" even in street wear; whereas, small towns and suburbs have a casual feel as you carry on your everyday shopping, lunching, and perhaps even working. The means of transportation you will use most of the time influences your choice of clothes. Warmer clothing usually is needed for public transportation than for private automobiles because you frequently must wait in the weather to catch a bus, train, or taxi.

Activities. Activities that you engage in outside of your occupation are important in wardrobe planning. Do you, for example, participate in sports or watch them? Are you a theatergoer or do you attend mostly small parties? What activities do you usually take part in during your vacation time? If any of your activities require clothes not found in the wardrobe of a person in your occupation, you will need to provide for them in the plan.

Local Customs. Certain standards of appropriate dress in an unwritten law sort of status do exist in some communities. You, of course, are not required to meet those standards, but you will be more comfortable in sharing in the work and play of your particular community if you do follow them. Surprisingly, most of the time, very good reasons exist for many of the customs. The custom of wearing darker clothing in the city than in the country, for example, evolved from the fact that the sidewalks and streets — indeed, the very air — is much dirtier in the city than in the country. Dark clothing at least does not look as dirty as light clothing after a trip from your apartment to your place of employment.

The custom requiring darker clothing during winter and lighter clothing in the summer seems to have fallen by the wayside in recent years. It originated because dark colors absorb heat and light colors reflect heat, helping to keep the body temperature comfortable in winter and summer. It still works, but the widespread use of central heat and air conditioning has eliminated most of the need for wearing color to regulate body temperature.

It is not necessary to adapt exactly item for item to what is worn most often in your community. The classifications — tailored, casual, leisure, and special occasion — are designations that guide you in adapting to local custom. For example, in one community a party in someone's home may require special occasion clothes; but in another home in another community, casual clothes. You can be well dressed in either category. It is not necessary to know if the casual party calls for pants or dresses. Anything in the casual category would be appropriate.

CLOTHES CLASSIFICATIONS

The lines of demarcation classifying clothes for the various times of the day are blurred and rarely play an important part in wardrobe selection today. There is also very little difference today between casual wear and street wear and practically no distinction made between formal and semiformal wear (except for members of wedding parties). Fabrics rather than style are important limiting criteria for many ensembles. Satin or peau de soie is not worn for street or casual wear, but may be worn for formal or semiformal wear, often in the same style of dress or pantsuit as that suitable for street or casual wear. Styles that are limiting are those that are revealing, such as a low-cut neckline or a backless gown, which are not suitable for daytime wear. Bouffant skirts of stiff fabric usually are not suitable for daytime wear. Very clingy, soft fabrics that mold and emphasize the figure are usually not appropriate for daytime wear but may be very good for evening home entertaining or a late dinner dance. Lacy blouses and dresses are not usually worn for casual or street wear but are good in the daytime and evening for teas, church, or other very dressy occasions. Beyond these extremes, clothes, because of their fabrics and styles, fit into various categories:

Casual Clothes. Casuals include those for informal activities and spectator sports. Casual styles have a simple, informal character and are suitable for many everyday activities. Campus wear is of the casual variety. Shopping, especially in the country, suburbs, and small towns is casual. Informal, impromptu dates and athletic events where you are a spectator call for casual clothes. Casual clothes are characterized by styles that are comfortable, with ease for freedom of movement. Pantsuits, sweaters, and skirts, are frequently casual in style (Illustration 12-1). Fabrics for casual clothes may be of any durable, easy-care cloth. Some fabrics that are especially popular are corduroy, double knit, tweed, gingham, and pique. They are usually of washable content, including cotton, washable wool, polyester, acrylic, and rayon. Colors for casual clothes are usually brighter and lighter than for tailored ones.

Vogue Pattern Service

ILLUS. 12-1 *A casual pantsuit is one with durable fabric and easygoing style.*

Tailored Clothes. Tailored clothes include those for church, business and office wear, travel by air or train, and street wear in large cities. Where casual clothes often have an unstructured appearance, tailored clothes achieve their good looks with fabric that is usually of a medium weight and that tapers with good seaming and cut (Illustration

12-2). Tailored clothes frequently, if they are not too detailed, can be dressed up or down so that they go from the very tailored look of the business office to a dinner engagement in town with the change of accessories or the removal of a jacket from a dress-jacket ensemble. Fabrics that wear well, are non-wrinkle, and that resist soiling are good for tailored clothes. Sharkskin, gabardine, double knits that are stable, quality broadcloth and flannel, shantungs, and linen weaves are good for tailored clothes. Fabric contents that wear well for tailored clothes are linen, silk, wool, polyester, acrylic, cotton, and rayon. Subdued colors are most attractive in tailored clothes. Bright colors are used in small amounts mainly for accents.

Vogue Pattern Service

ILLUS. 12-2 *Tailored clothes frequently are of classic styles that are good for career women. Most classic styles are very versatile.*

Special-Occasion Clothes. Special-occasion clothes include those for formal daytime wear, semiformal and formal evening wear, dinner dates, some parties, and some weddings. The customs of the community play a very important role in the design of these clothes. Long skirts as well as street-length ones are usually acceptable interchangeably, but you are usually more comfortable when you wear the same length as the local custom directs. If you don't know the local custom and appear in a length unlike most of the members of a group, do not consider yourself inappropriately dressed. The length is not as important as the fact that the ensemble is a special-occasion one. Fabrics for this category of clothing may be lace, satin, chiffon, velvet, soft drapey knits, or lightweight knits that float when you walk or dance (Illustration 12-3). In addition to the very fragile fabrics, more durable ones are appropriate, such as rayon for satin or taffeta; nylon for satins and knits; silk in its lustrous finish; cotton in its finest weave; and linen in fine, smooth weaves. The style of these clothes may vary according to what is flattering to the person selecting them. Color may be pastel, bright, or dark depending upon the special occasion, the age of the wearer, and personal preference.

Vogue Pattern Service

ILLUS. 12-3 *The halter style of this dress with a jacket makes it appealing as a special-occasion dress. Medium-weight fabric that is shaped is durable yet smart.*

Leisure Clothes. Leisure clothes are those you wear at home and in active sports. They may be almost anything you like. This is where you wear whatever appeals to you for your home activities. Some people, because they have frequent drop-in guests for whom they wish to be presentable, wear their casual clothes for leisure time. Others who engage in painting or other messy activities at home may wear faded, cut-off jeans and T-shirts, depending upon the mood and purpose. Probably the most popular leisure-time ensembles are the mix and match varieties of pants and tops (Illustration 12-4). Decide what your self-image and habits call for and plan for your leisure time those clothes that are really functional.

ILLUS. 12-4 *Leisure clothes frequently consist of pants and tops of the mix-and-match variety. They differ from casuals, which usually are of a coordinated suit style.*

Vogue Pattern Service

CLOTHES THAT ARE BASIC

There are clothes that have a greater capacity for versatility than is true of most clothing. These clothes constitute the "security blanket" of your clothing needs. When you don't know what to wear, one of these versatile basic items is sure to be suitable.

Career women are especially fond of the idea of a basic wardrobe as the core of their closet. A basic wardrobe has certain characteristics. It is not dated; that is, it is of classic lines with no faddish collars, buttons, sleeves, or lengths. Each item is usually of a solid or near-solid (monotone pattern) color in hues, such as beige, gray, brown, black, dark blue, very dark green, and very dark red — hues that mix well with many other colors. The basic wardrobe should be of fabric that does not wrinkle and that wears several seasons without fraying, stretching, or shrinking. Medium-weight fabrics are usually the mainstay of the basic wardrobe — versatility is its appeal.

The value of such selections to you when entering a business career is that with a minimum investment in a few purchases, you are prepared for all occasions. You are well-dressed while you are expanding your wardrobe and finding special styles and colors that meet your preferences and any particular needs of your job. The lines, colors, and fabrics of such a wardrobe probably will be so appealing to you after you wear them a while that you will automatically select according to those criteria when you are adding to your wardrobe beyond the basics.

Carefully observe the most successful woman in your organization to see if her clothes fit the basic wardrobe criteria of lines, fabric, and color. Chances are, she follows these very versatile ideas even when she can afford much more in variety and style. Basics simplify selection, upkeep, and good grooming to the point that most people who have once planned wardrobes around such criteria never vary from them.

The less attention the style of the basic wardrobe calls to itself, the more versatile it becomes. Accessories literally change the outfit to a completely new one. The suit that does not scream "Here I am again!" may never be recognized when the skirt is combined with a blouse and vest, or with a jacket and a turtleneck sweater. The basic dress, which is usually a one-piece model, may be worn with beads at the neck, a scarf, or with a pin — each with a different look to it.

A basic wardrobe usually includes: (1) a basic coat, (2) a basic suit, (3) a basic two-piece dress (matching jacket or coat), (4) a basic dress, (5) a basic special occasion dress. The characteristics of basic clothes follow certain criteria.

Basic Coat. A basic coat should be versatile, therefore, it should be neither too sporty nor too dressy (Illustration 12-5). For example, patch pockets are too sporty and jeweled buttons are too dressy. Neither are desirable for a coat that is truly versatile. The design of the coat should be neither too fitted nor too full since either extreme may date it before you have worn your money's worth out of it. A classic style collar that looks good with your face shape is one characteristic of your basic coat.

Vogue Pattern Service

ILLUS. 12-5 *A basic coat is neither too dressy nor too sporty. The cut is neither too full nor too fitted. The collar is not of an extreme style and the pockets are not prominent. The charm of the coat is in its simple line, quality fabric, and versatility.*

The fabric should be closely woven with a flat nap so that the coat will hold its shape and not shine on the seat and around the cuffs and hem after it is worn, cleaned, and pressed a few times. The buttons are the same color as the coat and may even be self-fabric buttons. The sleeve is long, covers your wrist bone, and is neither too full nor too fitted. It has some ease so that a dress with long sleeves fits comfortably under it. The trim is in the seaming but not in contrast colors or in fur. Pockets on your coat should not be prominent. A slit pocket is best and a pseudo pocket is even better since you won't be tempted to stretch it out of shape with hands, gloves, tissue, etc. Your basic coat should hang approximately one inch below the longest skirt with which you wear it. The color of your coat should be one with which you can wear almost all your other winter clothes — a more-or-less neutral color. A summer coat will probably be one of the all-weather fabrics, such as water repellant broadcloth, sharkskin, denim, or doubleknit. In warm, southern climates, this coat may be all that is needed for winter, too, especially if public transportation is rarely utilized. The versatility required of your coat rules out bright, strong colors that would limit your harmonizing colors. Some of the neutrals that are easy to coordinate in your wardrobe are black, brown, navy, gray, and beige. A solid color is probably best, but a subtle monochromatic pattern may be versatile enough for your needs.

A Basic Suit. A basic suit, if it is well chosen, may substitute in your wardrobe for two or three dresses. Such a hard-working suit must be chosen carefully, though. A suit that does so much will probably be relatively expensive. Therefore, you want to get more than one season's use from it. Select one of a classic style, which means that the collar is not extreme and the jacket is only semi-fitted and of a length suited to your figure height. There will be no pockets other than slits or pseudo-pockets. It will have pearl or other classic buttons and long or three-quarter sleeves (Illustration 12-6). The skirt will probably be eased according to your figure needs — either dirndl (slightly gathered), A-line, or straight. No extreme of any of the styles will be appropriate for the basic suit. It, too, will have no trim other than perhaps seaming within the garment. The neckline that does double duty (with or without a blouse) is the most desirable. For winter, a solid color that looks good with your basic coat is your best choice. In summer, the two are rarely worn together. A monochromatic tweed might be acceptable. The fabric should be firmly woven or of a stable knit and of a light weight if the suit is lined or of a medium weight if it is not. A suit of too heavy a fabric may limit you to wearing it without a coat, which might rule it out for truly cold days. A suit that includes a pair of matching tailored pants is very versatile.

Basic Dress. A basic dress is one that can be dressed up or down. It is usually of a dark shade of color. The lines are not extreme, but should be suited to your figure needs. This dress is often called the "little nothing" dress because it frequently has no collar, no belt, no trim, and either no sleeves or long sleeves that are tunnel with no cuff. That description may sound bland, but the dress appropriately worn is frequently smashing. Slight tapering at the waist and ease in the skirt makes such a dress a tremendous asset because of its versatility as well as comfort (Illustration 12-7). Understatement is its charm, since one piece of jewelry or one scarf can make the statement appropriate for any occasion. Your basic dress will be your favorite if you choose it of a beautiful, easy-care fabric and of a color in a dark shade that looks good on you.

Two-Piece Basic Costume. The two-piece costume should be a simple dress with a matching jacket or coat (Illustration 12-8). The jacket to this dress may have more detail than the suit jacket since this ensemble does not go to as many places as the suit. The dress in this ensemble, though, stands alone as well as with the jacket or coat. This

ILLUS. 12-6 *A classic-style suit with an A-line skirt and semifitted jacket may substitute for two or three dresses in a wardrobe.*

Vogue Pattern Service

Vogue Pattern Service

ILLUS. 12-7 *The understated style of a basic dress makes it very versatile. A dark color is even more versatile.*

Vogue Pattern Service

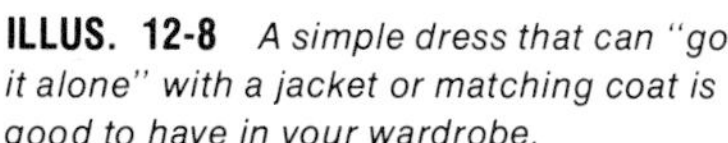

ILLUS. 12-8 *A simple dress that can "go it alone" with a jacket or matching coat is good to have in your wardrobe.*

costume may take you to church in the morning with the jacket or coat or to a party at night without the jacket. The dress is frequently worn with the basic coat, and colors and textures must be compatible. A solid color, again, is more versatile than prints, plaids, or tweeds, although muted monochromatic designs might be acceptable. Light-to-medium-weight fabrics are best for this ensemble.

Special-Occasion Basic Dress. A basic special occasion dress will be similar to your basic dress but will limit itself to after five and special occasions because of perhaps a lower neckline or a fabric that is for special occasions only. A street-length, special-occasion dress is more versatile than a long one in most locales. However, if your community seems addicted to the long dress, this is your chance to fall in line if you wish. With this dress you may carry your evening bag and wear matching shoes for extra-special occasions. Surprisingly, the cost of this ensemble may be less than the cost of your basic two-piece costume. Special occasion fabrics usually are neither as durable nor as expensive as the fabric you will purchase for daytime clothes. The best buy in special-occasion fabrics is still tightly woven or very stable knits of a medium-to-light weight (Illustration 12-9). However, if you like, this is the place to use the luxury fabrics, such as chiffon, lace, and peau de soie. Stiff fabrics such as taffeta will probably not be suitable because of their propensity to wrinkle and their poor packing potential. If the style is shaped, a knitted synthetic or wool fabric with a plain surface may be durable and versatile. Avoid fabrics that wrinkle easily, especially if you choose a long dress. Few ensembles look worse than one with a long, wrinkled skirt.

CLOTHES THAT ARE UNDERNEATH

Part of your wardrobe, of course, is your undergarments. There is very little to the style available in bras and girdles. The lace that is used is very functional and frequently is combined with some kind of stretch material to make it part of the foundation. Panties and slips (petticoats and half-slips included) do have some style to them. You may like the very tailored ones or those with lace trim. The only warning about lacy undergarments is to avoid those that are bulky. The undergarments you choose should not create bulk under your clothes. Color in undergarments requires some planning. White traditionally has been used for most ensembles, with black playing the supportive role for dark dresses and suits. Beige or brown may be a color you want to consider depending upon the natural color of your skin and the availability of the style of

ILLUS. 12-9 *A special-occasion dress may be long or street length. The shirtwaist style is a classic that is never dated.*

Vogue Pattern Service

undergarment you choose in beige or brown. Frequently, beige or brown is less noticeable under both light and dark colors because it blends with your skin color and is in many ways more versatile than either white or black. Try a bra of a color close to that of your skin under both a white and black blouse before you make a decision about the color of your undergarments.

For a girl who doesn't mind washing undergarments by hand each night, the rule of thumb in the number of each that she requires is three — one to wear, one to wash, and one to spare. This number does not include special items, such as the pant-liner girdle or a strapless bra if your wardrobe calls for one. If you can afford it, you may want to purchase one of each of the undergarments for each day of the week and wash only once a week, especially if you have access to a washing machine only once a week. The number you purchase depends upon your personal habits and preferences. Absolutely fresh and clean undergarments are required *every day* — no exceptions — if you are to be well groomed.

Your sleep wear depends, too, upon your personal preferences in the same way as your leisure clothes do. You will probably need three of whatever it is you choose for sleeping in — gowns or pajamas, or alternating the two. You probably will need two robes, one for cold weather and one for warm weather. If you live in a very warm climate, you may be able to survive with one medium-weight robe that washes and dries quickly.

CLOTHES THAT FIT A PARTICULAR COLOR SCHEME

Your wardrobe will look smarter, be more versatile, and seem much larger if it is built around a basic color scheme. When you are selecting that scheme, consult the hue chart and select the colors that you know look good on you. The basic color — the one in which you will probably purchase your basic coat and a set of accessories (shoes, handbag, jewelry, etc.) — will probably be most versatile if you will pick from black, navy, brown, beige, gray, or some other dark colors. Because you want your coat to wear several seasons, it is better not to purchase a new, faddish color that obviously will be dated and of which you will probably tire in a few months. After you select a color that fits the basic criteria and that looks very good on you, make a list of all the other colors you see in the hue chart that will combine well with your basic one. Check that list to see how many of the colors can be coordinated with each other so that the pieces of your wardrobe will be interchangeable when they are in those colors. Make a list of the colors you will use with your basic color. Some specific examples of color schemes that may or may not work for your complexion, but which will give you an idea of how to select colors follow.

With dark brown, use beige, orange, yellow, light blue, light red-violet, light red-orange, light blue-green, and light violet. With gray, use red, green, blue-green, light blue, bright yellow, orange, red-orange, and light violet. With black, use any light color in small amounts — beige, white, and gray. With navy blue, use bright green or red, light blue, red, violet, yellow, white, and light orange. With beige, use brown, black, red, bright blue, bright green, orange, and dark violet.

Because of the nature of color, you probably will be most satisfied with a dark basic color rather than with a light one. The larger the area in most instances, the more subdued the color should be. You probably will find it easier to use light colors for trim and accessories on dark clothes than to use dark accessories on a lighter basic color.

CLOTHES THAT ARE NOT BASIC

The basics are great because they save you money and indecision with their versatility. As your confidence grows along with your pocketbook, you may want to add some nonbasic clothes of specific styles and designs. Keep your personal tastes in mind and try to integrate each item into the lines you have chosen for the basic wardrobe. Try to use colors that will coordinate with the accessories you already own and perhaps that interchange with those that you have in your basic wardrobe.

Depending upon how you see yourself, the style you choose for your personality will characteristically have certain lines and textures of fabrics. Very often a person does not have a clear concept of herself that is consistent. A problem arises when part of her wardrobe is purchased when she sees herself in tweeds and country-styled casual clothes and part of it is purchased when she sees herself in fine silk at the finest restaurant in the city, and she expects to interchange the outfits because they are built around her basic color scheme. Another problem may arise when the basic coat is purchased in a length that looks best for her figure and legs; but she indulges the fashion scene by purchasing a dress in a new, longer length, and it hangs out from beneath the coat.

The style of your nonbasics is important if you are to interchange them with your basics. It will not be wise to mix ruffles with tailored items and expect them to look coordinated. A little-girl look with puffed sleeves will not coordinate with a tailored skirt. A classic jacket will be out of place with hip-hugger pants or those with extremely flared legs. A soft, flowing skirt probably will not be attractive with a bulky sweater. A bloused, shirtwaist dress may not go with a fitted jacket. A tailored jacket will not fit over a full-sleeved blouse.

Some of the lines that are more versatile are:

(1) Sleeves that are "skinny" — not flared or gathered.
(2) Collars that are man-tailored, small, or turtle necked.
(3) Skirts that are eased or A-line rather than full and gathered.
(4) Dresses with shaping at the waist rather than straight or tightly belted.
(5) Pants that have waistbands rather than elasticized or hip-hugger tops.
(6) Pants without pleats and, if pockets are included, slit pockets rather than patch or bulky ones.
(7) Pant legs that are straight without cuffs rather than flared or full with cuffs.

Some good choices in nonbasics would be a skirt or vest to wear with parts of your other two-piece ensembles and a tailored jacket to wear with a dress, skirt, or pants in your basic wardrobe (Illustration 12-10, next page). For your casual activities, a sweater set can brighten your skirts and pants.

Vogue Pattern Service

ILLUS. 12-10 *Add to your basics by selecting items such as a tailored jacket to wear with a dress, skirt, and pants in your basic wardrobe.*

Your Plan Calls for Coordinating Accessories

Hosiery, shoes, and handbags are accessories that are part of your wardrobe plan. The styles, colors, and quantity you need are important in making a workable wardrobe plan.

HOSIERY

Almost every shoe requires nylon hosiery. The exceptions are leisure-time barefoot sandals and tennis shoes, with which you wear socks. Hosiery protects your feet from hard surfaces inside your shoes and enhances the appearance of your legs. Pantyhose also frequently substitute for panties; and if they are control-top hose, for a girdle.

Pantyhose. Pantyhose are the most frequently worn style of hosiery since they require neither a girdle nor a garterbelt with fasteners to hold them up. They are available with a sheer, reinforced, or elasticized panty to provide for any need. The feet sections are available with reinforced toe and heel, reinforced toe only, and sheer ("sandalfoot") toe and heel. Pantyhose may be of the one-size-fits-all material, or they may be sized and preshaped for your feet and legs. Pantyhose also are made of the reinforced support material if you have problems with your legs. Almost all pantyhose are seamless.

Other Hosiery. Hosiery is also available in various lengths without an attached panty. They can be obtained with elasticized tops in lengths ankle high, knee high, and thigh high, and without elasticized tops in thigh-high lengths. Thigh-high hosiery is available with seams along the center back of the leg, but these are rarely worn today. The feet section of hosiery with and without elasticized tops are available with reinforced toe and heel, reinforced toe only, and sheer sandalfoot styles. They, too are available in preshaped and sized styles or in the one-size-fits-all material. Hosiery with elasticized tops sometimes create a problem if the elastic is very tight. Hosiery without elasticized tops require some kind of fastener or garter to hold them up.

Sheerness and Durability. The sheerness of hosiery makes it desirable for enhancing the appearance of your legs. The sheerer, the better. However, in addition to being more expensive, very sheer stockings are fragile and tear or run easily, making the cost to wear them very high. Less sheer hosiery is cheaper, usually more durable, and is very well suited for everyday wear. One-size-fits-all material looks opaque before it is stretched over your legs, but becomes sheerer as you put it on. This kind of fabric is usually very comfortable unless you have to stretch it very taut to make it fit. Then, your feet may be cramped by the too-tight foot section. If they are not stretched somewhat, though, these stockings are very thick and may not look good on your legs.

Preshaped and sized hosiery is fitted according to your height and weight in pantyhose and according to your foot size in other hosiery. Each manufacturer determines his own designations for your height and weight range. Some sizing is of the "A, B, C" variety and some is of the "1, 2, 3" variety. The criteria for the designations are explained on the back of each hosiery package so that you can select the appropriate size for your figure. Preshaped, sized hosiery is available in various degrees of sheerness also. You can probably satisfy your needs and your budget best by purchasing the less sheer, more durable hosiery for everyday wear and the more fragile, sheerer hosiery for special occasion wear.

Hosiery Colors. Colors in hosiery usually range from very light beige to very dark black. Generally the colors fall into groupings of beige colors, gray colors, browns, taupes, red-browns, blues, and blacks. They are available in pastel colors, opaque colors and patterns; but these are faddish and not usually worn by the well-dressed person. Your overall proportion and silhouette will appear more coordinated if you wear hosiery that is lighter in color than your shoes. An obvious exception to this suggestion is that light beige hosiery is usually worn with white shoes since white hosiery is not worn with tailored and casual clothes.

The more the color of your hosiery differs from the color of your legs, the more attention hosiery calls to your legs. Lighter colors do tend to enlarge the area they cover and darker colors tend to diminish the area. However, the sheerness of hosiery limits its capacity either to enlarge or to diminish; mainly it exposes your legs and their shape. If you have very shapely, well-developed legs, any shade of hosiery will look good on you. If your legs are not shapely, you will probably prefer very subtly colored hosiery. Very often a medium beige that is somewhat sheer can be worn with all your clothes. If you prefer, however, you can coordinate colors somewhat by using:

(1) Brown hosiery with brown, orange, red-orange, and yellow-orange clothes.

(2) Gray or taupe hosiery with red, red-violet, violet, blue-violet, and light blue clothes.

(3) Blue hosiery with dark blue, dark red, and dark green clothes.

(4) Black hosiery with black clothes.

A simple plan that allows for some variety in hosiery colors is to wear beige with oranges, yellows, and greens and to wear taupe with blues, violets, and reds.

Quantity and Style. Clean footwear daily is a necessity for the well-groomed person. If you don't mind washing hosiery every night, three pairs of the style and color you wear daily will be sufficient quantity for your daily wardrobe. Two pairs of the other styles that you wear only occasionally, such as the knee-high length with pants, will probably be what you need.

If you wear shoes with open toes and heels, be sure that you purchase hosiery with sheer toes and heels. Reinforced toe and heel hosiery are not worn with shoes that expose the reinforcement. Closed toe and heel shoes are destructive to a sheer toe and heel, especially where your toenail rubs the hosiery against your shoe. Therefore, you need to be sure to purchase reinforced hosiery if you wear closed toe and heel shoes. If you select ankle-high hosiery to wear with pants, be sure the tops do now show when you sit and cross your legs. Knee-high lengths are usually better for pants. If you wear pantyhose with control or reinforced tops, make sure that the reinforcement does not show from underneath your skirt as you bend and walk.

Care. Hosiery usually lasts longer if it is washed by hand in lukewarm water and mild soap, rolled in a towel to remove the water, and hung to dry. There are hosiery bags that can be used to protect hosiery in the washing machine and warm dryer. Machine washing, of course, is frequently more convenient than hand washing. You may sacrifice some durability in your hosiery if you machine wash, though, because of the additional wear and tear of the tumbling action in the washing machine and clothes dryer.

SHOES

Shoes as an accessory to your wardrobe are an item that does more than enhance your appearance. Shoes should support and protect your feet. The shoes in your wardrobe, then, should be chosen for fit, color, style, and material.

Fit. The fit of a shoe can be vitally important to a happy face all day long. Be sure that your shoes allow for movement of your toes and that either the shoe is flexible enough for you to "wiggle" your foot in its arch or that the shoe itself allows room to move the ball of your foot slightly by arching it. This is "breathing" room in your shoes that lets your feet expand when you walk without cramping them. Be sure that the heel of the shoe fits around your heel snugly and that the top of the shoe does not gap or pinch.

When you fit new shoes for your feet, do so both early in the day and again later when your feet may have expanded slightly from standing or walking. Many people have one foot larger than the other, and it is necessary to try on both shoes and walk around in the store to check the sizing for both feet before making a selection. The width of your feet may change as you gain and lose weight. It is a good idea to take this into consideration when you are purchasing new shoes and to try them on before you purchase them.

Colors. Colors in shoes are influenced by the same considerations as colors in the rest of your wardrobe. Bright, light colors attract attention to themselves and appear larger than they are. Dark colors of low intensity appear to be smaller and, in general, attract less attention. If your legs are not well formed or if your feet are large, subdued colors in shades of brown, gray, navy blue, and black are best for you. One surprisingly versatile shoe that seems to look good on every foot and seems to improve the shape of a less-than-perfect leg is a skin-colored shoe of a brown hue. Whereas the darker colored shoes stop the eye with an abrupt color change on most feet, the brown hues that are near the skin color seem to draw the eye in a vertical line, improving the appearance of the entire figure.

Style. The style of a shoe includes the shape of the toe (whether it is open or closed); the vamp (whether it is low, medium, or high); the heel height and width (whether the heel is open or closed); and the thickness of the sole. Trim on shoes also influences the style.

The classic shoe that seems to know no season or age is the small-heeled pump with a closed heel and toe, of a brown, black, gray, or blue shade. Quickly gaining on the classic pump is a small-heeled, closed toe and heel "refined loafer" shoe with a higher cut vamp (Illustrations 12-11 and 12-12). This shoe for many women looks good both with slacks and with dresses. The higher vamp meets the pant hem but does not fit high enough to widen the ankle with a horizontal line when it is worn with a dress. The refined loafer is considered good for tailored and casual wear, but rarely is worn for special occasions. A pump is good for tailored and special occasion wear but rarely is casual.

Vogue Pattern Service

ILLUS. 12-11 *Classic-styled pumps are good for wear with tailored clothes.*

Photography by Terry Webb

ILLUS. 12-12 *The "refined loafer" doubles for casual and tailored wear.*

A sense of proportion is necessary in selecting shoe styles for your wardrobe. The width of the heel will be influenced somewhat by the height you choose. The higher a heel, the more slender it usually is. Very wide heels tend to widen the leg, but very thin heels may make you appear to be teetering, especially if they are very high. Some shaping of the heel and a medium width usually improve the appearance of the shoe, the foot, and the leg. The shorter you wear your dresses, the shorter the heel of your shoe should be. The longer the dress, the higher the heel of the shoe needs to be to provide for good proportion. Thin, delicate legs and feet should avoid large chunky shoes. Large legs and feet should not wear very delicate looking shoes.

The thickness of the sole of the shoe varies with fashion. Usually one-fourth to one-half inch is the range of width for soles of shoes. Very thick soles are called platform soles and usually are considered faddish. Very thick platform soles usually look out of proportion on a person of average-to-small height. Tall girls, who rarely desire the additional height that platform soles provide, are the ones whose proportion is best for them.

Shoes with open toes and heels are of a style that comes and goes with the design of clothes. They are fashionable for a time but are not as lasting in style as shoes of closed heels and toes. Sandals with high heels are worn more often with special occasion clothes than with tailored or casual clothes. Traditionally, they are for summer wear, although fashion occasionally decrees them appropriate for winter when made of suede or calf. When in fashion, sandals with flat heels are worn with leisure wear, and sandals with blocked heels are worn with casual wear. A shoe with a closed toe and open heel is a "sling." It usually is worn with tailored and casual clothes when it is in fashion. Closed toe and heel shoes are more classic in style and probably will prove more versatile in your wardrobe than sandals or slings.

Materials. Materials for shoes may be patent leather, suede, peau de soie, leather, and some fabrics such as canvas for tennis shoes, and linen or satin for dyed-to-match shoes. A classic, versatile shoe for year-round wear is of a smooth-finish calf leather. Suede can be very good for winter, and patent leather is especially good-looking for summer. The color of the suede and patent leather, though, may make them acceptable for other seasons. Dark colored patents, for example, are sometimes worn in winter, and light colored suedes are sometimes worn in summer. Until you are very sure of your best groomed look, it will be easier for you to stick to the traditional patterns of wear. The most practical selection is a smooth leather shoe in a medium-to-dark color that looks good with the color scheme around which you have purchased your wardrobe. Both the pump and the refined loafer will take you through many seasons in well-groomed footwear.

Trim. Trim on shoes, as on clothes, draws attention to itself. Unless you want your feet to be the center of attention of your appearance, select shoes with very little trim. If your feet are long, avoid trim that accents the length, such as a line from the heel to toe. A horizontal line across the vamp or toe of the shoe will break the length and give an illusion of a shorter foot. If your feet are wide, avoid horizontal lines and select trim that gives an illusion of length or no trim at all.

Care. Caring for your shoes includes keeping them clean and in good repair. The finish on leather and patent leather shoes usually repels dirt and stains. They can be cleaned with shoe cleaning products that are either waxy or fluid, in aerosol cans. Calf leather shoes, of course, can be polished to a new shine if they become scuffed. Make it a practice to check your shoes before you put them away each day to see if they need to be cleaned and polished. Suede shoes are easily cleaned by brushing. Stains, however, frequently are permanent, and dirt on light colored suede is almost impossible to remove. Some suede can be sprayed, before the shoes are worn, with a waterproofing agent that repels moisture and dirt.

Heel caps and half soles are available for replacing worn ones on your shoes. If the upper parts of your shoes are still in good repair — not cracked or worn — the cost of replacing a heel cap or a sole is well worth the money. Shoes with run-down heels or that are scuffed can ruin an otherwise well-groomed look. Each time you take your shoes off to put them away check to see if they will need repair before you wear them again.

Quantity. The number of pairs of shoes you need for your basic wardrobe depends upon how well you have built your wardrobe around a color scheme. It is a good idea, too, to provide for alternating pairs of shoes daily. This practice seems to prolong the life of your shoes and to diminish the occurrence of calluses and corns on your feet. Leisure-time shoes may be sandals, loafers, tennis shoes, or anything that fits your leisure-time activities. You probably will need one pair. Casual shoes should look good with skirts and pants. The refined loafer with a medium heel and a high vamp will fit the needs of most people for a casual look. The same shoe may be worn with your tailored clothes, or you may select a pump for your basic tailored clothes. One pair of each style will provide for alternating shoes daily and for variety in shoe styles. An evening shoe may be of silk, satin, peau de soie, or of a smooth calf leather. It may be a sandal or a pump. If you are purchasing silk or one of the other fragile fabrics for special-occasion shoes, shop for an inexpensive shoe. You probably will not wear such shoes often and an inexpensive pair will probably look as good as a more expensive one for a long time. If you are selecting a pump that will be worn occasionally for special occasions and frequently with your tailored clothes, select one of good quality.

Quality. Well-constructed shoes should maintain their shape for many wearings. If they take the shape of your toes when you try them on, they are probably too flexible to give much support or protection to your feet. Leather-lined shoes of good quality should wear well and look good for a long time. They will probably figure to be less expensive per wearing over the long run than a cheaper pair of shoes that breaks down in a short period of time.

Your casual shoes should be of a good quality and leather-lined if possible because they, too, take a considerable amount of wear. You should be able to wear them several seasons without their breaking down or looking worn. Leisure time shoes may be less expensive, according to your needs, because tennis shoes and flat heeled sandals frequently are less costly to make and sell than shoes of more substantial structure.

Bootwear. Boots may be for protection, for warmth, and for fashion. Plastic overboots may be good to protect your shoes from rain and snow if you live in a very wet climate. Fur-lined boots, too, are good to protect your feet from extremely cold weather and from snow. When these are worn to and from work, your tailored shoes may be carried in a shoe bag so they you may wear them while you are working inside a building.

Boots for fashion come and go like most fads. If boots are worn at all, select a length appropriate for your legs and proportional height. All boots draw attention to your legs. Boots that stop near the ankle or at mid-calf cut your height and widen your leg. Be sure that you are very tall and very thin if you select such boots. Boots that come to the knee are best for most people. If you want a continuous vertical-line look to your silhouette, wear your dresses long enough to cover the top of your boots. If one or two inches of your legs are showing between the top of your boots and the hem of your dress, the vertical line is broken, making you appear shorter and, of course, wider. If you wear your skirts above your knees and boots below your knees, be sure the exposed part of your leg showing between the hem of your dress and the top of your boots is not unsightly because this arrangement calls attention to it.

Mini- and skimp-length skirts are fad looks that are worn with knee-high boots. These very short skirts should be confined to your leisure-time wear since they look out of place on the street or at work.

HANDBAGS

A smart-looking handbag that holds everything you need is essential to a well-dressed appearance. A handbag needs to be functional without looking like a travel case. It needs to be handsome without being superfluous. Handbags, of course, come in all shapes and sizes; with and without handles; in all colors, patterns, and textures; and are made of many materials. Finding one that fits exactly your needs takes only some forethought and careful shopping.

Style. The styles of handbags are classified as: inverted V, envelope, clutch, tote, box, or pouch. The inverted V because, of its tapering, usually does not enlarge the hip line when it is carried near the hip. The envelope and clutch bags are usually long and thin with no handles and are therefore inconvenient to carry. They, too, however, do not add inches to the hip line because of their slim line. The tote bag is usually large and unstructured. It is not considered in good taste for casual, tailored, and special-occasion wear. If you carry one at all, it should be with leisure-time wear when you perhaps stuff your swim suit or tennis balls inside it. Box or pouch bags, because of their shape, add inches to your hips when they are carried in that vicinity. While a shoulder strap is convenient, especially if you are carrying packages or books in addition to your handbag, it usually is more casual than tailored and will not be as smart as a bag with a regular arm/hand handle. All handbag handles should be flexible enough to be carried comfortably. Beware of clasps that are either too difficult to open — breaking your nails and scratching your hands — or so easily opened that they fall open at inappropriate times. Handbags without closures invite would-be pickpockets. Carefully avoid purchasing a handbag without a good closure.

A tailored handbag is one that is structured, with or without a handle, covered with leather or a leather-look material, and smart and uncluttered in design (Illustration 12-13). It may be the same color and material as your tailored shoes or it may be of a different texture or of a different hue of the same color as your shoes. Although shoes and bags do not necessarily match exactly in color, you will probably find it easier at first to coordinate your appearance with shoes and handbags of the same color in perhaps slightly different hues than to try to coordinate your bag with some other part of your ensemble.

A casual handbag is one that is somewhat less structured, usually with a handle or a shoulder strap, and may be of somewhat different materials. Besides textured leather and leather-like materials, decorated canvas, burlap, and wood in structured shapes are usually casual in style. In the tote style, which is completely unstructured, the flexible materials are usually confined to leisure-time wear.

An evening handbag usually is of a smaller size, intended only to carry touchup makeup aids, a comb, money, and your identification (Illustration 12-14). It may be leather, metal, peau de soie, silk, or satin, and may be covered in sequins or stones. These bags are usually fragile and intended only for very limited use.

Proportion. The shape and size of your handbag should fit the shape and size of your silhouette. The shape of the handbag should not

ILLUS. 12-13 *Smooth leather and leather-like material in a structured style are good for tailored wear. The unstructured tote bag is good for leisure and casual wear.*

Photography by Terry Webb

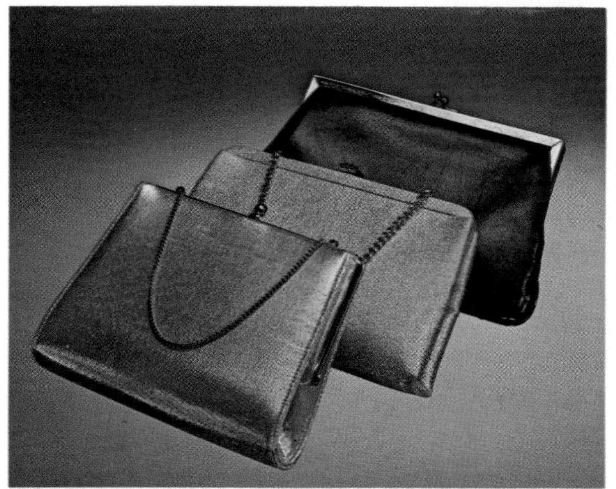

Photography by Terry Webb

ILLUS. 12-14 *Small, decorative handbags are good for evening wear.*

emphasize shapes in your silhouette you wish to conceal. Thus if you are rounded, a pouch type, rounded handbag with lumps will emphasize the lumps in your figure. If you are thin, with little shape, your handbag can have a more rounded shape. The size of your handbag should be in proportion to your own size. A small person needs a proportionately smaller handbag than a large person does.

Quantity. You will need a handbag for each pair of shoes in your basic wardrobe. Select the best bag you can afford in the casual and tailored styles since these will be worn most often. A somewhat cheaper leisure and special-occasion bag is usually your best buy because these take less abuse than the ones you carry to work or to class each day.

Care. Keep your handbag in good condition. Clean it out at the end of each day and arrange your articles in an orderly manner. Most handbags get more abuse from the inside, from disorderly arrangement and overstuffing, than from the outside. You can prolong the good looks and life of your handbag by carefully keeping its contents in order and keeping superfluous items out of it. An orderly, uncluttered arrangement can save you the embarrassment of endless fumbling for your keys or money. Keep your handbag clean, dust free, and polished if it needs it. Suede handbags need brushing. Leather and leather-look materials may be wiped with a slightly dampened cloth. Spot-clean fabrics if they become soiled.

When you store an unstructured handbag, stuff it with tissue so that it keeps its shape. Place your stored handbags in large plastic bags to protect them from dust. Small "feet" on the bottom of a handbag can save much wear and soiling. Also, the less metal on your handbag, the less tarnishing you will need to contend with. A shoe repair shop can repair most loose stitching, broken straps, and clasps on handbags. If your handbag is in good condition other than for one small problem, it will probably be worth the time and money to have it repaired.

SUMMARY

Planning your wardrobe to provide for activities and occasions in your life can save you many hours of indecision about what to wear and many hours of discomfort wondering about the suitability of the clothes you are wearing. Basic clothes, planned around a basic color scheme, certainly will get you started in being well-dressed. Knowing your own lines and colors will enable you to develop your own style in wardrobe selection that will be useful to you throughout your lifetime, regardless of fad or fashion trends.

Understanding Plans

1. What do you consider when you want to select clothes that "fit your life?"
2. How do casual clothes differ from leisure clothes?
3. How do you identify tailored clothes?
4. What characterizes a "basic" design in clothing?
5. What is the value of having clothes of basic design?
6. How do you plan your colors?
7. What are criteria for selecting hosiery?
8. How do you decide on a shoe style for your needs?
9. How do you decide on a handbag style for your needs?

Chapter 13

Buying and Accenting

When you go shopping, you may feel that there is a conspiracy to keep you from being well dressed. Think of it this way. Shoe designers consider themselves artists who express themselves in their designs. They shape and decorate shoes according to their artistic inclination, hoping to make shoes the center of interest in your appearance. Handbag designers, dress designers, coat designers, belt designers, and jewelry designers, each are vying for expression through their wares. Stores, in turn, market each item as if it were the point of interest in your ensemble. If you purchase such expressive designs, you may find that you have too many points of interest and are overpowered by your clothes. Stick to your own style, keeping in mind where *you* want to direct the observer's eye (and from where you want to divert it!). Keep lines and designs simple so that you can vary the ensemble by changing the accents to redirect the eye or to change the color harmony.

Before You Buy

The clothes you need to buy depend upon two things: the plan you've made and the clothes you already have that fit into that plan. To find out what you have and to keep your clothes organized, you will need to give your closet some attention. After you inventory and organize your current clothes, take a few moments to work out some technical problems concerning your wardrobe. Before you rush to the city for purchasing what you need, consider your budget, the way your clothes should fit, and how you will care for them.

CLOTHES THAT ARE IN STYLE

Your plans are built around styles that are classic and that are always appropriate. The style of a garment includes the lines, the color, the texture, and the overall image it reflects. Fashion, on the other hand, is the emphasis that is placed on a particular style, color, or image for a particular season. Sometimes a little-girl look is pushed, sometimes a country-girl look, and sometimes a dramatic, sophisticated look is in fashion. You know already that not every person looks good in each of these fashionable styles. A dainty, small-boned, very thin, short person may be perfect for the little-girl look, but when the dramatic, sophisticated look is "in" she will look like she is wearing her mother's clothes if she tries to be "fashionable." By the same token, the tall girl with a well-developed figure will look absurd in little-girl clothes but perhaps perfect in the sophisticated, dramatic clothes.

You may occasionally find a fashionable outfit that simply is too great to pass up even though it will not really fit into your wardrobe so far as your accessories, colors, and lines are concerned. You face a decision before you buy it. Can you afford to put the money it costs into a single item that (1) can be worn only occasionally because of its fashion, (2) does not expand or utilize the items you already own, and (3) you will need to accessorize, costing additional money before you have a complete ensemble? In order to justify such a purchase, you need to consider your investment partly entertainment expense, because you are indulging your senses for the immediacy of the feeling rather than using a rational approach to building a working wardrobe. Be sure that the joy of wearing such an item will outweigh the disadvantages of its relative expense, especially if you are on a tight budget. Items that fit into this category are the fad items that, after one season, are dated forever, or items in unusual colors that are popular briefly and are dated thereafter. The best way to avoid such temptation is to know what colors look good on you and build your basic wardrobe around those colors. Know the lines that flatter your figure and build your lines around them. Up-to-the-minute fashion clothes are not essential to being well dressed.

It is always better to know that the style, lines, colors, and textures that you are wearing make you feel that you are dressed as attractively as you can be. More attention should be paid to your overall appearance than to whether a particular garment you are wearing is up-to-the-minute in fashion. You can always make slight concessions to fashion, if you wish, with inexpensive accesssories and leisure clothes if you want to and if you can afford them. Fashion buying, though, is almost always a very poor bargain in the amount of wear you get for your wardrobe dollar. Style buying, on the other hand, is almost always the best value for your wardrobe dollar, especially when you know your style and buy it in lines, textures, and colors that integrate with the rest of your wardrobe.

CLOSET ORGANIZATION AND INVENTORY

Before you decide to purchase anything for your wardrobe, inventory and organize what you have. That means cleaning out your closet and placing your clothes in it in an orderly manner.

Closet Organization. To start your reorganization take some clothes out of your closet and place them in three stacks:

(1) Everything that you haven't worn in a year or more.
(2) Everything that can't be worn until it is mended, cleaned, or pressed.
(3) Everything that has nothing to coordinate with it, such as a skirt for which you have no blouse or a pair of pants for which you have no top.

Seriously consider why you haven't worn items in the first group for more than a year. If you don't believe you realistically will wear them again, give them to charity. Take whatever action is necessary to mend, clean, or press the items that need it so that everything you own and wear is ready to wear. Make a list of the items in the third group and decide what you need in order to make each one a working part of your wardrobe. Ask yourself seriously if added investment in coordinating items would be worthwhile for each item. You may want to add these items to those you give to charity if they show no promise for your current activities.

Examine your closet space. Designate a place for (1) blouses, (2) jackets, (3) skirts, (4) pants, (5) dresses, (6) long dresses (if you have any), (7) special items such as your robe, tennis dress, or horseback riding outfit, and (8) clothes that need washing, cleaning, pressing, or mending before you wear them again. Group each category by color, keeping colors within the category together, and line up the colors in the same order in each category. This organization has certain advantages in helping you to find and match items you want to wear together. A pair of pants, for example, does not get lost among two dresses of approximately the same color. You can at a glance look for all the parts of a particular ensemble because you know approximately where each will be hanging in its group. If you have already worn any part of the ensemble and it perhaps needs to be washed before you wear it again, you won't need to spend time looking for it. It will not be in its regular place but will be in another section of your closet for those clothes that need washing, mending, or pressing before they are worn again.

The other items in your closet — shoes, handbags, belts — need to be organized also. If you keep your shoes in shoe boxes, use a felt tip pen to designate color and style of the shoe. Keep your colors in order. Handbags should be stuffed with tissue paper and kept in plastic bags or individual boxes to keep them dust free. If boxes are used, write with your felt tip pen the color of the handbag. Belts sometimes can be hung on the neck of a hanger with the item with which they are worn. Frequently, though, belts that tie or use some other means of fastening will not hang well. Those may be placed flat in a box on a shelf in your closet. If you really want your closet to have some zip, you can line the inside of the box and also your closet shelves with adhesive plastic paper that is printed gaily and that brightens up your closet.

Closet Inventory. If you have the list you made in the color chapter of your wardrobe items, you can use it to classify the items according to where they will be worn. Your suitability list will be headed: casual clothes, tailored clothes, special occasion clothes, and leisure clothes. If you are a student who is studying personal development with an eye to entering business or a profession, you probably will find that you have many casual clothes that were good for student activities but few tailored clothes that are appropriate for business or professional wear. Be sure that you know the difference and do not enter the business office still dressed like a student. If you are a homemaker who is studying personal development with an eye to starting a career in the business office, you may have many leisure clothes and few tailored ones. Don't make the mistake of entering the business office in your leisure clothes. You will be uncomfortable if you are not dressed according to the custom of the business community in which you are working.

The lines separating the classifications are not always clear and are not always the same for every community. Some examples of each classification that are true for most business communities are illustrated (Illustrations 13-1, 2, and 3). While you are making your inventory, be especially alert for items that qualify for your basic wardrobe: a basic coat, a basic suit, a basic dress, a basic two-piece ensemble, and a basic special occasion dress. If any of these are missing from your present wardrobe, that probably will be the first addition you will want to make.

Using the color inventory and the closet inventory you have made, decide what you need in order to have a suitable ensemble for ten days without repeating the same one. Remember that a change of a scarf, the removal of a jacket, the substitution of a blouse, or switching of a skirt all make different ensembles. If you can't make ten ensembles with your present wardrobe, decide what you need to purchase and the color scheme you wish to build around. It may take a year or so to get your

Vogue Pattern Service

ILLUS. 13-1 *Functional for your at-home activity, leisure-time clothes would be out of place at work.*

ILLUS. 13-2 *Characterized by an unstructured freedom, casual pants are good for spectator sports and campus wear.*

Vogue Pattern Service

Vogue Pattern Service

ILLUS. 13-3 *Good style and fabric characterize tailored pants. If pantsuits are acceptable in the business community where you work, they probably will be of a tailored style and of a subdued color.*

wardrobe completely coordinated around a basic scheme if you have not been conscious of coordinating colors in the past. Be sure the ten days' ensembles are of the classification needed for your major activity (casual if you are planning for student activities, tailored if you are planning for business or professional work). When you have listed what you need to make ten ensembles, decide on a priority. The most pressing need probably will be to round out your basic wardrobe. List the items in the order you feel you need them.

YOUR BUDGET

There are two extremes in the cost of clothes. You can opt for one, which is to buy very inexpensive items so that you have more variety, but you must expect them neither to wear as long nor look as good as more expensive clothing. You can opt for the other extreme and buy designer clothing at very high prices and plan to have a few that look exquisite and last forever. Probably you will want to place yourself somewhere in between. The woman who works in the business world and aspires to the executive offices probably will place herself nearer the second extreme because the more expensive clothes that look better longer save her time in shopping. She doesn't have to shop as often and she is sure that she is as well-dressed as she can be. It is convenient to wear clothes of quality because they are usually easy to care for, wrinkle resistant, and the buttons stay on. They rarely stretch out of shape, and if they are of a classic style and are available in a color that fits her wardrobe scheme, they are versatile. With a few of them, she can have many ensembles that are different but appropriate.

A homemaker may find that she prefers variety for her everyday clothing and chooses less expensive clothing that can be disposable if she encounters a messy job in her home or with her car while running an errand. She may buy the bulk of her everyday wardrobe from the less expensive racks but purchase her basic items from more expensive lines, expecting to wear them for several seasons.

A student who is buying clothing for campus wear may find herself somewhere between the homemaker and the career woman. Most of the casual clothes she buys will be of a moderate price range, with a few leisure-time ones from the less expensive racks and the basic items from more expensive lines.

The length of time you can expect an item to look good depends, of course, on the number of times you wear it and the care you give it. The quality of the fabric and the construction, too, are important. Within those limitations, a good quality coat, suit, dress, or special-occasion dress of the basic design and color should wear well for you at least two years. That is, you should plan to replace those items every other year. Try to stagger your purchases so that everything does not have to be replaced during the same year.

If you can sew, you can cut down considerably on the cost of your wardrobe. To save money, women who sew, but who do not want to take on a big project such as a coat or dress, frequently make such items as straight skirts, sleeveless tops, and leisure-wear items. The saved money, then, is used to purchase the more intricately constructed garments. Be sure that your finished garments, though, look as good as those that are professionally made. If your home-sewn clothing does not look well made, you may be better off to spend your extra time earning money at a part-time job than at the sewing machine.

CLOTHES THAT FIT

Getting a good fit is perhaps the most important part of selecting your wardrobe. Clothes that are too big or too small, too short or too long, or that simply do not fit the shape of your figure, are not good buys. This is one area you cannot ignore and be well dressed. Before you decide to purchase something with an eye to altering it, examine it carefully. Be very sure that there is enough seam allowance if you are making it larger. Be certain that there is no trim near the hem if you are raising or lowering it and that the crease that already is there will not show if you are lowering the hem. Alterations on the top of a garment are much more difficult than on the hem. Unless you are very good with the needle and thread, avoid undertaking alterations on the bodice of anything.

Some considerations in checking the fit of a garment are:

(1) The collar and neckline should not pull or gap. You should be able to sit comfortably in a dress with a high neckline without its choking you (Illustration 13-4, next page).

(2) Shoulder seams should end precisely at your shoulder bone or possibly ¼ inch shorter than your shoulder bone, depending upon the style of the sleeve. The armholes of sleeveless garments should fit smoothly around your arm, not binding or gaping. Check to see that the armholes are not cut too low, showing your undergarments under your arm. Also, be sure that they are not too big so that a gap in the front shows your undergarments in front. Sleeve armholes must be comfortable — not tight, not sagging.

(3) Bodice darts should end at the fullest part of your bust. If they end before that point or if the darts themselves are placed too high or too low, the dress will not fit properly and will be almost impossible to alter.

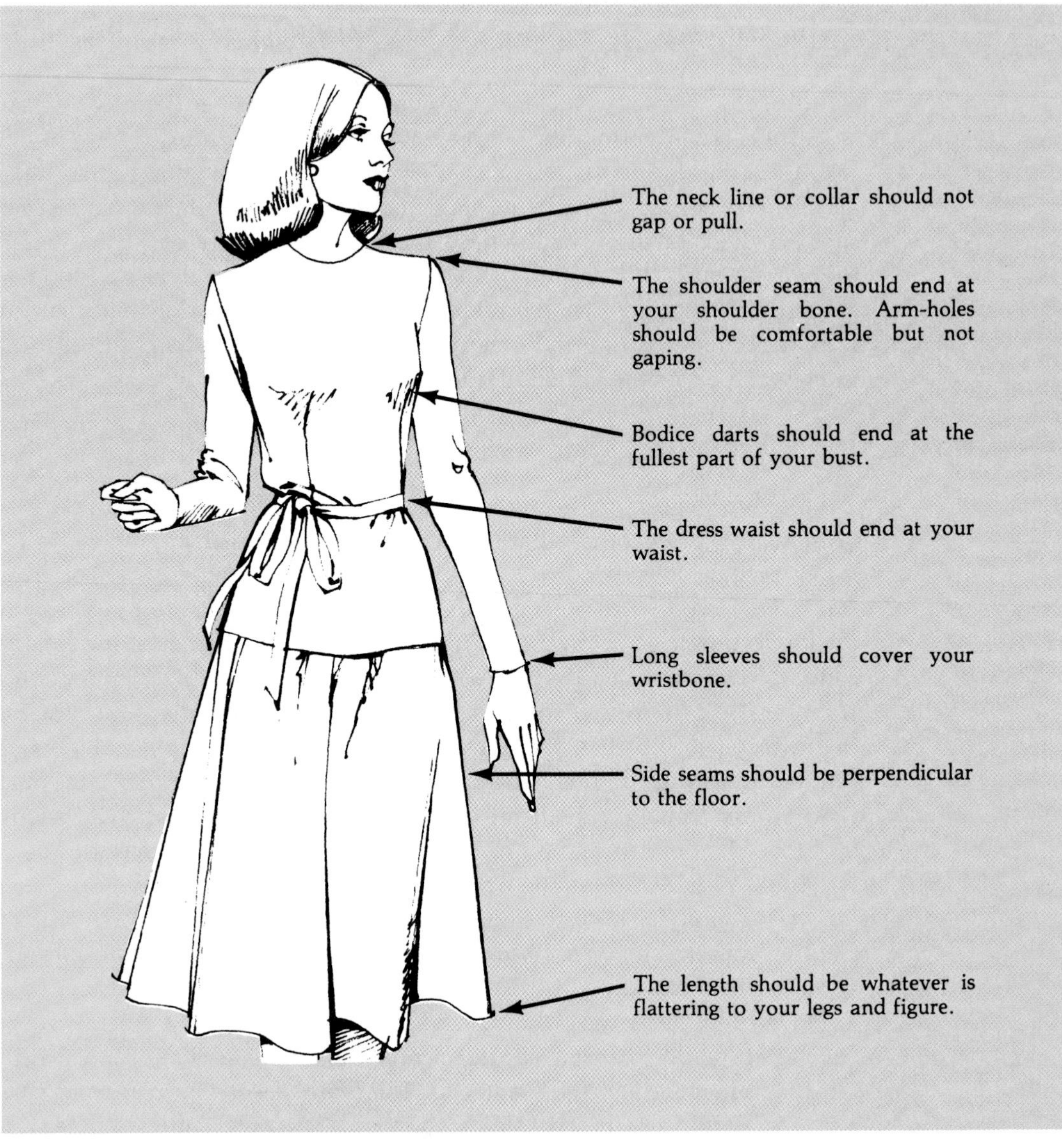

ILLUS. 13-4 *Check the fit of a garment at the designated points.*

(4) If the ensemble has a natural waist, be sure it hits you at your natural waistline. It is possible to wear the waist ¼ to ½ inch above your natural waist; but if the bodice is too long, it will appear wrinkled and too large for you.

(5) Long sleeves should be long enough to cover your wristbone but not to cover part of your hand. Bracelet-length sleeves should

stop just above your wristbone. Be sure you know which you want and that the ensemble is balanced well with whatever sleeve length you choose.

(6) Side seams should always be perpendicular to the floor. If they hang awry or are stretched to the back or front, the garment does not fit properly.

(7) The length should be whatever is flattering to your figure and legs. Wear the same height shoe you plan to wear with the ensemble, when you try it on, to get a good idea of the best length in proportion to your figure.

(8) Wear the undergarments you plan to wear with the garment. If you plan to wear a certain girdle, control top pantyhose, or bra, be sure you have it on when you are trying the garment.

(9) Allow for ease in your clothes. Across the back of the bodice between the armhole seams and in front across your bust, there should be some ease to allow for movement of your arms. There should be some ease in the waist circumference of a dress. Straight skirts should have approximately two or more inches ease so that you can sit comfortably in them.

(10) When you try a new garment, be sure you can walk, bend, reach, and sit comfortably before you make it your own.

FABRIC SELECTION AND CARE

When you select your clothes, read the fiber content and care labels carefully. These bits of information can make a big difference in your decision to buy or not to buy. The fiber content of the garment and whether it is washable or dry-cleanable only will appear on the label. Beyond that information there are some other facts about fabrics that will help you in selecting and wearing them.

Cotton. Cotton, one of the four natural textile fabrics, (the others are wool, silk, and linen) is frequently used in clothing for warm weather because it absorbs perspiration and facilitates your body's cooling system efficiency. Cotton is usually washable but wrinkles easily unless it has been treated. The wrinkle-resistant finish may deteriorate with repeated washings. A hot iron is used on the wrong side of the dampened fabric to remove the wrinkles. Check to see if any cotton garment you buy has been preshrunk or Sanforized. If not, expect it to shrink when you wash it (Illustration 13-5, page 293).

Wool. Wool is often used for cold-weather clothing because its "breathing" action holds the warmth of your body. Wool, too, is absorbent and can be effectively used for warm-weather clothes. Unless wool garments specifically call for washing (which automatically means cold water washing), have them dry cleaned. The heat of a clothes dryer and the heat of an iron can shrink and destroy wool. To press wool, always use a press cloth, steam, and the wrong side of the fabric if possible. Wool rarely wrinkles much, and the wrinkles that do occur usually "hang out" without pressing (Illustration 13-6).

Linen. Linen washes easily but wrinkles very easily, too, unless treated. A hot iron on the wrong side of the dampened fabric is necessary to remove the wrinkles. Linen is used often for warm weather clothing because it is absorbent. Linen is usually most satisfactory when it is dry cleaned since moisture makes it wrinkle readily (Illustration 13-7).

Silk. Silk is a fragile textile fiber usually used for tailored and special-occasion clothes. It does not wash well and requires a cool iron for pressing.

Synthetic Fibers. There are three synthetic fibers that have similar characteristics and are important in your wardrobe: Polyester (Dacron, Trevira); Acrylic (Acrilan, Orlon, Zefran); and Nylon (Qiana, Antron). All are wrinkle resistant, and all wash easily and well. If pressing is needed, a warm iron on the wrong side is used very lightly. Clothes made from these fibers usually wear extremely well year round and probably will be the mainstay of your wardrobe.

Acetate is a synthetic fiber that is fragile and that does not launder well. Plan to have it dry-cleaned and to handle it carefully. It wrinkles easily and should be pressed with a warm iron on the wrong side.

Arnel is washable, but it has a tendency to wrinkle easily. A hot iron is needed to press it. Rayon, used extensively in clothing, has a tendency to stretch out of shape when wet, and should be dry cleaned rather than washed. It wrinkles and should be pressed with a warm iron.

Frequently you will find that two fabrics have been blended in a garment. Be sure that you treat it (washing, cleaning, pressing) according to the more fragile of the blended fabrics, not the more durable. Blends of polyester and wool, polyester and acrylic, and silk and wool are common and make excellent clothing fabrics.

Fabric Weaves. The fabrics themselves may be woven, piled, or knitted. Some woven fabrics are broadcloth, shantung, organdy, sharkskin, and denim. Velvet is the most common pile fabric. Knitted fabrics are delightful for clothing because of their "give," allowing for comfort in movement and wearing. Single knitted fabrics are usually thin and may stretch out of shape. Double knits range from light weight to heavy weight and usually do not stretch out of shape. Cotton and acrylic double

Vogue Pattern Service

ILLUS. 13-5 *Cotton is cool and usually washable. It wrinkles badly, however, unless it has been treated.*

ILLUS. 13-6 *Wool is warm but rarely is washable. It does not wrinkle easily.*

Vogue Pattern Service

Vogue Pattern Service

ILLUS. 13-7 *Linen is cool but may wrinkle if it becomes damp.*

knits will stretch somewhat under repeated strain, such as on the seat of a skirt, if they are not lined for shape retention.

Before you purchase a garment, think about the cost of keeping it cleaned and pressed. You may find that the double-knitted polyesters, acrylics, and nylons that wash easily and do not wrinkle will save you time and money in the long run, even if they should be more expensive initially than garments of other fibers.

Vogue Pattern Service

ILLUS. 13-8 *Knits are very comfortable to wear. They rarely wrinkle and many of them are washable.*

Mending. It is always better to anticipate a repair such as a loose button or a loose stitch and take care of it before it occurs rather than after it embarrasses you. For most garments today, cotton-covered polyester thread is available in multiple colors for mending. Some bees wax, available at sewing notions counters, is excellent for coating thread to keep it from knotting as you sew and for stiffening thread for sewing on buttons. Dental floss, because of its strength, is excellent for sewing on buttons but should be used only for buttons where the thread doesn't show, because it comes only in white.

Some emergency mending measures can be used. If your hem falls out and you have no needle and thread but do have cellophane tape, you can tape it temporarily. A dark button can be sewn on with light thread and colored with an ink pen so it won't show. Cuticle scissors you carry in your handbag are good for cutting stray threads.

Shopping

One of the most important things you do for your wardrobe is to plan your shopping for it. You already have a list of the items you need with the most needed items at the top. Think about where you can reasonably expect to find each item and jot the name of the store down beside the item. Write the top limit price you will pay for each item.

BRAND NAMES

After you have purchased clothing of the style you need for a while, you will become familiar with the brand names that seem to meet your needs best. If you already know some that you like, you can place a few phone calls to the local stores to find out whether or not they carry the lines. If they do, ask about how complete their stock is or when they expect it to be replenished. If you are not familiar with the brands that suit your needs, take note of those that you try on that you especially like, if they fit and are within your price range. If you are alert when you shop, you will soon find certain stores and certain clerks that simplify your shopping by having and knowing what you need and like. After you have shopped with them a few times and they know what you want, some clerks will call you when they receive items in which they think you will be interested.

SALES

Beware of sale merchandise. Stores usually have two kinds of "sales." One sale is usually a bargain and one is not. The best kind of sale which offers quality merchandise for a lower than regular price is the only one that will interest you for your wardrobe. The other kind is one in which the store buys "sale" merchandise to market during its "sale." This sale merchandise is rarely of the quality that the store usually handles and frequently is a very poor investment as a permanent item in your wardrobe. Learn which sales are the ones that offer the kind of merchandise you need.

One of these sales may be the end-of-season sale when all seasonal merchandise that has not been sold is marked down before the new season's goods are put out. Be very careful, however, of buying anything of an extreme fashion during these end-of-season sales, because next season you may find it passé and therefore a waste of your money. Also, be careful of tying up your money in next year's clothing when you really need it for next season's clothes. In March, it would not be wise to spend the money you planned for spring clothes on next winter's coat if you don't have appropriate spring clothes for April, May, and June of this year. Taking advantage of end-of-season sales can provide quality merchandise at lower-than-normal prices, but it also ties up this year's money in next year's clothes. Be sure you can afford to do that before you indulge in the end-of-season sale.

Sale items themselves can be traps. It is important that you be objective when considering a sale item. Be sure that it is something you would buy at the regular price, if money were no object, before you consider buying it at the sale price. No matter how inexpensive an item may be, if you don't use it, it is a waste of your money. Sometimes items are on sale that have buttons missing or a belt missing. Before you decide to purchase the items and replace the buttons or belt, check the cost of that kind of replacement. If it brings the total cost of the item up to or above the price of one with all the buttons and belt in place, you will be wasting your time in repairing a sale item.

There are sales that offer the kind of merchandise you will need. Be vigilant in learning the patterns of sales of the stores in your community and in learning which ones usually offer the kind of merchandise you want on sale. A sales clerk who helps you regularly can be your best friend in helping you to know the difference between the two kinds of sales.

Some items that you can buy cheaply without sacrificing your appearance are those that are not subjected to daily hard wear and those that are not constructed. Evening accessories that are worn infrequently may be of an inexpensive line, and scarves that have no seaming or buttons to worry about may be of an inexpensive line without affecting your appearance. You may find other items that can be bought from inexpensive lines that serve your needs without breaking the bank.

TIMING

Try to plan to do your shopping when you are not tired or hurried. If it is possible, plan to shop when the stores are not crowded, or at least at times other than the peak crowded periods. Be considerate when you shop. Explain what you want to a clerk and consider the clerk's suggestions. If the store's stock does not meet your needs, say so, thank the clerk, and leave. Sometimes, because the clerk does not fully understand your needs or does not thoroughly know the stock, items may be shown to you other than what you have described. Be firm in sticking to your shopping plan, and resist trying on items that do not fit your plan. You will save yourself time, wear, and tear on your nerves and energy, and the objectives of your planned shopping trip.

STORE POLICIES

Some stores are more cooperative than others about letting you purchase items "on approval." This means purchasing something, keeping your receipt, taking the item home, trying it with whatever you plan to wear it with, and returning it (without wearing it, of course) for a refund if it doesn't work with your ensemble. Check the store policy if you wish to use this procedure. It is, of course, better to take the item you want to coordinate with you because you save yourself the trouble of taking something back that doesn't work. Too, you have a better chance of coordinating if you use the item itself, rather than your memory, to match or contrast a color, line, or texture.

BOUTIQUES

Boutiques have sprung up around the country and are popular because they are rather small but carry a few lines of all the items you need for an ensemble, and you can coordinate the whole outfit in one dressing room. Large department stores do not offer this particular advantage because their merchandise is departmentalized, and one clerk cannot help you with all the items you need for an ensemble. You must go from department to department, coordinating the items you need. However, department stores usually have a larger variety of merchandise from which to select.

Accenting

Jewelry, scarves, gloves, and hats are the accessories you may want to accent your wardrobe. Jewelry and scarves are used to provide a center of interest and to emphasize an existing center of interest. Gloves and hats may be used to give a "completed" look to a particular kind of ensemble and to provide warmth on cold days.

JEWELRY

Jewelry may range from genuine precious stones set in 14 carat gold to colored glass in painted metals. It may be of a delicate design, a chunky, casual design, or an uncluttered, tailored design. It may be set to show the brilliance of a genuine stone or it may be set to provide an accent color to a suit or blouse. Jewelry may be thought of as jewelry to show the beauty of the jewel and jewelry to accent the beauty of the wearer. Genuine stones in gold may be designed to do both. They are appropriate in many special occasion situations, and, when in simple designs, for every day. Often expensive ornate pieces are not considered appropriate for everyday casual and tailored wear. Costume jewelry is designed for the wearer, not the jewel. It is costume jewelry that you will select for everyday accessories to your wardrobe.

Uses. Jewelry may be used to intensify a color by repeating it. It may be used to draw attention to a particular area of the costume or to draw the eye away from a particular area of the costume. It also can give a completed look to an area of the ensemble (such as beads on a plain neckline), or provide a complementing or intensifying color to the basic ensemble.

Jewelry worn near your face draws attention to it and away from other parts of your ensemble. Necklaces and earrings especially draw attention to the shape of your face. The length and shape of these pieces should be selected carefully. If you have a rounded jawline or a square one, be sure that your necklace is long enough to give a V look that will offset the rounded or square shape of your jaw. Select earrings that are oblong, or slender, not round or square. If your neck is long, however, dangling earrings and long necklaces will emphasize the length of your neck. A short necklace and rounded earrings shorten the neck and widen it. Rounded earrings and square ones widen the jawline but can be worn by people with thin faces.

A bracelet can be worn in the same metal or color as earrings or a necklace, to intensify the metal or color by repeating it. Bracelets may also be used to pick up a color in the costume or may, themselves, be a center of interest if you have pretty, well-cared-for hands.

Rings, especially those of semiprecious stones, can be used to repeat a color in the costume or provide a slight hue variation to a color you wish intensified in the costume. A smoky-colored topaz ring worn with brown or beige, for example, can be stunning. A turquoise ring with a blue-green dress is equally attractive. Tourmaline stones in many hues can be coordinated to your basic color scheme.

Quantity. Jewelry can be overdone. Usually two pieces of jewelry are quite enough for a well coordinated ensemble. Save your gaudy costume rings for every finger for your way-out, leisure-time wear. If you choose to wear a necklace and earrings at the same time, make your earrings of the smallest, least obtrusive kind you can find. A necklace OR earrings with a ring OR bracelet is usually in better balance than a necklace with earrings. Your wrist watch, unless it is of a very ornate design, is not considered as one of your pieces of jewelry (Illustration 13-9).

Style. Keep your jewelry the same style as your clothes. If your clothes are tweedy and bulky, choose chunky jewelry. If your clothes are

ILLUS. 13-9 *Choose your jewelry carefully. Usually two pieces are enough for accenting an ensemble.*

Vogue Pattern Service

tailored and uncluttered, keep your jewelry simple and of moderate design. The size of your jewelry is important, too. A small ring on a large finger looks out of proportion. A large ring on a small finger is equally out of proportion. Long, dangling earrings on a person who is relatively short are out of proportion. Small earrings, though, seem to look good on most people, even tall ones.

Basic Pieces. In your basic wardrobe, you will find simulated pearls very useful in a necklace. A gold-plated (or 14 carat if you can afford it) bracelet, pin, chain necklace, and earrings (not to be worn all at the same time) are very versatile for your basic wardrobe. Silver and white gold are good with blue ensembles, but generally are not as complementary to most complexions as gold colored jewelry is.

Select the shape of a pin (which can be worn instead of a necklace) to repeat lines in your ensemble that you wish to emphasize. Round pins emphasize roundness and soften angular lines. Square and angular-shaped pins emphasize angularity and de-emphasize roundness. Rings of round-shaped stones shorten fingers; oblong and marquise-shaped stones lengthen the finger.

Care. Keep your jewelry clean. A bottle of jewelry cleaning fluid or silver polish enables you to do this job at home. Many jewelers are happy to clean your rings at no charge just to have you come in their store. If you clean your jewelry yourself, use a soft, lint-free cloth to dry and polish your jewelry after you have rinsed the cleaner off in warm water. Pearls have to be cleaned professionally since regular jewelry cleaner will discolor them. Most stones and gold or gold-plated rings, chains, pins and bracelets can simply be dropped in the fluid or rubbed with polish at home for cleaning. While you are cleaning your jewelry, about once a week, check for loose stones and weak clasps. These are easily repaired by a jeweler and can save you the unhappiness of losing a favorite piece that is in poor repair.

SCARVES

Scarves are the ultimate secret weapon in putting a wardrobe together. The color, shape, and placement of a scarf can completely disguise an ensemble that you wear frequently, giving it a completely different feel and look with each change of scarf. The key to wearing a scarf as an accessory is to wear it with authority.

Colors. Try several different scarves with each ensemble to get the effect of various color combinations. Try multicolored, bright scarves with dark, single color ensembles. Wear scarves of one pastel color with ensembles of multicolors. Use scarves to bring a color near your face that looks especially good with your complexion. A black dress, for example, can be softened considerably with a pastel or multicolored scarf near your face. Use colored scarves to repeat — thus intensify — a color in your ensemble. Or, use them in an analogous color of a darker shade to dull an ensemble color that seems too bright. Be careful not to use a scarf of a brighter hue of the color of your eyes because it will dull them. You can intensify their color, though, by using a tint of the eye color or by selecting the complementary color to the eye color for your scarf.

Lines. Arrange and tie scarves to accent your best lines. If your neck is rather thick, avoid a horizontal line around it. Instead, wrap the scarf to a V in front with ends inside your dress to soften the width of your neck. If your neck is short, allow only a small portion of the scarf to cover your neck. Arrange most of the scarf lower on the neck of the dress or tuck most of it inside your dress. If your neck is long and slender, cover more of it with your scarf, and don't be afraid of horizontal lines tied around your neck (Illustration 13-10).

The length of the trailing ends of a scarf can accent the width of your shoulders and silhouette if they point in a horizontal direction. Choose

Square and rectangular scarves of short and medium lengths may be wrapped once (1) or twice (2) and tied in a double knot. The ends may point horizontally (2) or vertically (3). The ends may be tucked inside the neckline (4).

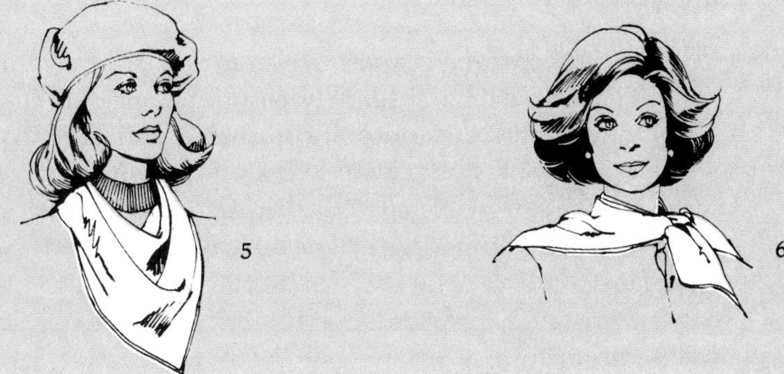

Square scarves of all sizes may be folded to a triangle with the third corner worn in back, in front (5), or to the side (6).

Long, rectangular scarves may be wrapped once (7) or twice (8) and tied tightly or loosely. They may be worn above (9) or under (10) the collar.

The long, trailing ends may be in front (7), in back, or split with one to the front and one to the back (9).

ILLUS. 13-10 *Emphasize your best lines with scarves.*

scarves of sufficient length to hang in a vertical line if you plan to wear them with the ends trailing outside your dress. The easiest arrangement and frequently the one that is very appealing on most people is a scarf wrapped around the neck with the ends tucked inside the neckline of the dress. It can be arranged to give a horizontal line if needed or to give a V shape to compensate for a rounded face or a wide neck.

Uses. Color in scarves can be wildly extravagant, bright, and forceful. Because you can carefully control the amount of color that shows in a scarf, you can use it in much stronger color than other items of your wardrobe. A scarf, like jewelry, can be used to complete an area of your costume. For example, with a scarf you can fill in a neckline, repeat a color to intensify it, call attention to your face, draw attention away from other parts of your silhouette, or soften the effect of unflattering colors in the ensemble.

Care. Accessory scarves are made of silk, nylon, polyester, and rayon. They must be absolutely clean and wrinkle-free to be effective. Nylon and polyester fabrics are washable and they dry quickly, almost wrinkle-free. Silk and rayon wrinkle somewhat more and are prettier when they are dry-cleaned. Take the dry cleaning cost into consideration when you are comparing prices. Silk is considered the most luxurious scarf fabric and usually costs more than the synthetics. Nylon and polyester, however, provide superb fabrics for scarves that are durable as well as beautiful.

Other Scarves. Scarves for warmth are made to wrap around your neck, muffler style, during cold weather. A scarf of this kind needs to be coordinated with the basic coat and gloves you wear to keep warm. Muffler scarves are made mainly from wool, a blend of wool and nylon, and acrylic. Acrylic is washable. Wool and wool blends usually require dry cleaning unless they bear a label specifically stating that a cold-water wash is acceptable.

GLOVES

Gloves for dress wear with tailored clothes are rarely worn today. They are appropriate, however, if you wish to wear them with tailored clothes. A most practical choice, if you want to purchase a pair of gloves, would be of cotton or opaque nylon in a neutral color and in a length that covers your wrist bone. Gloves of kid leather, although luxurious, are hard to keep clean. Dirty gloves are always inappropriate. Select gloves that are well made, with smooth seams, well-fitting fingers and of a smooth fabric. If you wear them with a long-sleeved ensemble, push the cuffs of the gloves to a crushed look around your wrist. All jewelry that you wear on your hands and wrists goes under your gloves. Rings will usually fit better if the large part of the ring is turned to the palm side of your hand while you are wearing gloves.

Gloves for warmth in cold weather, of course, are frequently worn with your coat. They are available in textured leathers, wool, and acrylic, and may be color-coordinated with your coat, a knitted hat, or scarf that you wear for warmth.

HATS

Hats as accessories to an ensemble come and go in fashion. If you need one at all today, it will most likely be in a church or for a special occasion. Select a style that complements your face shape as well as your relative height. Any hat with a brim that makes a horizontal line will widen the face and shorten the silhouette. A hat that makes a more vertical line for the eye to follow will lengthen the face and silhouette. The brim of a hat should be as wide as your hair style, and, if you wear eye glasses, the brim should be as wide as your eyeglass frames. If you wear eyeglasses, avoid "crowding" your face with a veil or a hat that covers part of your face. Eyeglasses require that you wear your hat slightly off your face.

Since a hat will be very near your face, choose it in a color that looks especially good with your complexion as well as your ensemble. Keep the size of the hat proportionate to the size of your silhouette. Don't perch a small hat atop a large figure, and don't smother a small figure under a large hat.

Hats for protection from the weather are frequently knitted from wool or acrylic. Select one that coordinates with your winter coat. Match it either to the coat or to your gloves. A more coordinated look is achieved if either the gloves and hat match, the gloves and scarf match, or if the scarf and hat match. The effect is too spotty if all three match in a color that contrasts to the color of the coat. Gloves that are the same color as the coat with contrasting hat and/or scarf draw attention away from your silhouette and to your face.

Eyewear

Corrective eyewear should be considered as a miracle for people with eyesight deficiencies. Notwithstanding the contribution of this miracle, people have hated their glasses anyway and have even endangered their own well-being and that of others by driving cars, operating equipment, and squinting at movies without their glasses in order to avoid the woe of feeling unattractive. How you feel about yourself is, of course, the key to your well-being. If you think you are unattractive, it makes no difference if others think you are pretty. If you think your glasses are unattractive, how you really look in them will make little difference to you. Following some guidelines in selecting frames that look good on you may be helpful. If you are still unhappy, consider wearing contact lenses to correct your vision.

EYEGLASSES

Eyeglasses are framed in many styles and of many substances. Metal and plastic are the most popular frame materials. The shapes can be of several styles. Color is available in almost every shade. Good choices in each of these areas can achieve for you eyewear that enhances your appearance while correcting your vision.

Frames. Metal frames including gold and gold-plated ones are usually heavier than plastic ones. They may have the separate nose pieces of plastic to provide comfort for the wearer. Plastic frames, available in patterned styles and many colors, are usually very lightweight.

Shapes. The shape of the lens frame varies from a narrow, cat-eye shape to a large, round shape. A person with a rounded face probably should avoid the rounded eyeglass frames because they call attention to the roundness of the face. A person with sharp, angular features should not wear the square frame or one with sharp corners of any kind because they further sharpen the facial features. Most people need eyeglass frames between the two extremes of the large, round and the narrow, pointed look. Ear pieces that are narrow allow for more light in the eye area, allowing your eyes to be seen. Ear pieces and thick frames that shade the eyes tend to make the eyes look dark and circled.

Color. A frame of a soft, muted color is preferable to one of a strong pure color. The soft, muted color blends more easily with other colors, making your frames more versatile than they would be if they were of a strong, pure color. Select a color that complements or blends with your eye color. Remember that complementary colors intensify each other, and that a lighter hue of the same color intensifies eye color. If your eyes are blue, for example, the complementary color, orange (in a very light tint, of course) will intensify the blue, as will a frame of a lighter tint of blue than your eyes. Gray eyes can be intensified with a lighter gray or blue-gray frame. Brown eyes can be intensified with lighter brown frames or with very pale blue or blue-violet frames. Analogous colors can also be used. A very pale yellow with brown eyes can be pretty if yellow can be worn near your face. Use all your "color sense" in selecting the frame to complement your complexion and eyes. Very dark-colored frames can be worn by people with dark complexions and dark hair and eyes. On others, dark frames tend to dominate the face. Frames should be an accessory, not a center of interest. Avoid decorated ones. The less attention they call to themselves, the more versatile and the less tiring they will be to you.

Proportion. Select the size of the lens according to the size of your facial features. Oversized, round frames on a person of small features look out of place. Small, narrow, pointed frames on a person of average or large features look squinty and tend to perch on the nose. Gently curved, oval shaped frames of an in-between size, perhaps somewhat larger than the eye area, are good for many people. The more eye area that can be exposed without having frames that look oversized for the face, the prettier the eyes will appear. And the more light that surrounds the eye, the more shadows that tend to age and darken the face will be eliminated.

Tinted Lenses. Tinted lenses other than those tinted for sunglasses are worn sometimes. Often tints are prescribed by physicians for light-sensitive eyes or eyes exposed to glare. Dark tinted lenses, though, have usually been categorized as faddish, and one who wears them indoors risks their becoming passé rather quickly.

Sunglasses can be a bit more dashing than those glasses that you wear indoors. Stronger colors and more extreme shapes and sizes can be worn in sunglasses because we expect them to be somewhat dramatic. The larger the lens in sunglasses, the better the protection for the eyes from the sun. Consideration again must be given to the relative size of your face as well as to the shape of your face when you select the frame for your sunglasses (Illustration 13-11, next page).

Care. The cleanliness of your glasses and frames makes a difference in your appearance. Lenses can look oily from your skin oil; and your earpieces and lens frames pick up cosmetics from your hair and face. Most glasses can be carefully washed in warm, soapy water to remove these secretions and should be bathed carefully every day either in the morning before you put them on or at the end of the day when you take them off. Special tissues can be obtained to clean the lenses. These are available to carry in your handbag. Window, mirror, and glass cleaner is

ILLUS. 13-11 *When you select frames for your glasses, try not to repeat a line in your face that you don't like.*

good for cleaning the lenses. Never lay your glasses on a surface with the lenses down because small particles of grit can scratch the lenses. Fluid lens cleaner is available in small bottles for your desk drawer or your handbag. It is a good investment for keeping your lenses clean and oil free.

CONTACT LENSES

If you need corrective lenses and do not like to wear glasses, you might consider contact lenses. Contact lenses may be either hard or soft. Each type has different advantages and disadvantages. Like all corrective eyewear, a doctor can advise you on whether or not your eyes can be fitted with contact lenses. He can also advise you as to whether he recommends soft or hard lenses. Generally, the adaptation time for soft lenses is shorter than for hard lenses. The comfort in wearing soft lenses is greater than for hard ones. Soft lenses, however, have not been as good as hard ones for correcting vision, especially for eyes with astigmatism. Hard and soft lenses also have other special characteristics you should consider.

Hard Lenses. Hard lenses require strict cleanliness — of your hands, your lens case, your lenses themselves. Even your eyes must be "clean." If there is makeup oil or eye secretion of an oily nature in your eyes, it will cloud and smear your lenses. Hard lenses usually should not be worn for longer than eight or ten hours without a break. Many doctors recommend that they be removed for thirty minutes to an hour at the end of each eight-hour wearing period. Sometimes that is inconvenient for the wearer. If the lenses are worn too long without such a break, though, the eyes may become very irritated. Secretions in the eye caused by hay fever frequently interfere with contact lens wearing, as does mascara that flakes off into the eye during the day. The hard lenses tend to attract such particles in the eye. Dust that is blowing in the air frequently is deposited on the lenses. Most hard-lens wearers wear their sunglasses religiously when they are outdoors for protection from such dust particles.

Other disadvantages of hard contact lenses are that many people experience contact blur when they remove the lenses at the end of a wearing period. Contact blur means blurred vision for several hours, even though regular eyeglasses replace the hard contact lenses. Glare is another problem experienced by the hard contact lens wearer. Many people find themselves much more sensitive to light and sunlight with hard contact lenses than they are with ordinary glasses. Hard contact lenses also occasionally "float" off the cornea of the eye. The wearer usually needs a mirror to locate the lost lens in the eye so that it can be replaced on the cornea.

The advantages to hard lenses are numerous. First and most apparent is the fact that no frames are seen around the eyes. Eyeglass frames, which can be uncomfortable as well as unattractive, are eliminated. Hard contact lenses are available in colors as well as in clear plastic. Your eye color can be enhanced. If your eyes are blue, you can accent the blue with blue lenses or you can make them grayish blue with gray lenses. Usually the color in the lens is not strong enough to change the color of your eyes. Brown lenses on blue eyes, for example, will not make the eyes brown, but will make them brownish blue, not a very good color for eyes. The vision correction with hard contact lenses is usually better than with regular eyeglasses. It has been suggested that deterioration of vision is curbed with the wearing of hard lenses, but science has yet to support such a claim.

Soft Lenses. Soft lenses, like hard ones, require strict cleanliness. They are treated somewhat differently, though. Hard lenses require certain commercial solutions for cleaning and insertion into the eyes. Soft lenses are of a material that is of a very high percentage of saline solution (salt and distilled water) and are cleaned, stored, and inserted with such a solution. They are also boiled for a specific length of time each day in distilled water. The main disadvantages to soft lenses as compared to glasses and hard lenses is that the vision correction usually is not as good, and frequently the soft lenses cannot be worn by people with astigmatism.

Because soft lenses are still being developed, they have yet to be made in colors. Currently they are available only in transparent material of no color and they are difficult to see when you are handling them. Difficulty in seeing them makes them easy to lose. They are also much more fragile than hard lenses and can be torn easily if you pick them up with a fingernail or if they are pressed against any sharp or pointed object. They are not as easily scratched, though, as hard lenses. The advantages of soft lenses are that they are much more comfortable than hard lenses for most wearers and they do not float off the cornea of the eye. They can be worn for longer periods of time, up to twice as long as hard lenses without a rest period. They do not attract grit or oil in the air or in your eyes. There is no contact blur and no glare experienced by most soft-lens wearers. Sprays, however, especially hairspray, can permanently damage soft lenses, and sometimes the lenses become discolored for no apparent reason.

Motivation. Before you decide to try contact lenses of either kind, carefully evaluate your motivation and discuss your vision correction needs with your doctor. Motivation is probably the key to successful contact lens wearing, provided, of course, that they are properly prescribed and fitted and that your doctor supervises your adaptation period.

Putting anything in your eye is traumatic at first; it is also uncomfortable. Be sure that you are willing to suffer some discomfort during your adaptation period before you invest in contact lenses. Tenacity in forcing yourself to insert the lenses in your eyes at an appropriate time each day is important. Cleaning the lenses carefully without fail is a must. Suffering somewhat while you are becoming accustomed to them can be expected. Maintaining clean hands and appliances for handling, storing, and cleaning them is imperative. All this, in a nutshell, is what wearing contact lenses is all about. Be sure that the motivating forces you have for considering them are strong enough to overcome the irritating discomforts you may experience in wearing them.

SUMMARY

The key to dressing well is getting and putting together what you know looks good on you. The inventory you make of your current clothes gives you practice in observing objectively lines, colors, and styles. Maintain this cool objectivity when you shop, and you may amaze yourself with your effectiveness in getting just what you need. Be courageous in putting together colors, lines, and textures that blend well. Accent with flair, and wear your ensembles with authority. You may just be the best dressed person in the city!

Understanding Buying and Accenting

1. How does style differ from fashion?
2. What categories can you use to organize your closet?
3. What are budget considerations for an office worker?
4. What do you look for in a good fit?
5. What fabrics appear to be good for tailored wear?
6. How can recognizing brand names help you in shopping?
7. Which "sales" are likely to have good buys?
8. What basic pieces of jewelry do you need?
9. How does a scarf affect the line of your clothes?
10. What are considerations in selecting either eyeglasses or contact lenses?

Projects for Part 3

1. Assume you are going to work in a downtown office in your city or in a nearby area. Considering your own complexion, your figure, your community, and the office you select, make a color plan for your wardrobe, explaining your color, hue, value, and intensity choices.
2. Assume that you are designing for yourself and your particular figure and job. Describe a dress, a suit, and a pantsuit, detailing the silhouette, neckline, sleeve, and length of your perfect design for yourself.
3. Make a list of wardrobe items you need for your own life, assuming that you work in an office. Include line and color considerations.
4. Research the lines of clothes that fit the color, design, line, and cost you desire for yourself. Determine which local stores in which to shop and how much you can expect to pay for the items in a basic wardrobe.

Part 4

Fourth Dimension Your Relationships

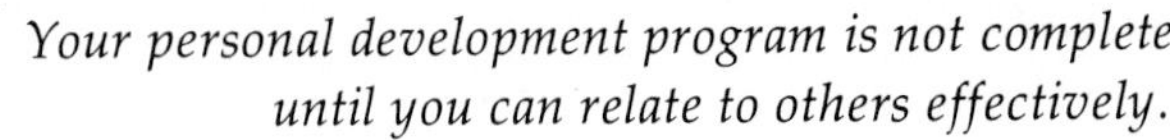

Your personal development program is not complete until you can relate to others effectively.

Relating to others well begins with understanding and liking yourself. Recognizing what motivates you, how you spend your time, and why you react as you do is the beginning of knowing yourself well. As you learn to understand yourself and others better, you function in professional situations more effectively.

Much of your success depends upon your ability to communicate with others. Facility in both verbal and nonverbal communication can open avenues of expression for your ideas and feelings.

Social and semi-social situations can add much variety to your life. The skills and customs for these situations conclude the fourth dimension of your personal development program.

Chapter 14

Personal Relationships

If you have been working at improving your figure, posture, complexion, hair, and clothing, you may already feel a change in your personality — an uplift in your morale. You may have even noticed a difference in your relationships with other people as you become more attractive and self-confident.

Each of us has a goal in life to be happy with ourselves and to get along with others. It is possible to overlook the necessity of being happy with ourselves and to look outside at other people or other situations to make us happy. Happiness from outside is temporary and cannot provide lasting serenity and satisfaction within you unless you are happy with yourself — in your beliefs, your actions, and your accomplishments. If you want to improve relationships with others, first learn about yourself.

No matter how attractive and pleasant you may be, no matter how efficient you are on the job, you will not make real progress unless you know how to relate to other people. This means learning how to evaluate and to take criticism; learning how to deal with and keep from creating problems; and learning how to cope with yourself when you don't feel well and with people who may not be easy to work for or with. You can improve your personal relationships by learning to understand why people (including yourself) act and feel as they do.

Your behavior is determined by your personality traits. A normally developed personality has three identifiable characteristics. These are:

(1) a set of suitable principles by which to live, (2) the capacity to enjoy living, and (3) the ability to evaluate objectively. A personality has two strong motivating forces: the pursuit of recognition and the need to structure time.

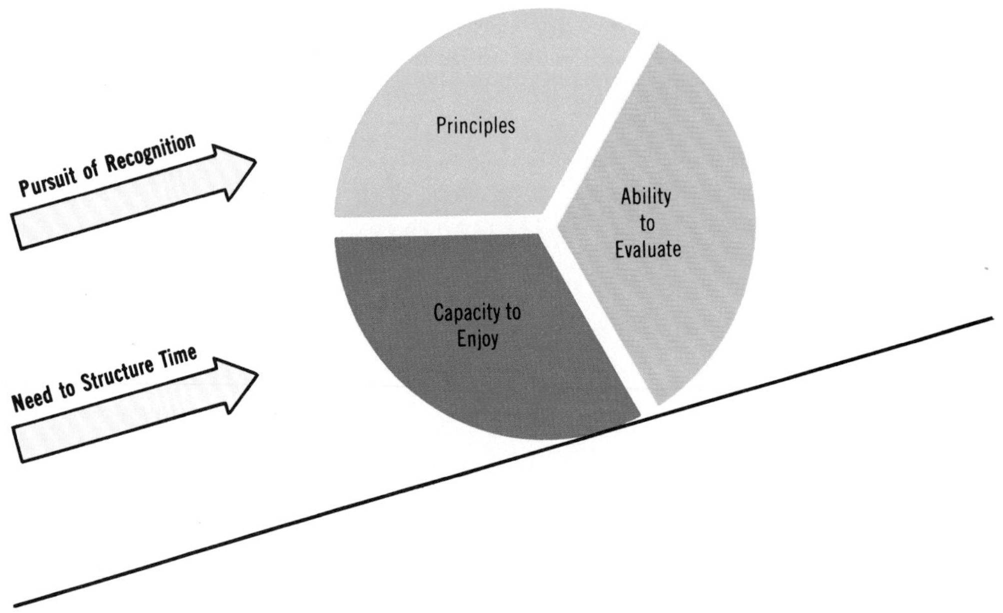

ILLUS. 14-1 *In a normally developed personality there are two motivating forces —pursuit of recognition and need to structure time. There are three identifiable characteristics —a set of principles, the capacity to enjoy, and the ability to evaluate.*

The System of Terms

Dr. Eric Berne developed a system of terms to describe human behavior that may be helpful to you in identifying and discussing people's feelings, actions, and reactions in personal relationships.[1] There are many theories employing different terms to describe behavior including the best known ones of Sigmund Freud who used id, ego, and superego. Dr. Berne, however, developed terms that are easy for you to understand and to use because they relate to situations with which you are already familiar.

Dr. Berne's system is named Transactional Analysis. The TA terms that will be most useful to you in discussing behavior are: Parent ego state (that set of suitable principles by which to live); Child ego state (the

---

[1]Eric Berne, M.D., *The Structure and Dynamics of Organizations and Groups* (J. B. Lippincott Co., 1963)

capacity to enjoy living); and Adult ego state (the ability to objectively evaluate). The personality needs are called strokes (the need for recognition), and the methods of time structuring are called: withdrawal, rituals, pastimes, games, activities, and intimacy.

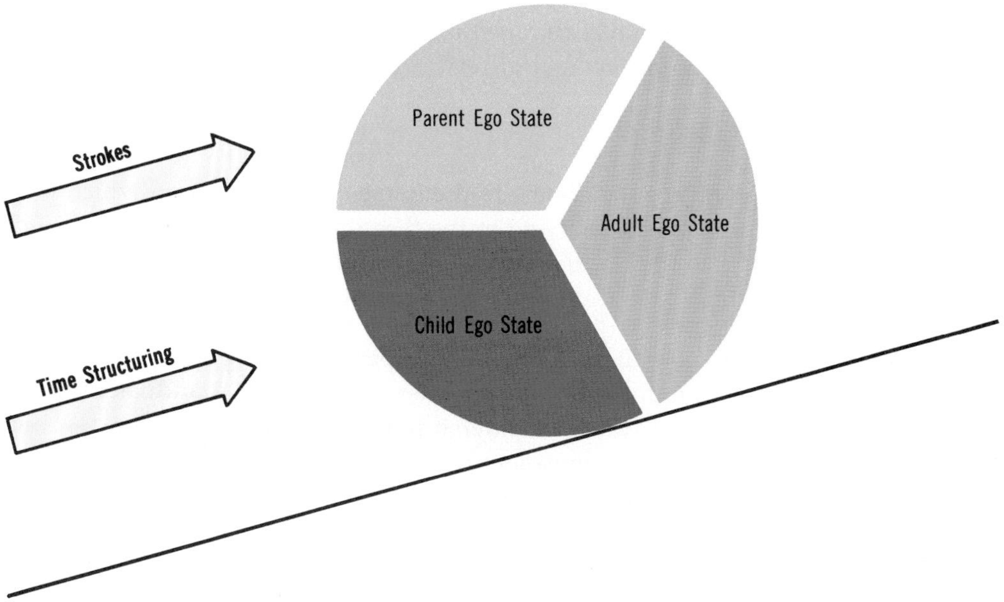

ILLUS. 14-2 *In Transactional Analysis terms a human personality and its behavior are described as having: Parent Ego State (principles), Child Ego State (capacity to enjoy), Adult Ego State (ability to evaluate), Strokes (pursuit of recognition), and Time Structuring (the need to structure time).*

THE CONCEPT

Everything that has happened to you since before birth seems to influence your current behavior and is believed to be "recorded" either in your conscious or unconscious memory. These memories in TA are called "tapes" and further termed Parent or Child tapes depending upon the nature of the remembered event. Feelings usually are in Child tapes. Ideas usually are in Parent Tapes.

Tapes store all your memories of the events and your responses to them in your brain, which acts similarly to a tape recorder. They can be "played," providing the same responses today any time you encounter an event similar to one you've encountered before. Problems seem to arise when people respond automatically from an old tape to a new situation under circumstances that require reevaluation and a different response. Frequently people making such automatic responses may cause themselves unnecessary problems without knowing why. The way to avoid such problems for yourself is to learn what may be "taped" in your mind by examining your automatic responses and then by changing the responses if you need to do so.

Inappropriate responses will cause misunderstandings with other people and will make you uncomfortable about your own reactions. By learning what the typical taped messages are and what motivates people to act, you can improve your relationships with them.

EGO STATES

The term *ego state* refers to the frame of reference from which you are responding. When referring to the three ego states, capital letters will be used for Parent, Child, and Adult. Capital letters will not be used for parent, child, and adult when they refer to people.

Parent. The Parent can be any person having authority over your life. This could include your parents, a baby-sitter, grandparent, teacher, minister, friend, or even older brother or sister. These are the people who have given you messages of "right" and "wrong." They are also the people who nurtured you in childhood.

Memories recorded on Parent tapes are of both a nurturing and critical nature. If you fell and a nurturing Parent picked you up and kissed you, you recorded a nurturing experience. On the other hand, if you ran into the street and a critical Parent scolded you and spanked you, you recorded a critical experience.

From the beginning of your life you heard things from authority, mainly from your parents or those having authority over your behavior. These things may have been good, sound statements that are true for all time. They may have been true for situations at that time. They may have been false from the start. As a youth, though, you were unable to tell the difference and you recorded them in your Parent ego state as true for all time. They now may play back automatically whenever a similar situation arises unless you consciously control them and keep them from coming on.

"Airplanes aren't safe" may have been true in grandmother's day but not at present. "Do not walk in front of an automobile" is still true. "It's bad luck to walk under a ladder" may never have been true (Illustration 14-3).

As you examine responses that emanate from a Parent ego state, you probably will find many that give good direction for many occasions. Such direction as "Keep everything in its place," "Everyone ought to do his part," and similar generalities are appropriate for many occasions;

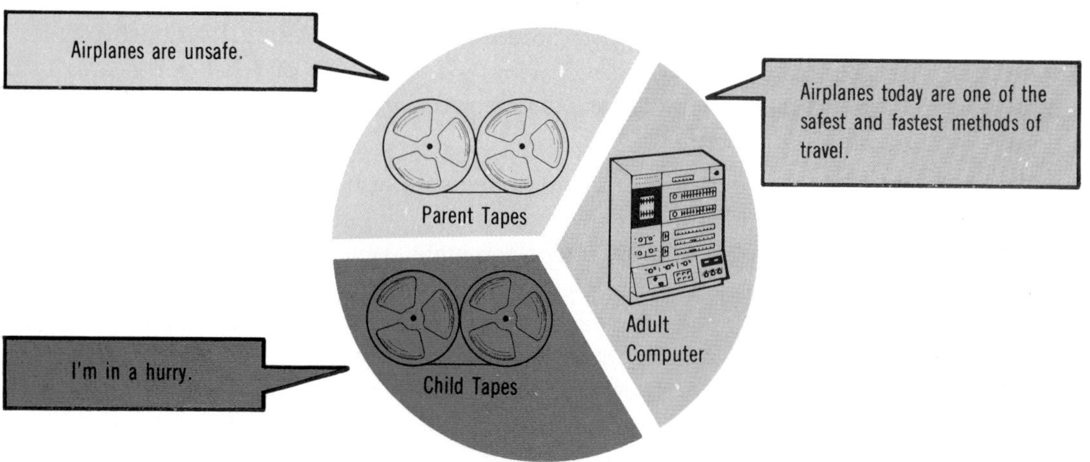

ILLUS. 14-3 *Sometimes messages are recorded on old Parent tapes. These messages may be outmoded and may need to be reexamined in light of current facts.*

and you would not want to erase those opinions from your tape. You simply want to be able to activate them in appropriate situations and avoid them in inappropriate ones.

For example, "Keep everything in its place" is a good edict for most of your life. However, if you are about to miss your bus to work, you probably should not take time to straighten the bedroom before you run for the bus. You should evaluate the circumstances — the time you have to make the bus and the importance of keeping everything in its place — then decide which is most important to you for the present circumstances. All things being equal, you probably will find it more important to catch your bus and arrive at work on time for the day than to spend the time now to straighten your room. Better management of time would help you schedule yourself in the future so that both stimuli may be responded to if they are important to you.

Much of your Parent programming is reflected in the form of your conscience. Parent tapes that tell you not to cheat or lie are useful to you every day. Rigid conscience decisions, though, may make you uncomfortable when the circumstances do not merit discomfort. "You should always tell the truth" is a Parent statement, and it is one that concerns your conscience. It may cause you discomfort though when you think of a date, "You are dull and uninteresting, and I don't want to date you," but you want to lie and say, "I'm sorry, I have other plans."

You could reconsider the Parent truth edict and select a response to rephrase the statement objectively and truthfully to say, "I don't believe we have enough common interests to make a dating relationship enjoyable from my viewpoint." This is a statement of what you see as fact, and it takes the judgmental statements about "dull" and "uninteresting" out of the picture.

Nurturing instincts and statements also come from the Parent. "I'll take care of you," "Let me help you," "Let me do it for you," all are statements from your Parent ego state. When one of your colleagues in the office seems distressed, you may automatically respond with your nurturing Parent tapes and offer to rescue the person in distress. It may be more beneficial both to you and the colleague in distress, however, to evaluate the situation. Decide if there is reason for distress, if it is work related, if indeed you can help without letting your own responsibilities suffer, or whether it is better for the person to get out of the dilemma without help. You can then make an appropriate response rather than an automatic one. Doing something for someone that should be done by that person is not a rewarding experience for either of you and will probably produce bad feelings in you about the person.

It is possible to have a nurturing Parent tape that automatically plays for others in distress but not for oneself. The need for sympathy and help is needed by you from yourself as much as it is needed by others from you. Learn to recognize when you are suffering from real distress — when you can benefit from self-indulgence. Learn to nurture yourself in these circumstances of pain and genuine distress. It is possible, of course, to be overindulgent both with yourself and with others. That occurs when you are enjoying sympathy and concern over the unfortunate circumstances more than the relief resulting from your avoiding the circumstances that bring the distress.

Many prejudicial statements come from the Parent ego state. Statements that say, "Husbands must be older than their wives," "Long hair is untidy," and "Adults don't understand," are prejudicial statements that may not apply to the current circumstances. Before any of these preconceived ideas are applied to a situation, all current facts and information should be evaluated.

It may be necessary for two people who are about to be married, for example, to evaluate whether they are of approximately equal maturity rather than age. Should one have more experience in life than the other? If so, which one? Should they be of equal experience? Which one is likely to live to an older age, leaving the other alone in old age? The two people can then make a decision about desirable relative ages from the facts. Lifelong discomfort can result without evaluation and information in light of the current facts.

There are some characteristic words, postures, and attitudes that are found in the Parent ego state. If you learn to recognize them, you will have an edge in determining whether they are appropriate or just automatic replays of old tapes that are not necessarily suitable to the present situation.

An authoritative tone of voice is easy to recognize as a Parent tape. It may be accompanied by a stern look, compressed lips, a pointing index finger, arms folded across the chest, or resigned sighing. Words that are characteristic are those that are moralizing, judgmental, nurturing, punishing, sympathizing, criticizing, and perhaps giving orders. Typical Parent words are "should," "have to," "ought to," "must," "always," "never," "stupid," "disgusting," "ridiculous," and "If I were you" (Illustration 14-4).

It is important to recognize these gestures and words so that you can realize when you or another person is acting or reacting from the Parent ego state. It is also important to appreciate that these characteristic features and words may be appropriate to various situations. You want only to be able to evaluate the situation and to select the proper response rather than to respond automatically with an old tape that may be unsuitable.

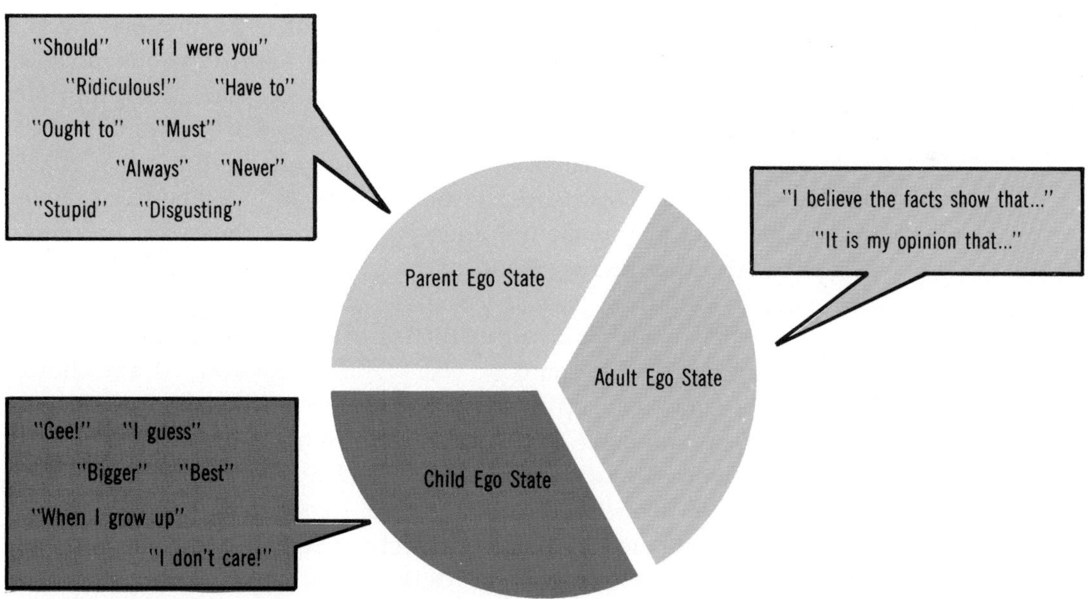

ILLUS. 14-4 *Each ego state has typical statements, phrases, and words that help you to recognize which one you or someone else may be reacting from.*

Child. Everything natural, spontaneous, and creative originates in the Child ego state. Fearfulness, self-indulgence, self-centeredness, and temper also are part of the Child. The Child contains memories of all the impulses that come naturally to a small child. Most of the feelings you experience are from your Child tapes. The Child also contains responses to all your early experiences as you saw and felt them and has stored the attitudes you took when you reacted to these experiences.

Recorded on Child tapes are such things as you did to get attention, to manipulate people to get your way, and to pass responsibility for your actions from yourself to others. The way you handled your situations to get the best results for you is the way your Child tapes will play back to you. If you were able to get your own way by crying, tears may still be your weapon. If you received attention by being either very good or very noisy, these modes of behavior may be your methods even today. All the feelings you got from past activities and your concept of yourself are recorded on your Child tapes.

Much of what is attractive about you is found in the responses from your Child tapes. An easy laugh, an affectionate nature, and a sensitive quality are traits that are usually very appealing in a person. These are termed your "natural" or "free" Child responses.

An adapted Child is another part of your Child. This part learned early in life through trial and error that in response to stimulus one could withdraw, procrastinate, or comply. These kinds of adaptations are still there. Sometimes they are suitable ones that make expressions more acceptable to oneself and to others. Sometimes they are inappropriate, making a person feel that she can never be the person she wants to be.

Some adaptations that make life easier for you are those that enable you to share, to be courteous, to be sociable and to take turns. Some adaptations that may make life uneasy for you are those that make you comply with all authority, good or bad, without question; those that cause you to withdraw because it is easier than facing the circumstances; and those that make you procrastinate to keep from doing what you should, perhaps so that someone else will do it for you. All the choices are available and will replay automatically even when you don't want them to unless you make a conscious decision to change them.

A child who has had her own way may have serious emotional difficulties trying to live in a world that requires cooperation and sharing. A child who has adapted by being a model of obedience may find that she is criticized in the working world for lack of initiative.

Unsuitable Child responses bring discomfort when, for example, an automatic Child response to the making of a mistake is severe distress regardless of the seriousness of the error simply because severe punishment followed the making of mistakes when you were a child. It is not necessary to experience such severe reactions to mistakes now, though, especially for those of minor importance or for those which you could not avoid. It is better to evaluate the severity of the mistake and to decide what to do about it than it is to indulge bad feelings simply because you made it.

Characteristically a person who operates from a Child ego state most of the time may try to associate with people who operate from the nurturing Parent ego state so that the nurturing Parent will take care of the Child who will not have to think for itself. That relieves the Child from making its own decisions or from taking responsibility for its own behavior. Frequently, a person acting from a Child ego state shows little conscience, and seeks to be babied, punished, rewarded, or applauded.

It is necessary to recognize the importance of the Child. It contains the natural curiosity, humor, emotion, creativity, and spontaneity, without which any grown-up would be a very dull and monotonous person. The child also contains the desire to explore and the originality, without which there would be no new inventions or progress.

Child feelings are frequently expressed with smiles, laughing, crying having tantrums, having fun, or getting into trouble. Other Child signs are pouting, a whining voice, shrugging shoulders, teasing, or squirming. These movements are frequently accompanied by words such as "far out!" "Golly!" "I wish," "I want," "Gee," "I guess," "bigger," "best," "When I grow up," and "I don't care." Refer to Illustration 14-4, page 319.

When you recognize the above signs and sounds in someone else or in yourself, you can feel sure that they are coming from a Child ego state.

Adult. Automatically playing old tapes is easy because it requires no reasoning or thinking on your part. The response to stimulus is automatic and is not subject to evaluation in your brain — not until you choose to evaluate it. That choice usually comes when such response makes you uncomfortable.

If you are reacting from old tapes that you collected when you were growing up, you are reacting from a Parent or Child ego state. The problem with old tape reactions is that they often are not suitable to today's circumstances and frequently do not reflect what you really feel. For example, children who feel afraid, excited, anxious, or guilty may have real reason because of their station in life. Adults, though, experiencing the same response to similar stimulus probably will find these extreme responses inappropriate to the circumstances. If you can identify them, you can change improper responses to those that are right for an adult.

An Adult ego state has little bearing on a person's age. It is related to today's reality and impartial collecting of information. The Adult is logical and objective. It tests reality and estimates probabilities. The Adult actually works like a computer, making decisions after evaluating information from three sources: (1) Parent tapes; (2) Child tapes; and (3) data the Adult has collected and is collecting to determine the reality of the situation.

An Adult ego state is not necessarily "grown up." The Adult actually begins to emerge when you are less than one year old. You, as a child, begin to gather data from your surroundings. You begin to find things out for yourself rather than from the teachings of your Parent or the natural feelings of your Child. If this emerging Adult is not discouraged too much, it will continue to develop normally.

The decision making that goes on in your psyche is in the Adult ego state. This ego state can evaluate, reason, gather, and store technical information; and it can be selective in all responses. Responses from each ego state are necessary to a well-rounded person, but the Adult is essential if you are to ever attain the awareness and self-direction to select and evaluate responses you wish to make.

Decisions made in an Adult ego state will not always be correct. They depend upon the education and experience you have in the area of the decision. You cannot always wait for complete information, and sometimes you have misinformation with which to deal. The most you can expect of your Adult ego state is to use what you have attained through education and experience to reality-test and to estimate probabilities of your decisions. Then, knowing you've done your best, resolve to live with your victories and your mistakes.

Sometimes the Adult accepts an edict from the Parent or a feeling from the Child without evaluating it or testing it for reality. When this happens, the Adult is not functioning independently and is said to be contaminated. Once the Adult is receiving messages and evaluating them, you must be constantly on the alert to spot periods when you accept incorrect data at face value from other ego states. It is tempting to accept such incorrect data without question because you've "always done it that way," but it is better by far to evaluate the facts and change behavior when it should be changed.

When your Adult is in charge, you will deal with a stimulus by examining what it really means to you rather than by merely responding automatically with a Parent or Child tape. You will be able to evaluate before acting and be more willing to take full responsibility for your thoughts, feelings, and behavior.

When your Adult ego state is in charge, you will be able to referee between conflicting messages from the Parent to the Child. For example, when your Parent is playing, "Everyone should go to college and work hard," and your free Child is saying, "I want to party all night and sleep all day," your Adult can evaluate what is best for you in terms of the goals you want for yourself and referee between the opposing forces.

Your Adult can also decide when it is time to indulge the desires of your Parent programming or your Child programming. After a hard week's work, it may be necessary to allow your free child to dominate for a few hours on the weekend, being self-indulgent, self-centered, and aggressive. On the other hand, you may find after periods of such freedom, it will be necessary to have some very structured, quiet time for Parent programming such as, "Take time to meditate everyday" or, "Pay attention to your spiritual welfare."

The Adult signs and sounds vary with each individual but they usually indicate alert, responsive listening with some facial movement. Typically the words of an Adult ego state differentiate clearly between fact and opinion with such words as "I believe the facts show that," and "It is my opinion that." Refer to Illustration 14-4, page 319.

Balance of Ego States. Because all three ego states are useful to you and are essential to your well-being, it is necessary to provide for the expression of all three in your daily living. That means that some variety between work, play, meditation, evaluation, feeling, and being objective are necessary for a satisfying life. Too much of any area at the expense of the others will deprive you of a feeling of balance in your life.

If you operate mostly from the Parent ego state, you can be bossy and domineering, surrounding yourself with people who operate mostly from the Child ego state. In this manner the overactive Parent can take control of situations. People with overactive Parent ego states may go to the other extreme and spend all their time nurturing and helping other people, sometimes making other persons overdependent.

It is also possible to operate mostly from the Child ego state, not wanting to grow up, make decisions, or accept responsibility. This constant Child looks for an overactive Parent to do all these things for it.

The balance needed for your life depends upon keeping the Adult actively evaluating circumstances in light of current facts and selecting appropriate responses (Illustration 14-5, next page).

MOTIVATORS

There are some other aids you can use to help you understand better your own behavior and that of others. These aids are found in the things that motivate people to act. Basically, there are two kinds of motivating stimuli. One is a hunger for recognition; the other is a hunger for structured time.

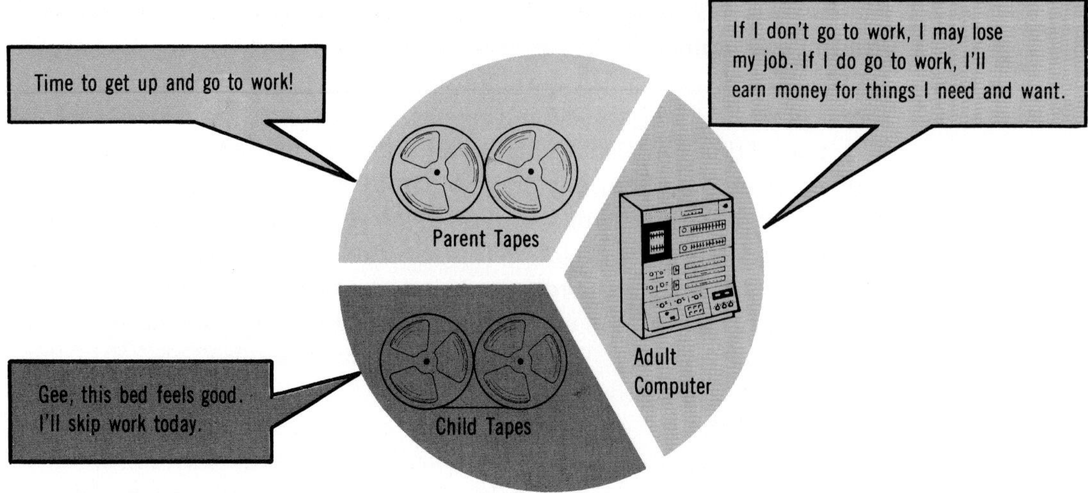

ILLUS. 14-5 *Often, one ego state plays one message while another plays a conflicting one. The Adult evaluates the information and makes the decision.*

Strokes. Your hunger for recognition (or attention) is appeased through "strokes" (units of recognition) from other people and from yourself. Everyone needs strokes, and it has been demonstrated that babies may become ill and die without them. Strokes may be negative or positive, and you may be seeking both kinds at different times.

All of us need positive strokes to be emotionally healthy. We need to be recognized as worthwhile persons who have something to contribute to life. These positive strokes may take the form of a simple "Hello" from a passing acquaintance in the hall. They may be, "You're really a nice person," from a good friend. They may be simply an approving smile from someone dear to you. Positive strokes are commonly called "warm fuzzies" and may be "doing" or "being." You need both kinds. "Doing" strokes tell you what you do well and get you approval for performing well. "You did a good job" is a doing stroke. "Being" strokes simply appreciate you for the person you are — you don't do anything to get them. "I care for you" is a being stroke.

Often, "doing" strokes are easily given and taken even within yourself, but their effect is temporary because you must continue "doing" to get them. It takes a bit more understanding and awareness to like yourself and others enough to give and take "being" strokes. Just feeling happy about being the person you are is a way to give yourself being strokes. Being strokes are permanent and powerful because they reinforce your good feelings about just being yourself.

It is important to be able to recognize the difference between when you are seeking approval, compliments, appreciation, and other positive strokes and when you are seeking negative strokes, such as punishment, bad feelings, being ignored, or being disliked. When you are not able to get positive strokes, you may turn to negative ones because they are better than no strokes at all. For example, if you cannot get positive strokes through approval of your accomplishments in school, you may choose to call attention to your failures so that you can get negative strokes. It would be better to accept your average school ability that produces no strokes, and seek positive strokes elsewhere in your life.

Negative strokes are always painful but are better than no strokes at all. Your psyche will demand strokes and will not survive without them. If you are unable to attain positive strokes, you probably will seek negative ones just to survive. Negative strokes may occur when you are laughed at, teased, ridiculed, or treated as insignificant. Negative strokes that you get from others and that you give yourself are put-downs to your Child ego state feelings because they automatically make you feel bad just as they did when you were a child.

If you get negative strokes and you don't want them, you can deal with those that come your way both from within and without by evaluating them to see if they really apply to you in your current circumstances. If they don't, consider the source and ignore them. If they do, rather than feel bad, try to develop a program to improve the situation. Don't indulge bad feelings about yourself just because someone throws a negative stroke your way. You may not deserve it.

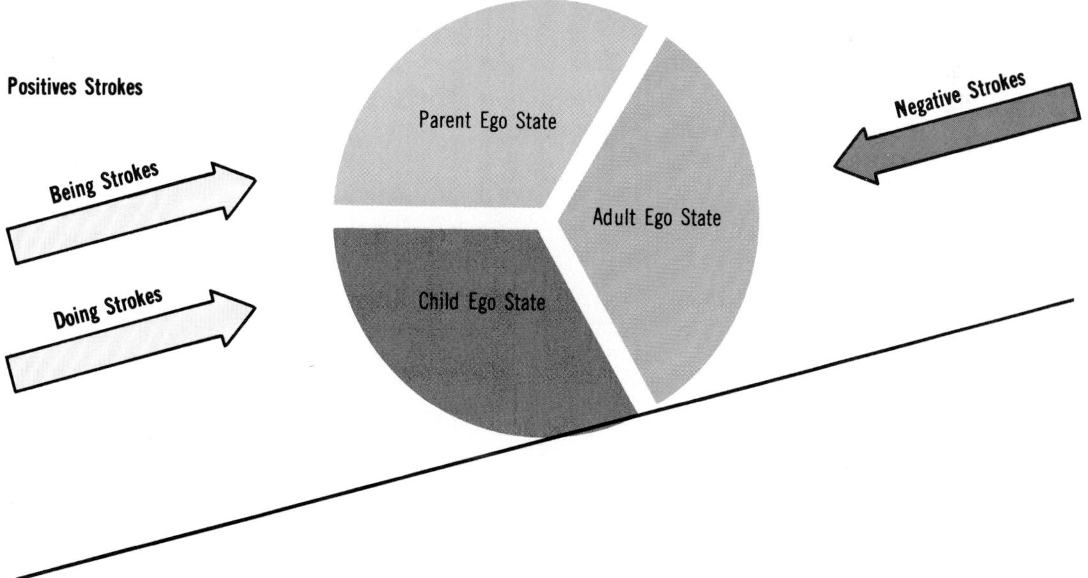

ILLUS. 14-6 *Positive strokes may be either "being" or "doing." They make you feel better. Negative strokes may make you feel bad if you let them.*

TIME STRUCTURING

If your need for strokes is not satisfied in your regular activity, you will begin to structure time so that your needs are satisfied. The ways in which it is possible to structure time are innumerable. However, some classifications that are good for examining and identifying the use of your own time are: withdrawal, rituals, pastimes, games, activities, and intimacy.

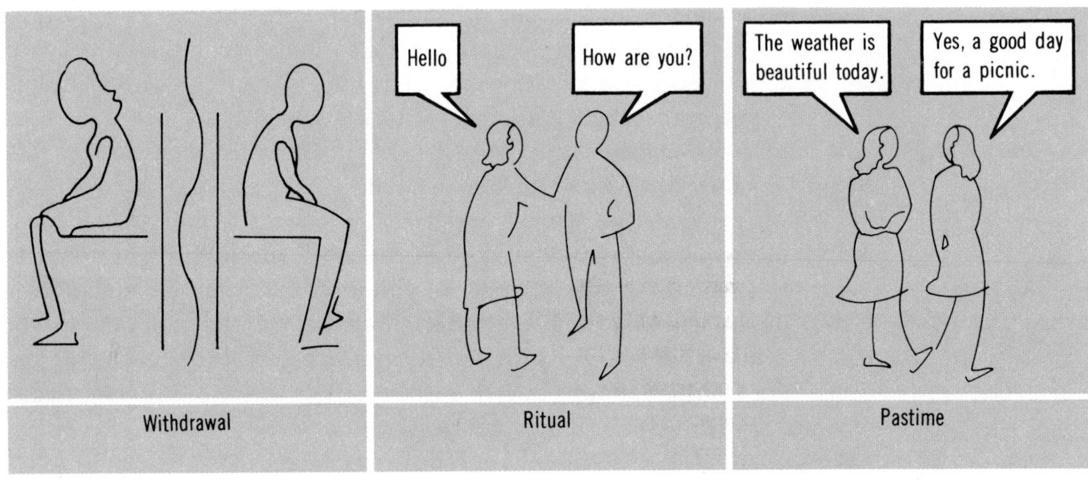

ILLUS. 14-7 *Ways to Structure Time*

Withdrawal may be a conscious decision to take some time for oneself for meditation and recuperation. Such a decision would probably be an Adult decision. It may also be psychological removal from reality because reality cannot be handled. That usually is a Child decision. It may be the avoidance of a confrontation because of an edict from the Parent "not to fight." Daydreaming and allowing your mind to wander may be withdrawal. Strokes in withdrawal may come from people seeking your physical presence or from doctors and loved ones seeking your psychological presence. The strokes may be from yourself in the form of congratulations for not fighting, or they may result from meditation and self examination which turns up worthwhile aspects of your personality.

Rituals are said to grease the wheels of social interaction. They are the polite "Hello, how are you" and "Good morning" that pass from one to another very casually. Usually very little personal involvement is included in a ritual. Rituals provide light, positive strokes and provide a vehicle by which to receive and give them without real involvement with other people.

It is important, though, to practice rituals only in selected areas where they are useful and not to build your life around them. Any activity may become ritualistic if it is done without involvement and feeling, including those in your home life and religious services. Use rituals when you cannot afford to become closely involved in people's lives; for example, with everyone at work. Don't use them to pass time while avoiding involving yourself in meaningful relationships with close friends and family members or in a meaningful worship service.

Pastimes are those activities that people use to take up time with one another without becoming closely involved. They include light party conversations — subjects such as the weather, the state of the economy, and the price of eggs. These conversations, trivial though they seem, do serve the purpose of allowing people to become acquainted so that they may judge whether or not they wish to know each other better. Pastimes are useful to feel out another person to see if you share common interests. They provide light, positive strokes that may lead to more powerful ones. It is a good idea to develop the facility of structuring time with pastimes so that you will have a vehicle for getting to know others better when you want to.

Games (psychological games) are ways to structure time that recreate old feelings that brought strokes as a child. They are different from social games or practical jokes. Psychological games usually are patterns of behavior and/or conversations that we unconsciously fall into in order to show that "Mine is better than yours," (providing a positive stroke for ourselves and a negative one for someone else), or to get someone to

"Kick me," (providing a negative stroke for ourselves because we think we don't deserve a positive one).

If you played a "Mine is better than yours" game as a child and achieved satisfaction from it, you probably play a form of the same game now to get strokes. If you got strokes, negative though they were, from misbehaving, you probably still play a "Kick me" game to reinforce your strokes when they are low.

Games usually have the ulterior motive of creating bad feelings for the person being "hooked" into the game and another ulterior motive of either good or bad feelings for the initiator. Games usually are played from a Child ego state and result in some form of payoff in terms of strokes.

Games are destructive, but everyone is guilty of playing them at some time. Many people play them almost all the time. Check to see if you are initiating behavior or conversations that provide you with positive or negative strokes and others with bad feelings or negative strokes. If you are having many bad feelings about yourself, or if people around you seem not to like you very much, it would be wise to pursue the study of games further. Entire books have been written about games.

Activities are those useful things you do, such as your work, getting dressed, typing a letter, and cleaning your apartment. These are the things you have to do of necessity or things you want to do, such as hobbies. They are a way to structure your time constructively to get strokes. A problem for many people is that they depend solely upon activities for strokes ("doing" strokes) and feel lost when there are no activities to be done. It is very important, of course, to get strokes from everyday chores and activities, both those you do alone and those you do with someone; but it is also important to be able to feel good about yourself and others without doing anything.

Intimacy is open and honest interaction with another person. Intimacy may last only for a moment or it may be for hours or longer. It is a time of relating to someone with no ulterior motives, freely sharing yourself with another person. Intimacy with someone indicates genuine caring, not superficial manipulation to get something for yourself. Only people who are honest with themselves and with others are capable of intimacy.

Intimate acts can be mistaken for intimacy. If a truly open, warm, loving relationship does not exist outside intimate activity, the activity itself will not provide intimacy. Intimacy requires no activity. It may be only a feeling of openness, closeness, and honesty with another person.

The relation of intimacy between two people does not need withdrawal, rituals, pastimes, activities and games. The important thing is that during the time structuring, neither person is on the defensive — both people feel relaxed. Intimacy is a game-free relationship that can exist only when the Adult is in charge and allows the creative, loving, natural Child to emerge.

Strokes from intimacy are "being" strokes that are powerful and lasting. It is worth the effort it takes to get yourself to the point of relating honestly with others so that you can experience such time with a person about whom you care.

SELECTION OF MOTIVATORS

The kinds of strokes you seek and the way you structure your time are influenced by a concept you have of your life pattern called your life script. Each person is born with unique characteristics, capacities, and potentialities with which to develop, express, and experience life. That means that you have everything you need to grow up to be a successful person just by being yourself. A problem arises if you allow cultural or family pressures to influence you to become less than you are capable of being.

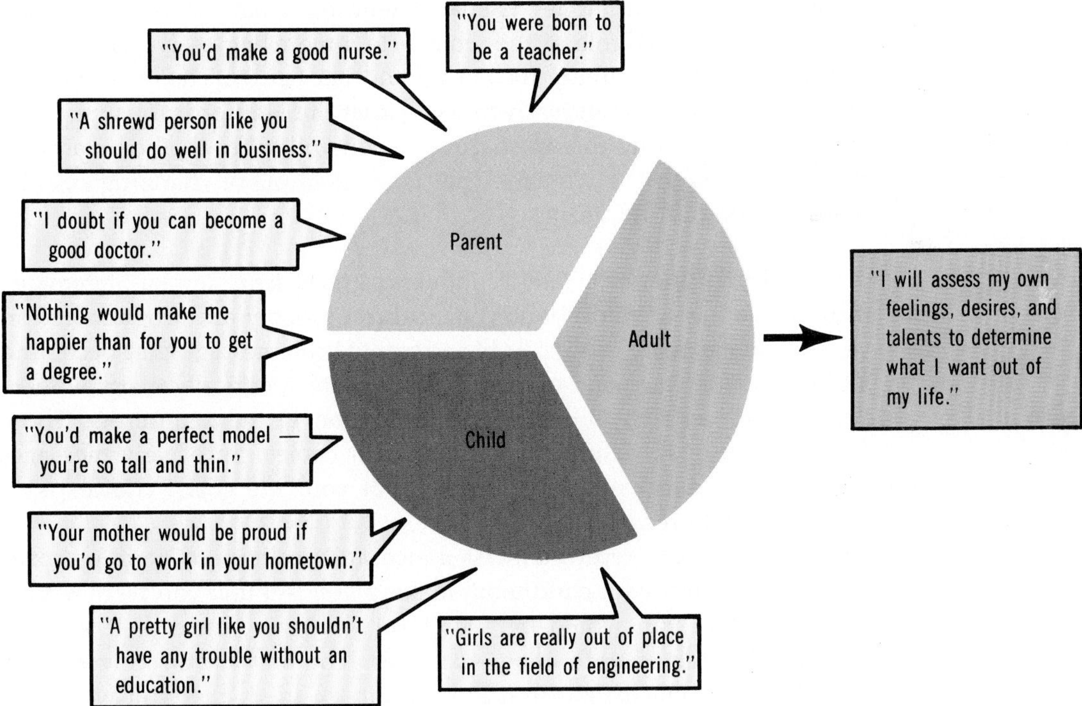

ILLUS. 14-8 *Your achievements, feelings, and the kind of person you become are influenced by cultural and family messages you receive throughout your life.*

Cultural Influences. Scripts differ according to the culture in which you live. A century ago, working women were looked upon with disdain in this country. Scripts also differ among ethnic groups. What is considered normal behavior for some people is not for others. Suicide was acceptable and honorable to the Japanese at the same time that it was considered an unforgivable sin in many other cultures. In some groups an affectionate embrace between members of the same sex is perfectly acceptable. Among other groups, this behavior would be considered very peculiar.

Some of the cultural influences that have been destructive are at last changing. "Girls who are intelligent are not lady-like" is one that fortunately has fallen by the wayside. "Girls who are attractive can't be intelligent" is another. "Boys should be strong and girls should be weak" is another that is hopefully gone forever.

For many years in this country, women played a passive role in society, bearing and raising children and caring for the home. Men were scripted to become aggressive and forceful in making money to support the family and home. Now, fewer children are born, and the woman's obligation in child raising is shared with the man. Likewise, the man's obligation in making money is shared with the woman. The culture has changed the passive role of the woman to a more aggressive one so that she can help make a living for herself and her family. The male role has changed from one of aggressiveness against the land or in business to a more accommodating role in sharing responsibility for the home and for child raising with the woman. That is an example of changing cultural influences on our life scripts.

Family Influences. Family influences take many forms. Statements made to you as a child about your future probably are programmed in your Child ego state. You may have received the message that becoming a career person was your goal, or perhaps more specifically that you were "born to be" a leader in business, a profession, or the community. Those statements probably influenced your career choice. Such early messages influence not only your career choice but your life goals, choices, successes, and failures.

You may have received reassurance and feelings of your personal worth throughout your childhood, making you feel that you were worthwhile and that you would be successful whatever you did. If so, you probably have lived with many successes. You may have received messages that you would fail no matter what you tried, that you would be unhappy no matter what your accomplishments, or that you simply were not a worthwhile person. This kind of programming, too, can permeate your life script unless you choose to identify and change it.

A System of Change

There are some questions you may want to ask yourself. Have you really been getting along as well with yourself and other people as you would like? Do you like yourself? Are you pleased with the way you spend your time? Can you give and receive strokes? Do you allow yourself time to withdraw alone occasionally, or are you always in a frenzy of activity? When you are indulging in pastimes — talking to other people about such things as hobbies, TV programs, school, or work — do you use these occasions for getting to know people better or for holding them at arm's length? Are you a happy person? Do you think pleasant thoughts most of the time? You are the only one who can answer these questions, and you are the only one who can decide if you want to make specific changes.

Walter Fountaine, Director of Glemby Specialists, Glemby International

ILLUS. 14-9 *Take a good look at yourself.*

Some change is inevitable. You probably have heard that the only thing that can be relied upon constantly is change. That is never truer than when it is applied to you and your life. Human beings, because of their continuing experiences, change somewhat every day. New ideas that are introduced into their minds, new activities in which they participate, or the simple repetitions of the routine of life make changes in their lives. You are changing each day and, if you want to, you can choose the direction your life takes.

Your choices range from becoming more of what you are, to becoming simply older at what you are, to becoming somewhat different from what you are, to becoming completely different from what you are. You can control your life if you want to, and you can select the course you want to take. Three basic areas of change may be useful to you if you choose to direct the course of your life.

Becoming consciously aware of your feelings is the first area. Another area concerns "where" you are in relation to the present. It is related to your awareness. The third area concerns your script and changing the "characterizations" you do not wish to "play."

AWARENESS

If you want to change, you need to make an analysis of yourself. An analysis of what you are is a good way to define what you like and don't like about yourself. Take a few minutes to think about what words you would choose to describe yourself. What are your personality characteristics? What do you accept as rules? What do you have strong feelings about? When does cool reason overrule emotion? What motivates you to action? How do you structure your time?

This part of analyzing yourself is the beginning of awareness, but it is not as easy to identify all of those areas as it looks at first glance. Awareness, though, is the basis of all your relationships, both with yourself and with others. It is necessary to know yourself well before you can relate to or know anyone else well. Advancing in the process of awareness takes a little time and effort and a great deal of honesty in examining what you are. Keep in mind as you examine yourself that you will find both things you like and things you don't like. But, keep in mind, too, that you do not have to stay the way you are. You can change whatever characteristics you want once you know what changes you want to make. It is only those who do not wish to recognize negative characteristics about themselves who must go on living with them. These people deprive themselves of the opportunity to change.

Awareness and the choice to change what you don't like about yourself can bring you the ability to be self-governing, spontaneous, and selectively intimate at will, and to enjoy a truly fulfilling life. If you do not examine yourself, then you have already made a choice — the choice to maintain the status quo. The choices to make are whatever you like; however, you cannot escape making a choice.

Awareness is developed by analyzing what you feel at any given time in response to various stimuli. The next time you feel bad, for example, examine the bad feeling. Are you embarrassed about something you said, did, or did not do? Are you afraid of the reaction of someone to something you said, did, or did not do? Are you ashamed of some act or something you said? Decide on the nature of the bad feeling and decide if your act or word or lack of action or words really merited the bad feeling you experienced. If it did — really did — feeling bad about it may be a choice you made so that you could "pay" for the act. If it did not, you may be responding as a result of an old tape that has control of your responses and which you want to examine. It may be that you could avoid experiencing unmerited bad feelings and the resulting discomfort by gaining conscious control over your responses.

Awareness cannot be taught or bred into you. The obvious characteristics described in this chapter can be helpful to you in determining which ego state your psychic energy is reacting from, but they are not foolproof. It is possible, for example, to put an "It is my opinion" prefix on a Parent statement, which really does not apply in light of the facts, and pass it off to others as an Adult statement. Only you can know the difference by being scrupulously honest with yourself — all the time. Dishonesty to yourself is dishonesty to others simply because you are not able to recognize the truth. Good relationships result only from truthful ones. Becoming aware of what you are feeling does not itself alleviate the feeling, just as ignoring it does not make it go away.

It is important to realize that the feelings exist whether you acknowledge them or not and that they are part of you. If you refuse to acknowledge your feelings, you refuse to accept part of yourself. Such rejection of yourself can hinder your self-image and destroy your ability to give yourself positive strokes. The need for such strokes, both positive and negative, frequently results in games, making your relationships with others and with yourself very uncomfortable. Learn to recognize your own feelings and to accept them, whatever they are, simply because they are a part of you and you are a worthwhile person.

Becoming aware of the ego state from which you are responding is important. It is possible for you to go through life responding from the Parent or Child ego states; and unfortunately, people do so without ever knowing why they make statements, behave, and feel inappropriately about events that affect them. We are all equipped with an Adult ego state which can receive messages, evaluate them, and select appropriate responses. If you desire, you can put your Adult in charge of receiving stimuli, processing them, evaluating them, and choosing the response that is suitable from either your Parent or Child. Your Adult can even choose not to respond at all.

It is when your Adult is in charge of your psychic energy that you become autonomous (able to choose appropriate responses that reflect what you really feel). Your Adult will not be infallible. Its efficiency depends upon your education and experience (the quality and quantity of the information it has to evaluate situations), upon practice, and upon the freedom with which you allow it to function. The key to liking yourself is to put your Adult in charge of your responses and to give it the best information you can. When your Adult selects a response in your best interests with the best information available, allow yourself to behave accordingly (Illustration 14-10).

BECOMING TIME COMPETENT

It is possible to become too consumed with the future and the past to enjoy the present. Life is now; if you don't experience it now, you lose the opportunity of this moment. It can only be remembered, not experienced. It would be sad indeed to have a storehouse only of memories of experiences missed when you look back on your life. It would be just as sad to look back only at times of expectation or anxiety, which is all that a person who lives in the future has. Become time-competent by learning to live each moment one at a time, feeling, seeing, hearing, smelling, and tasting.

The Present. Living in the present means that you check yourself when you begin to play old tapes from your past. Instead of depending upon inappropriate responses from your past, you engage your Adult in the present to evaluate and select a suitable response. Living in the present means that you are not overly anxious about the future. Your Adult is prepared to accept the stimuli of the future, and you can trust it to do the best it can for you with what it has to work with.

If you live in the present you are aware of the input to your senses. You taste what you eat; you sense "where" other people are in their ego states; you play to enjoy; you see what is actually before you; you hear what people are saying to you; and you are facing current problems with current responses. Most of the time you are comfortable in your surroundings. If you are uncomfortable, you are aware of the discomfort, and you can identify its scource.

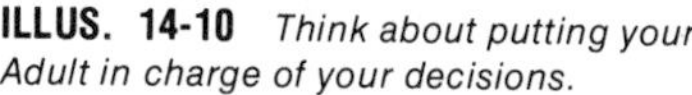

ILLUS. 14-10 *Think about putting your Adult in charge of your decisions.*

Vogue Pattern Service

Some insidious ways we keep ourselves from living in the present and identifying what we feel are by projection and by using judgmental words instead of describing feelings. Such statements as "I feel ugly," "I feel stupid," and "I feel foolish" are statements that do not make sense. "Ugly," "stupid," and "foolish" are not feelings, they are descriptions of objects and acts. An ugly person doesn't feel ugly; he looks ugly. A stupid person does not feel stupid; he acts stupidly. A foolish person does not feel foolish; he acts foolishly. What each of these persons may feel is embarrassment, disappointment, disgust, or depression. But, until the actual feeling is identified for what it is, there is no hope of gaining control of it so that the response can be changed.

Beware of thinking of yourself in judgmental terms (from the critical Parent tapes of the past), and begin to describe your feelings for what they really are. Once you identify them, your objective Adult evaluation of the current circumstances may reveal to you that such bad feelings are not justified and that you need no longer feel them. Think of the improvement in your life if you need experience only those bad feelings that are justified by the present circumstances rather than those brought on by old unsuitable tapes.

The Past. Living in the past prevents you from living in the present. The past has no value except that it provides you with experience for the Adult to use in evaluating the present. Your past should not be allowed to provide improper responses to current stimuli.

Characteristically, if you are living in your past, you will experience times when you respond to situations with greater fear, anger, or terror than is merited by the circumstances. These extreme responses come from old Child tapes on which your childhood feelings are stored. Actually few situations call for extreme emotion, and if your Adult is allowed to do so, it usually will find satisfactory solutions to current situations without trauma. You can save yourself much discomfort by putting reactions of the past in their place — in the past — and selecting more appropriate reactions suitable to the present.

Living in the past also can prevent you from being aware of the present. You will not see those you meet as themselves. You will see them as similar to someone you know from your past, and you may project characteristics of the past on them rather than learning about who they really are. You may constantly compare people you meet to people you have known, finding your current acquaintances constantly short in good qualities as compared to former acquaintances. You will not see current situations as they really are but will project aspects of past situations into the current picture, making a good evaluation and selection of response impossible.

Living in the past can only keep you from dealing effectively with the present. If you do not really see those you meet today, you can never expect to have a good relationship with them. If you cannot really see the aspects of a current situation, you cannot hope to deal with it effectively. A new boss, colleague, or employee, for example, will suffer all the inadequacies or attributes of the old boss, colleague, or employee in your mind, never having a chance to become whatever the person really is. You will suffer because you will miss the opportunity to know another worthwhile person — perhaps even the opportunity of a warm, positive stroking relationship. You will neither appreciate nor be appreciated simply because you choose to live in the past rather than the present.

If you do not really hear what is being said today, you will assume it fits the pattern of what has been said before in similar situations. You will "tune out" the present and listen to the past. Unfortunately, the past can't tell you where the person "is" who is talking, what he feels, or what is desired of you. Only by really listening — being aware of the words and the context — can you respond appropriately.

It is in hearing from the past that you find yourself in destructive games instituted by others. Instead of hearing what is actually being said and discerning what is actually being felt by the other person who is initiating or "hooking" you into a game, you allow an old tape from the past to interpret, and you respond from your Parent or Child ego state. If you stay in the present, you will not be "hooked" into others' games. You will recognize "where" the game player is, evaluate the situation, and respond in such a way that you will avoid the game.

The Future. A person who lives in the future usually is a worrier, constantly fantasizing about trauma and catastrophies about to occur. Or the person may be a rainbow chaser, dreaming of what Santa Claus will bring. If you live in the future, you may find yourself trying to control the outcome of events rather than preparing yourself now to respond appropriately to whatever occurs. You may worry if events do not take the course you expect them to take and be thrown by spontaneous actions of others. You may suffer an unproductive life because Santa Claus never actually arrives, and you have spent your life waiting instead of living.

If you do experience the present, it probably will seem more like play-acting a predetermined part you have rehearsed in your mind rather than reality. You may find yourself responding according to your predetermined plan rather than according to what current circumstances call for.

Living in the present means identifying, appreciating, and trusting your feelings. It means allowing your responses to be a result of your current feelings. Becoming what you want to be necessitates that you identify with the present and put the past and future in proper perspective. Before you can change a feeling, you must identify it, appreciate the reasons for it, and trust your Adult to evaluate and select according to what you consciously want to become.

STRUCTURING TIME RESPONSIBLY

When you become aware of what your feelings are in the present, you can begin to use your time according to what you really want. If you need a light, positive stroke, you can seek it through yourself in withdrawal or through others in rituals, pastimes, or activities, depending upon the circumstances. When you want to punish yourself or to experience bad feelings, instead of "hooking" another person into a destructive game or withdrawing and "kicking yourself" emotionally, you can evaluate the situation and expend energy improving yourself. When you want the satisfaction of a job well done, you can throw yourself into whatever you consider worthwhile activity, such as your job or volunteer work.

The awareness you have developed enables you to experience the best strokes of all, those of an intimate relationship with another person. You can spend time in being open, honest, and sincere, accepting yourself and another person, giving and getting powerful "being" strokes.

You improve your efficiency because energy and time are not lost in playing tapes of the past or in anxiety about the future. What you are doing at the moment is appropriate to the circumstances; what you acknowledge that you are feeling is what you actually feel; what you are seeing is what is actually before you. In short, you are aware of your life and surroundings. You are expending your energy for current situations only.

As you strive for awareness and living in the game-free present, be tolerant of yourself. You may have long-standing habits to break, and new ones are not formed in a day. You may slip into games, the future, or the past. You may play old, unsuitable tapes occasionally. If you are alert and diligent in examining what you feel, especially when you feel bad about yourself, you will find those times fewer and fewer.

CHANGING CHARACTERIZATIONS

Once you become aware of your feelings and gain control over them, you may find that your new goals do not fit the old script by which you were living. If you had destined yourself to a mediocre life — winning sometimes, losing sometimes — you may find that losing seems a waste of your energy and does not provide good use of your time. You can write yourself a new script if you can identify specifically those areas you want to change and make a commitment to yourself to change them.

If you have been a procrastinator, for example, hoping others would do your work for you, you can decide for yourself that the harassment and bad feelings you experience from procrastinating more than offset the energy you might expend getting the job done and the good feeling resulting from doing it. You may rescript yourself by deciding to evaluate the time needed for the job, the time you have to do it, and set aside the appropriate time for doing the job.

If you have been failing at small things because you believe that you probably are not "as good as" someone else (usually because of Parent programming) you may decide that the bad feelings from these failures are more painful than expending energy to be a success at small things, whatever they are. If you come to such a decision, you can set out to undertake things you usually fail at with new interest and determination to succeed.

If you have felt that pretty girls were not intelligent but now decide that the negative strokes you get for your unkempt appearance (although you are intelligent) are not as good as positive ones you might get for a well-groomed appearance (in addition to being intelligent), you can make an Adult decision to be both well-groomed and intelligent, disarming the prejudiced old Parent tape that has produced numerous negative strokes for you in your life.

If you spend much of your time being unhappy, you may decide that being happy would be a more satisfying life. You can identify the ways you make yourself unhappy by analyzing the situations each time you feel unhappy and beginning to change them, one at a time. Becoming what you want to be is a matter of wanting to change, making a definite plan for change, and taking specific action.

SUMMARY

You are constantly becoming — either someone you don't like or someone you do like. It is your choice. To improve your relationships both with yourself and with others, work on becoming self-directing and aware. Learn to understand other people and yourself. Begin to hear, see, smell, touch, taste, and speak in accordance with the reality you are experiencing now. Put your Adult in charge of receiving, processing, and evaluating your experiences.

Structure your time responsibly, using the social skills in rituals and pastimes to get to know others better. Engage in activities that are fulfilling so that you won't be tempted to engage in games to get strokes. Choose wisely and carefully the circumstances in which and the people with whom you share your intimate feelings.

Allow yourself to live spontaneously without a destructive script and in the present time frame. You are a worthwhile person relating to other worthwhile people. The time and effort it takes to improve yourself and your personal relationships are well spent.

Understanding Personal Relationships

1. How are your memories classified in Transactional Analysis terms?
2. Describe a typical critical Parent action or statement. A nurturing Parent action or statement.
3. Of what importance to you is your Child ego state?
4. Why aren't Adult decisions infallible?
5. Why do all three ego states need to be active?
6. How can you give positive strokes?
7. How can you handle negative strokes you get?
8. Of the possible ways you can structure your time, which do you employ most often?
9. Give an example of a cultural influence on your script. A family influence.
10. What part does awareness play in a system of change?
11. How can you know if you live in the present?
12. What is wrong with living in the future?

Chapter 15

Professional Relationships

Your primary purpose at work is to work! Although work serves many purposes in your life, basically it provides money for the necessities of life and for your other activities. Equally important to your emotional well-being, though, work is a way to structure your time constructively, and it is a vehicle for obtaining and giving strokes. Work can be gratifying because it is possible to be creative and to develop skill and excellence. Work can give you an opportunity to express many different talents and abilities. The attitudes you develop about your work and your co-workers will greatly influence your personal happiness and success on the job.

Time Structuring on the Job

Most of your time on the job should be spent in work-related activities. There will be other opportunities, though, to simultaneously structure time in other ways such as withdrawal, rituals, pastimes, games, and possibly intimacy. You should be aware of how you are spending your work time since it will influence your success on the job and your professional relationships.

Ideally, on the job you should process stimulus with your Adult in charge. You should spend your time in the activities of work if employers and colleagues are to appreciate you. Sometimes, when such a position does not bring you and others around you the strokes needed, other means of structuring time may be employed. You may be initiating alternates yourself, or your colleagues may be initiating them. Neither of you may be aware of employing unacceptable means of structuring time unless you consciously analyze what is happening.

WITHDRAWAL

Withdrawal in a work situation rarely works for very long. It is an absolute necessity to be able to deal with people effectively on the job. The most frequent reason for discharge is that people can't get along with people. Withdrawing may be acceptably used occasionally when you need some recovery time to ponder a situation or problem, but it cannot be your standard method of structuring time at work.

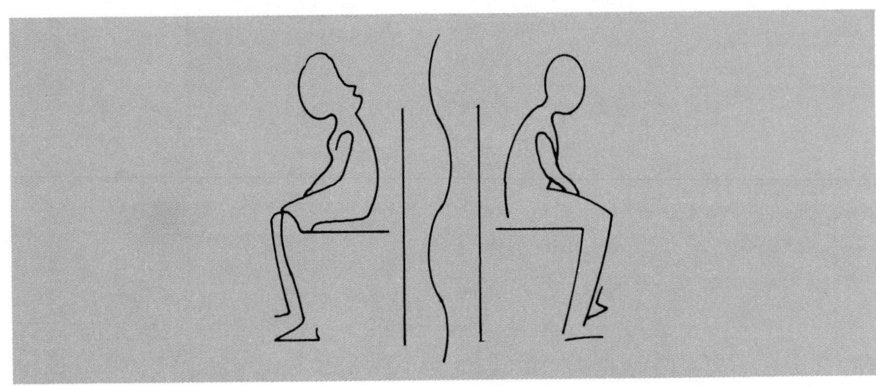

ILLUS. 15-1 *Withdrawal is rarely appropriate at work. Most of your time probably will be spent in interacting with others.*

Occasionally, you may have to work with people who prefer withdrawal. Deal carefully with those who seem to need "alone" time. It may be that working with others is too difficult for them or that they are temporarily shy. When it is necessary or desirable for you to work with such people, be considerate. A person has a right to his or her basic privacy, and you should respectfully observe the boundaries of such a right. Unnecessary chatter and superfluous activity may be irritating to such a person. Although it may not present a pleasant atmosphere for your office, it is not your duty to reform a person who withdraws. It is your duty to work as effectively with that person as you can.

It is a good idea to observe the privacy of others at all times. Prying into people's reasons for acting as they do is never in good taste. You should concentrate on conducting yourself appropriately and let others seek their own methods of fitting themselves into the world and into their work atmosphere. Excessive withdrawal can be treated by a doctor but not by a colleague at work.

RITUALS

Rituals are a desirable and acceptable means of giving and getting strokes during work time. Characteristically, they take very little time away from the primary responsibilities of your job; and they do a great deal of good in making people feel happy about themselves and you.

Every day at work you will probably come in contact with many people. It is neither practical nor desirable to become friends with each one of them. It is practical and desirable, though, to give all of them the feeling that you recognize them and in general to show a warm feeling toward them.

A "Good morning, how are you," a smile as you walk down the hall, an offer to bring someone a cup of coffee or to take the mail to the mailroom as you take your own — all show simple consideration. These gestures provide units of recognition without involvement with other people. Such recognition shows that you are aware of them and that you appreciate them without obligating work time to cultivating friendships.

ILLUS. 15-2 *Rituals, such as opening the door for someone, saying "hello," and other casual but routine words and acts, provide ways to show others that you are a friendly and concerned person without indulging in time-consuming conversations or more involved acts to communicate your goodwill.*

A ritual, such as opening a door for a colleague, bringing a flower for the receptionist's desk, or helping someone with a coat, can show that you think kindly of them and are a friendly person. Rituals, though, mean that you are not necessarily involved in the life or thinking of the other person. When you are on the receiving end of such activity, do not mistake it for something more involved.

Rituals provide the vehicle for you to express good will to all people. You will be pegged as friendly or unfriendly according to your facility with rituals. It is appropriate to speak or smile in acknowledgment to everyone from the lowest person in the organization to the highest. All people need and appreciate recognition in the form of these positive strokes.

PASTIMES

Pastimes are not appropriate for time spent on the job. They are reserved for coffee breaks and lunch. It is a good idea to remember that your principal concern at work is to do your work. Human relationships are a by-product and an important one; but they should not be placed in a more important role than the work itself. Your own time after work is the time when you should place emphasis on developing warm human relationships. Your work time merely necessitates your maintaining good working relationships with others.

Pastimes are useful for when you have time to chat with a colleague at coffee break or lunch. It is tempting when you see people every day to decide that they are warm friends and confide in them all your personal data. That is definitely inappropriate, even on coffee breaks and lunch. Confine your conversation to the pastime variety with people at work so that no problems will arise with exposing your private life.

ILLUS. 15-3 *Coffee-break time is one of the very few times that pastime conversations are appropriate for work.*

Often when you have bared your soul to someone at work, a conflict will arise in the tradition of "familiarity breeding contempt." Make every effort to confide only in close friends away from work. The everyday, constant exposure to people at work can become irritating if you allow your entire personal life to surface. Keep such items to yourself on the job, and show your attitude of friendliness and ability to recognize the worth of others by conversing with them on less personal subjects.

It is rarely appropriate to discuss controversial issues such as religious beliefs and political preferences during pastimes. Such conversations evoke strong responses in people. Your coffee break and lunch break are designed to relieve your mind from stresses of work. It is better to choose pleasant subjects, such as a television show you have seen, the new fashions shown in the stores, or something interesting that happened on the way to or from work.

Avoid negative statements during pastimes because these will provide bad feelings for you and for others. If colleagues decide to employ negative conversation, personal information, or controversial subjects in the time you have to relax, it is appropriate to acknowledge their speaking with a smile or look of concern, but refrain from joining in. You may want to alternate your coffee break companions and lunch break partners frequently so that you will be exposed to new ideas and new people with varying interests.

It is never a good idea to discuss with people at coffee or lunch what goes on in your work. Work is performed for the purpose of making a profit. Knowledge of the inner workings and inner conversations regarding work can provide opportunities for a competitor to cut into sales and profits. Even interoffice relationships within a company are affected by a secretary's or manager's willingness to talk about the work in the office. Sometimes hard feelings among others in the office are a result of distortions of things you may have said casually at coffee break or at lunch, without realizing the effect they might have on others within the company (Illustration 15-4, next page).

It is not appropriate to discuss your feelings about others in your company with company people, either your likes or dislikes. If you are asked a direct question about how you like working with someone, try to find an objective statement with which to respond. It is far better to say "Mary and I work well together" than it is to say "I like the way she organizes her work, but that constant chatter really gets on my nerves." Chances are that Mary will hear only about the part after the "but" in the statement, and you will find yourself working in a strained situation the next time you have to work with Mary.

ILLUS. 15-4 *Be careful not to reveal confidential information about your job. It can cost your company money, and it can cause strained relationships among your peers.*

It is important, too, to remember that other's statements about yourself may be distorted if and when they are reported to you. It is much better to ignore unpleasant statements about yourself, if they surface, than to get excited and respond as a hurt Child. You always have the option of not participating in discussing someone's personality. If you are asked, just smile and say, "I don't know her well enough to comment." You have the right also not to respond to unkind things that may be said about you.

GAMES

Unkind statements frequently are parts of games that are played to provide good or bad strokes for the initiator and bad strokes for the one who is "hooked." Try to avoid games at work at all costs. They are destructive and definitely not productive. Only strained relationships can result from game playing.

"Let's You and Him Fight" is a favorite game of people who cannot stand smooth-running, tranquil atmospheres. The method employed is to get Person A to say something about Person B, which Person C immediately reports to Person B with appropriate agitating comments. Person C, in effect, initiates a fight between Persons A and B for the feeling of power he gets from it through controlling the activity of A and B. If you simply ignore reported statements about yourself and refrain from making inflammatory statements about others, you will not be a victim of the "Let's You and Him Fight" game.

"Mine is Better Than Yours" game is one everyone must be alert to, both as an initiator and as a participant. Person A may be feeling that she is not getting recognition or strokes that she needs so she proceeds to explain what a good job, good boss, or other good situation she has, with the undertone or implication that it is better than anyone else's. Person B, not wishing to feel put down by Person A's good situation, then describes what a better situation she has. On and on it goes until Persons A and B end up not liking each other because they are afraid the other has a better working situation or perhaps gets more strokes.

If you are "hooked" in this game, you may be inclined to reveal information about your office that you shouldn't. Carefully avoid comparing your own situation with someone else's. You can simply agree with Person A that she does, indeed, have a good situation and you are happy for her. Refrain at all costs from comparing yourself or others to her.

The "Kick Me" game is played when Person A feels bad about herself and desires confirmation that she is, indeed, a "bad" person. Person A may describe a situation or even create a situation in which she makes a stupid mistake or an offensive remark that cannot be ignored. Person B then allows her critical Parent to severely criticize or "kick" Person A, providing the negative stroke Person A needs to confirm the "bad feelings." Person A then gets to feel sorry for herself because she has been kicked. She also gets to feel bad toward Person B for kicking her, further relieving herself of pain. Person B, in the "Kick Me" game, becomes a victim now. Person A "gets" Person B by saying, "You are supposed to be my friend, but I've always known you were faking it. You are a rotten person for criticizing me" (Illustration 15-5, next page).

You can stay out of the "Kick Me" game at work by avoiding being critical about anyone's actions or statements. Try to be understanding but not critical. If you cannot be understanding, you can choose not to respond at all or to deal only with correcting the situation and not the person.

ACTIVITIES

Activities are the appropriate means of structuring time on the job (Illustration 15-6, next page). Your preparedness in performing the activities to which you are assigned in the office is important in determining

ILLUS. 15-5 *Work is not the place for games. Be careful not to be "hooked" into a "kick me" game.*

ILLUS. 15-6 *Most of your time at work should be spent in activities.*

the satisfaction or strokes you get from performing them. If you are well prepared and the tasks are varied so that some are easy for you while others present a challenge without discouraging you, you probably will find the job satisfying. If your work is not satisfying, you probably will find yourself seeking other ways of getting strokes.

Try to find a job that does present the kinds of activities in which you are interested and those that you are reasonably able to perform. In order to allow for growth in your job, you will want a situation that provides for opportunities to tackle challenging tasks and for moving up in the organization.

A satisfying work situation is the best way to avoid employing games and pastimes at work to get strokes. If you are happy in the work you are doing, you will not be inclined to initiate or to be "hooked" into games. The work itself and your pride in doing it well will provide the strokes you need. Recognition from your boss and others with whom you work will be reflected in their appreciation of your carrying your part of the load and carrying it well.

INTIMACY

Work is not the place to cultivate intimate relationships. There may develop open and honest communication among employees, but the warm, free sharing of personal lives is not appropriate to the work situation. There is a tendency for people at work to see each other as best friends, especially when they do not cultivate friends outside of work. The danger, though, of having "best friends" at work is that your personal life may be brought into the office, perhaps causing you discomfort and embarrassment.

Dating relationships in the office are often detrimental to the harmony of the office staff. Jealousy and gossip frequently result from the most innocent dating relationships and do not contribute to good working relationships for other members of the staff.

Married people who may be having trouble at home sometimes are tempted to discuss their problems with the nearest ear at work, seeking solace and understanding. Carefully avoid involving yourself in such a situation because it can only bring you discomfort both personally and professionally.

The best policy for relationships at work is to keep them friendly but impersonal. Allow conversations to include only noncontroversial topics and nonpersonal situations (Illustration 15-7, next page).

ILLUS. 15-7 *Keep your personal life personal. Don't discuss strictly personal things at work.*

Getting and Giving Strokes on the Job

Whether you are the manager or the one being managed in the office, there are qualities in people that you want to cultivate both in yourself and in others. If you are the manager, you can provide many strokes by recognizing and encouraging growth in your employees. If you are the employee, you can provide for growth in yourself and obtain recognition and perhaps even promotion, if you desire it, by cultivating these qualities.

These are two kinds of qualities that are appreciated by office workers. One category is reflected mainly in your attitude. This is possibly the most important part of your personality. Some of the "being" attitudes that are most appreciated by office personnel are to be thorough, considerate, prepared, courteous, attentive, prompt, flexible, private, efficient, loyal, honest, respectful, and realistic.

The other category for which you will be recognized and appreciated are for the things you do. Some of the "doing" things that bring acclaim are to ask questions, take notes, work independently, learn the rules, learn expectations, show your good attitude, follow protocol, and keep growing.

GETTING AND GIVING BEING STROKES

The most powerful and lasting strokes are the "being" strokes. These strokes are units of recognition for what you are, not for what you do. Frequently, what you are is reflected in what you do, but it is what you are that is appreciated even when what you do does not immediately reflect it. What we all strive for is recognition of our innate good qualities and appreciation for them.

Being Thorough. Being thorough means that you appreciate the whole problem of the work in which you participate. It means that you appreciate what went on before you received a document and that you provide for what goes on when the document leaves you. Being thorough leaves no room for the attitude that "I think that is wrong, but it is not my job to correct it."Thoroughness leaves no stone unturned to find the correct answer to verify questionable data. It means that work is not half-done or sloppy. Work is complete and neat. Consideration for those who prepared the data before you and for those who use the information after you is part of being thorough in your job. Understanding the implications of your activities to the success of the company and being guided by them marks you as a thorough person.

When you are given sketchy instructions, take time to fill in the details and do a creditable job with the data. Being thorough is a good way to be recognized as one who accepts responsibility for her actions. Accepting responsibility is one step up the ladder of promotion, a jewel we all treasure.

Being Considerate. Being considerate on your job means that you do not make things difficult for others in your office. Supplies are kept neatly arranged, file drawers are closed when you are not using them, and your personal items such as your coat and handbag are placed in suitable places out of other people's way. Your personal habits such as smoking, laughing, and speaking are never offensive in the office.

Being considerate means observing office rules. If no smoking or eating is allowed at your desk, you carefully observe the rules. If others are working very hard, and you are caught up with your own work, you can offer to help. Being considerate means that you think of the comfort and effectiveness of others. You refrain from doing anything that would cause discomfort and distraction to them.

Show consideration by anticipating what your boss needs before you are asked. If the mail comes to your desk, pull files you think the boss may want before they are asked for. If you anticipate that airline reservations or telephone numbers will be needed, look them up and have the schedules or numbers ready.

Being considerate means that when others may be having a bad day you do not contribute to their troubles. You handle gently their feelings and refrain from prying or intruding on a pensive attitude.

Being considerate means listening when instructions are given so that you don't have to interrupt someone later to find out what you are supposed to do. A sign of consideration is minding your own work and business without interrupting others when they are busy.

Being Prepared. Being prepared shows that you think ahead and that you care enough about doing a good job that you are willing to put some forethought into it. Good preparation requires good organization so that you can find materials you need when you need them. Being prepared shows that you know what is needed for your job and that you are able to anticipate your needs. You don't borrow from others or ask others to cover for your inadequacies. When you take time and effort to prepare for your work, you show that it is important to you, that you care about doing a good job.

Being Courteous. Courtesy is one of those signs of "good breeding" that everyone appreciates. Courtesy may be simply a "Thank you," holding the door for someone, helping with a coat, or other similar act. The act, word, or gesture is not as important as the thought that shows that you are willing to help — to put others before yourself and acknowledge their needs and importance.

It is courteous to step back so that someone may pass before you through a doorway, to wait your turn in line for coffee or lunch, and to avoid interrupting a conversation between other people. In general, you put others ahead of you in small ways by recognizing that your own needs and feelings will be taken care of in due time but that you are not so important as to merit the immediate attention of others (Illustration 15-8).

Being Attentive. Listening to what is being said to you is a powerful stroke to the one who is speaking. It shows that you really want to know what the person has to say. It also shows that you are conscientious enough to want to hear the information completely and correctly the first time it is said.

Being attentive means paying attention to the work that you are doing. It includes such things as checking dates to see that they are correct and that they coincide with a day of the week that may also be mentioned. Attention to your work and the instructions for your work leads to greater knowledge of the company and its workings. The more you know about the work, the more you are worth to the company.

Being Prompt. Being prompt is one of the most noticed attributes of an office worker. It shows that you respect others enough not to keep

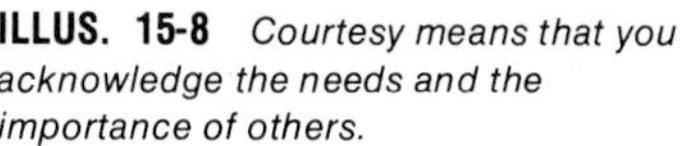

ILLUS. 15-8 *Courtesy means that you acknowledge the needs and the importance of others.*

Photography by Terry Webb

them waiting for you. It has been said that being late is an obscure way of punishing someone who is waiting for you. That could be a childish and destructive way to conduct your work.

Promptness at work keeps you in the good graces of others who also get to work on time. People who are late to work or coming back from coffee or lunch are always noticed and always begrudged somewhat. Make it a point to observe scrupulously the times for reporting to and leaving from work. Staying late somewhat will win you honors with some companies, depending upon the situation. Arriving on time will win you honors with all companies.

Being prompt in doing your work makes those depending on you appreciate your organization and efficiency. Be careful about holding up the work of others at any time because of your own inefficiency or lack of organization.

Being Flexible. It is convenient and efficient to "plan your work and work your plan"; but don't make it a rigid part of your life at work. If you are asked to drop everything to help on a rush job, do so cheerfully. If you are asked to stay for an hour or so after work to help your boss get some rush items out, do so cheerfully. A person who is unable to change plans in midstream when the change is needed to complete the work of the team is not very valuable to the overall workability of the company.

Being Private. Your life has different areas. You should have an active and interesting private life and a profitable and enjoyable professional one. The two, though, should be kept separate. If you do lead an interesting private life that others are interested in hearing about, try to refrain from discussing it at work. There is neither time for discussing it nor reason to do so. It may even cause jealousy that could be avoided.

Try to keep your professional life out of your private life. Work diligently and effectively when you are at work; but provide for variety by leaving work at work and enjoying private time in different kinds of activity. The perspective of your total environment will be more realistic if you are able to keep both areas of your life active but separate (Illustration 15-9).

If you should hear others discussing their private lives, refrain from passing the information on to someone else in the office. Let it die with you. If you wish to become friends outside the office with someone in the office, realize that you risk invasion of your privacy and possible repercussions at work if the friendship fails or becomes somewhat strained. A better policy is to cultivate friends outside of work and maintain a professional relationship with people at work.

Being Efficient. You can make yourself prime material for promotion by becoming efficient. Study your work habits so that you can weed out inefficient movements and activities. Efficiency shows up in neat, well-organized work areas, a well-groomed person, and work that is done correctly and promptly. Efficiency is often the product of good training, attentiveness to the work at hand, and creative thinking about the procedures for doing the work. Waste will not be in your vocabulary. Both time and materials are valued and used with care. Efficiency means not only that you are able to do more work, but that you do it almost effortlessly because of your ability to organize, perform, and streamline the tasks.

Being Loyal. Loyalty to your company and your boss are necessary to a good working relationship within the company. Being loyal does not mean that you cannot make your own decisions about using the services or products yourself within your own home. It means, though, that you do not make statements about the product or services that would indicate that you think they are not good. You are not required to support every claim for the product or service; you are merely required to refrain from making derogatory statements about it.

Being loyal to your boss means that you do not criticize him to other people and that you never belittle him, even subtly, to yourself or others. Loyalty is the natural state of affairs within a person. When a situation

ILLUS. 15-9 *An active and interesting personal life is important. Keep it private by refraining from discussing it at work.*

Vogue Pattern Service

is such that you cannot be loyal, you probably will become disgruntled trying to function as a part of the office team. If you find yourself in an organization or working for someone you cannot support, it would be wise to seek another position.

Being Honest. Honesty with yourself, others, time, and materials is a characteristic that will provide good feelings for yourself and for others who either recognize or exhibit the trait. Being honest with yourself and others takes much self-examination and effort in correct and accurate communication. Being honest with time and materials means that you spend the time for which you are being paid actually performing the work and that you use the materials appropriately and efficiently on the job — never carrying them home for your private use (Illustration 15-10, next page).

You refrain from conducting personal telephone calls or personal business while you are at work. You never use company supplies and materials for your personal business. Even though others may be pilfering from the supply cabinet, you will like yourself better if you do not. Even when others place and take personal phone calls at work, you will feel better about your own integrity if you do not. It will be tempting to do as others do when it seems to provide them fringe benefits. You must

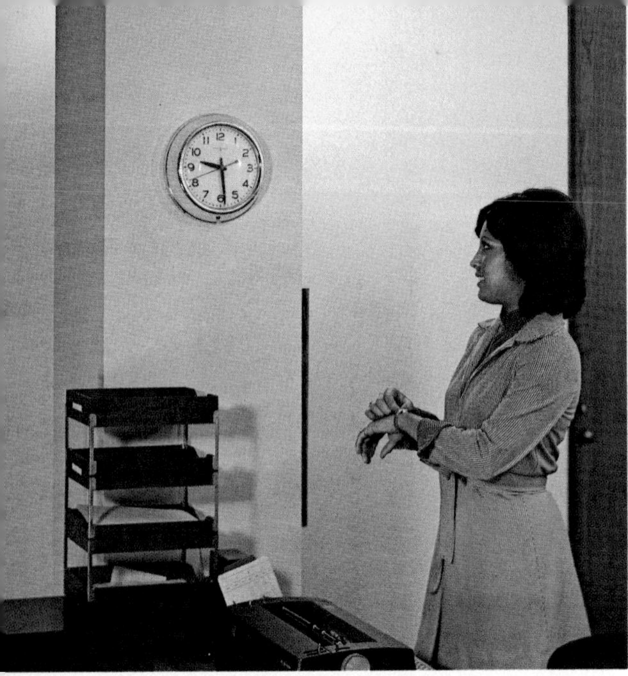

Photography by Terry Webb

ILLUS. 15-10 *Make your time at work strictly for work. Honest use of time is always appreciated.*

face and live with yourself. Conduct your own business and yourself so that you like what you are.

Being Respectful. The office is not a place for wisecracks, pet names, and rowdy activity. Be respectful to your peers, your superiors, and all other office workers. Respect for those with jobs beneath yours as well as for those with jobs above yours is expected from a well-trained person.

Calling out down the hall or across the room to a friend shows little respect for the quiet others need for their work. It detracts from the dignity of the office and the decorum of the company. You are wiser to be more reserved than you think is necessary than to be more chummy than you think is appropriate.

Showing respect for others means that you do not offend with your person in the form of loud fragrances, unorthodox clothing, or unacceptable speech. It means that you acknowledge the presence of others when they arrive at your desk and that you respond with a friendly word or smile of recognition.

People are shown respect by calling them Mister, Miss, Mrs. or Ms. with their surnames until you are specifically told to use the given name. Even when your boss calls you by your given name, you are expected to use the title and surname.

Being Realistic. Be realistic with yourself and others about what you can do and what you can expect of others. Appraise your work so that you can know what reasonable deadlines you can expect to set and meet and how much help you can give or expect from others. Refrain from making promises for work that can't possibly be done by a given time. Refrain from depending unduly on others by judging accurately how long it takes you to perform certain duties. Obligate yourself for extra assignments only when you know you can work them into your regular schedule without letting priority work suffer.

Being realistic shows that you value the integrity of your work and your word enough that you are willing to work at keeping it. It means that you know enough about what you are doing and your ability to do it to make accurate statements about it.

GETTING AND GIVING DOING STROKES

Doing strokes that you get and give are usually from learned activities that aid you in your work as opposed to being strokes that result from your attitudes and from being the person you are. Some of the things you can do to make your work go better for yourself and for others are:

(1) Ask questions when you don't understand.
(2) Make notes about new procedures.
(3) Work independently, not requiring constant assurance that you are on the right track.
(4) Show your good attitude.
(5) Learn the rules, both the written and unwritten ones.
(6) Learn what others expect of you and of your work.
(7) Follow protocol.
(8) Keep growing.

Ask Questions. Asking questions about your job and the procedures for performing your duties is an indication that you want to learn to do your work correctly. It is better to ask a question than it is to do a task incorrectly. Redoing work that could have been done correctly had you asked a question is very expensive and will not keep you in the good graces of your boss.

On the other hand, asking questions that are not relative to your work and that make you appear to be nosy will not win favors with anyone. Asking questions about information you should have read or that you have been told before will not bring you acclaim. Before you phrase a question, think about what you already know about the procedure or problem. Try to relate what you know to what you don't know. Think about the information you have, both written and oral. Try to work the answer out for yourself. If you cannot, then phrase the question as clearly as you can. If you recall having asked it before or having been told the answer or procedure before, apologize for your lapse of memory. Write the answer down this time, and make sure that you do not forget again.

Take Notes. Do not rely on your memory for instructions that may be blurted out as your boss is leaving for the day; take notes. It is also an excellent idea, especially for a new employee, to make notes on the procedures for handling various aspects of the job.

Frequently there is an office procedure manual that is provided new workers. If you get one, read it carefully. You may want to make notes of your own that will amplify the instructions in the book as you perform the work.

If you do not get a manual of instructions, keep copious notes, even if you have to write them up at home for the first few weeks of your job. Use them to assemble your own procedures manual. You will find that such an assemblage of notes will save you much time and make you a more efficient worker (Illustration 15-11).

Work Independently. One way you can convince others of your ability and desire to improve yourself and your work is to learn to work independently. It is comforting to have the reassurance and company of another person when you are working, especially when you are doing something new. Few companies can afford this kind of overlapping responsibility for a job that should be done by one person, and they will not look kindly on your needs in this area. Be sure that you understand what is to be done, and take the responsibility to do it — alone.

Working independently includes providing all your own supplies, getting your own reference documents, and providing for proper follow-up activity. It means that you are not chatting with others constantly during your work time and that you are not asking them to do things, such as getting files for you, that you should be doing for yourself.

You will be appreciated if you carry your share of the responsibility and load in your work. Others will notice that you are a contributing member of the team and will know that because of you their own work goes better.

Learn the Rules. There are some written rules in work situations usually applying to the time of arrival at work; time allowed for lunch and coffee breaks; and time off for personal illness, holidays, vacations, or business.

There are many more unwritten rules, however, that you should become aware of and observe. These will vary with your company. Some of them may be that you may not enter the boss's office without knocking;

ILLUS. 15-11 *Compile and use a procedures manual.*

Photography by Terry Webb

that you never sit at someone else's desk; that you do not eat, drink, or smoke at your own desk; and that your coat and handbag are kept in certain places.

Often older members of the staff feel that their seniority entitles them to certain prior claims on various places to sit in the coffee room or for placement of their desks near windows. You will do well not to infringe upon these prior claims but to be happy with what you have until "your time comes" for improvement in these small things. Usually these unwritten rules are not worth making enemies over. If you do break one unknowingly, carefully apologize and go on with your work. It is not necessary to upset yourself simply because you made a mistake.

Observing such unwritten rules will win you much approval. You can win cooperation for yourself by cooperating in small ways with those who have worked longer than you have. Constantly disregarding small unwritten rules, even though they may make little physical difference in the life of the company, can threaten the confidence of an older person and make you an outcast forever.

Learn Expectations. What is expected of you on the job often is stated either orally or in a manual. However, many things are expected of you unconsciously and are therefore not verbalized. You may be expected to do small things like straighten your boss's desk, empty an ashtray occasionally, or check the lamps and lights before you leave. You may be expected to cover mechanical equipment like your typewriter or adding machine at the end of each day. Sometimes you are expected to notify someone nearby to listen for your telephone or your boss's intercom while you are away from your desk. You might be expected to let someone know where you are going when you leave your desk, even if it is to the restroom for just a few minutes.

Learn what is expected of you and observe the requirements. Usually there are very good reasons, and you are expected to follow them closely. Sometimes expectations have arisen from times past when someone less responsible than you held your job, but they may be hard to change even if they are outmoded. Accept such expectations with good will, and try to keep things running smoothly. Reforming people, especially when you are new in a job, is not the way to become a roaring success. The best approach is to respect the current practices and to observe their effectiveness or lack of effectiveness before you make quiet, well-thought-out suggestions.

Show Your Good Attitude. You can show your good attitude by being cheerful and accepting gracefully compliments as well as criticism of your work. Know that you are doing your best and do not take personally comments about the work that you may not have done perfectly. Criticism is usually given to help you do a better job. Separate your work from yourself. Work should reflect your efforts and your ability to perform, but it should not be the determinant of your worth as a human being.

You can have a good opinion of yourself even if you are not the best at your job. Not being "the best" could simply be an indication that you are in the wrong job, but not that you are not a worthwhile person.

Determine in your own mind that you want to do a good job and that you will work to that end. Exhibit the attitude that you care about the work that you do. Help people who work around you feel comfortable with you. Your attitude will be appreciated.

Follow Protocol. Usually in a work situation there is a chain of command. The same chain applies to appeals. There will be times when you desire a change or to register a legitimate complaint about your work. You may want only to ask for time off for a certain purpose. It is important that you do not bypass anyone in the "chain" even though you know that person must go further up the chain to get the decision. Often the duty of passing the request up the ladder is considered the right of persons above you. If you bypass them, you offend them.

Usually, too, you do not ask people above you to join you for coffee or lunch; you join them only if you are invited. These ideas of protocol may seem petty and reminiscent of kingdoms past. Sometime, they are just that; more often they are rewards in terms of recognition and respect for having risen above a particular level in the company. One would think that attaining a particular position would be reward in itself. Very often, though, these small deferences are more treasured than the job. If they are, you will fare better by observing them than by criticizing or bypassing them. Change comes slowly, and you may have to wait to effect it until you reach a position of authority yourself.

Keep Growing. Keep in mind that you have never "arrived." You may become very proficient in your particular job but you always have areas in which you can still grow. You grow emotionally as well as professionally. Your growth in both these areas will make life better and better for you if you allow the growth to occur. Growth means change, and sometimes change can be frightening. Each new level of attainment, though, is important in your becoming a more effective and mature person.

Emotional growth means that you may change beliefs you have held for many years. It may mean that you change behavior that you have practiced for many years. Don't be afraid to admit that what was right for you in the past is not right for you now and may not be right for you at some future time. Learn to accept the changes that take place as you gain experience and information about living effectively. It is easy to take pride in maintaining something you have always done as being infallible. Few things, though, are suitable for a lifetime; and the more easily you recognize and make adjustments when they are merited, the more satisfying life will be for you.

Professional growth may mean that you acquire additional training. It may mean that you take on more responsibility. Be sure that you desire to grow and that you like what you are getting into before you accept a "promotion." Just because a promotion is offered does not mean that it is a better position for you. Examine the characteristics of the job and be sure that they are what you want.

Don't shy away from more responsibility if you want to grow. You are as capable as you want to become, and you can depend on those making the selection to assess objectively your capabilities as well.

If you desire professional growth and you are not offered the opportunity, ask what you should do to prepare yourself for the job you want or the responsibility you desire. Asking sometimes brings you into focus as a prospect for a job. If you do it honestly and objectively, asking always shows that you want to do your part in preparing for progress and that you do not expect someone else to do it for you (Illustration 15-12, next page).

Photography by Terry Webb

ILLUS. 15-12 *Additional training marks you as a person who wants to improve herself.*

SUMMARY

Getting along with colleagues at work will provide you with many benefits. Others will appreciate you if you use your time and conduct yourself so that the work is done in pleasant circumstances. You can make others feel good about themselves, too, by recognizing and appreciating their efforts in work. A major part of your life will be spent at work. Concentrate on developing the being and doing qualities that will make it a very rewarding part of your life.

Understanding Professional Relationships

1. Is it ever acceptable to "withdraw" at work?
2. How are rituals used to your benefit at work?
3. What topics of conversation are good for pastime time-structuring? When can pastimes be used during the work day?
4. How can you avoid initiating games?
5. How can you avoid being "hooked" into games?
6. How do you get strokes through activities?
7. What kinds of problems may result from intimate relationships at work?
8. What is the difference between a "being" and "doing" stroke?
9. What are some ways you can provide "being" strokes to others?
10. What are some things you can do to get "doing" strokes?

Chapter 16

Communicating

Your facility with communication mechanics and techniques will greatly influence how you get along with people. Your voice, gestures, words, and what you are saying combine to make an impression on the listener. You want to get your message across and to make a good impression while you are doing it. Good personal relationships depend upon your ability to interpret your feelings and needs into some form of communication. Good professional relationships depend upon your ability to interpret the information you have and the information you need into some form of communication.

There are many ways to communicate. The most obvious is one that many people think of exclusively — speech. The use of the voice certainly is vital to the area of communication. Other means of communicating include writing and gestures. Each form of communication requires certain mechanical procedures to make it effective. Speech, for example, requires that the voice be pleasant and audible, with varied pitch. Words must be articulated and pronounced clearly and correctly.

Writing, of course, must be legible. If handwriting is used for personal and informal messages, the more legible it is, the more attention the reader pays to the message and the less attention the reader pays to the handwriting. If the message is typewritten or printed, skill is needed so that the form itself does not take away from the message. If a gesture should be used, it must be visible and easily understood like a nod or shake of the head, and it must be an appropriate form of communicative response.

In addition to the mechanics of communication, there are skills you can improve to make you a more effective conversationalist. Listening is a vital skill that can be improved. You can even learn to listen responsively and to make your own words easier for your listener to comprehend. The words you select are important in improving your communication skill. The special area of telephone communication is so vital to career people that it should be emphasized in your improvement program. Communication confidence is basic to all improvement. Your confidence will be improved with thoughtful practices and ideas.

Mechanics of Communication

Speaking, gesturing, and writing are the mechanical ways of communicating. You can improve each method by concentrating on the parts that make them more effective. Selection of a suitable means of communicating, too, is vital to getting good understanding and response.

SPEAKING

Your speaking voice is the most used method of communication. It may be employed with or without your physical presence, and it should be developed so that you can communicate effectively with or without visible gestures that enhance your communicative ability.

Developing the mechanics of your speech requires only that you pay close attention to how you sound when you speak. It may be a good idea to ask a friend to help and to use a tape recorder to play back the sound of your voice. Listen for huskiness, nasality, and breathiness. Decide whether or not you speak too softly, too rapidly, too loudly, or in a monotone. Listen for good articulation of sounds and for correct pronunciation of words.

A Pleasant Sound. The sound of your speaking voice is as important as any singer's voice. It becomes part of your overall image and either adds to or detracts from your effectiveness and appeal. A harsh or raspy voice can alienate people, making them want to avoid hearing you speak. A high-pitched, shrill voice, too, makes you an undesirable speaker. The human ear is offended daily by many sounds ranging from grinding to shrieking. Try to make your voice a sound with a melodious quality that relieves the ear of further offensive attacks.

A voice of pleasant quality usually is one with little or no nasality, huskiness, or breathiness. You can check you nasality by pinching your nose so that no air can pass through it. Hold it while you repeat the alphabet. The only letters which should produce vibrations noticeable to your fingers pinching your nose are "n" and "m". All other letters should be pronounced easily without nasal vibration. Be especially careful to avoid nasalizing "i" and "y" sounds.

Huskiness in your voice may result from a physiological disorder, including laryngitis and other throat irritations. Correcting such conditions usually eliminates the problem. Sometimes huskiness occurs when you try to lower the pitch of your voice unnaturally. There is very little you can do to change the pitch. You can make improvements in a high- or low-pitched voice by utilizing the resonance chamber (your mouth) to produce rich and varied tones within your pitch. Breathiness may occur when you try to alter your pitch to a lower level. It may also occur when you speak too softly. Avoiding either misuse of your voice will eliminate the problem.

Take care in excited moments not to shift to a high-pitched, piercing sound that may offend. Keep your composure and your voice in control. You will appear to be much more poised if your voice shows no sign of wavering from its usual pleasant range.

Your telephone voice, especially, is important since you cannot enhance your communication with your physical presence or with gestures. The sound of your voice and what you put into the words you say are all that the listener has to work with. Many people put a "smile" sign on the telephone or nearby because they know that their voices sound more pleasant when they are smiling somewhat. You can check yourself by tape-recording your voice with and without a smile.

ILLUS. 16-1 *Concentrate on making your telephone voice pleasant.*

Photography by Terry Webb

Speaking Speed. Carefully observe your listener to determine the correct rate of speed with which you should speak. The rapidity of your speech makes a difference in your articulation and in your listener's ability to understand. Never speak so fast that you are forced to mispronounce words. If you are giving directions that must be "digested" and "followed" in the listener's mind, give them slowly. If you are simply relating an incident with which the listener may be familiar, you may speak more rapidly. Try to gear your speaking speed to the needs of your listener. If the listener's facial expression indicates difficulty in understanding you, slow down. If the listener seems bored or tries to help you find the correct words to complete your sentences, speed up.

Audible Speech. A voice must be heard. A very soft voice that is not audible frequently is irritating to the listener. The message is lost and the listener is alienated. Fear and uncertainty usually evoke the urge to speak too softly. It is sometimes frightening to enter a new situation, such as a new job; and you may be inclined to speak softly because of such fear. A person sometimes speaks too softly, also, because of uncertainty about the validity of what is being said. Learn to overcome this handicap if you have it, and cultivate a volume that does not expose your fears and uncertainties at inopportune times. Sometimes hearing yourself speak confidently helps you overcome fears and uncertainties.

A voice that is too loud can be a handicap to you, too. Loudness is related to abrasiveness and aggressive behavior. Sometimes, one speaks too loudly to cover insecure feelings about what is being said. Loud talking too can be used as a "cover-up" for uncertainty. "Loud makes right" is the theory behind this concept.

Sometimes loudness is just thoughtlessness. Loud talking frequently is distracting to those about you, especially to people trying to concentrate on work. Make your voice loud enough to be heard clearly, but not so loud that it is offensive.

It is natural to speak loudly when you are excited and to speak softly when you are meditative or sad. Try to keep your emotions on an even keel when you are at work. Controlling the volume of your voice will help to give the impression of a person in control of all situations.

Monotonous Speech. Vary the pitch, speed, and tone of your voice as you speak to give it some interest to the listener. A speech presented in a monotone, no matter how interesting the subject matter, is boring. A monotone can be avoided if you:

- Learn to emphasize important points as you speak by slowing down slightly and using an emphatic tone.
- Learn to express fill-in information more rapidly in a somewhat lower pitch while articulating very clearly.

Such techniques make it easier for your listener to follow your thoughts and to discern the important points of the communication.

You can make your speech more interesting if you try to vary your sentences so that all of them are not short, simple ones. Learn to put less important information in dependent positions such as dependent clauses and more important information in simple sentences or in independent clause positions of complex sentences. For example:

(1) You can be successful. Work is required to become successful. Success can be attained at any age.
(2) If you work, you can become successful at any age.
(3) To become successful at any age, you must work.

The first example is three short simple sentences. The second one emphasizes "successful" in an independent position. The third emphasizes "work" in the independent position. Whatever you choose to emphasize, either of the two latter examples are more interesting than the first.

People "tune-out" a continuous loud sound as easily as they "tune-out" a continuous softer one. Varying volume, though, provides some interest and relief, allowing you to emphasize important points with a little louder sound and to de-emphasize less important ones with a softer sound. Vary the volume of your voice so that your listener gets a break from one monotonous sound.

Articulation. Distinct, clear articulation makes your words easy to understand. To achieve such articulation, be careful to pronounce word endings such as "ing," "s," "d," and "t." Talk slowly enough to speak each word distinctly without slurring it. "Whatcha" for "what are you" is an example of slurring words together.

Learn to project word sounds so that you won't be guilty of mumbling, which is a common articulation problem. Note whether you have regional slurs and drawls that you need to alter. It is not usually desirable to rid all of your speech of its regional flavor unless you plan to become a public speaker or work in verbal communications such as television or radio. Some regional flavor in your speech provides variety throughout the country and even charm in some instances. Your regionalisms, however, should not be so heavy that your articulation is poor and you cannot be easily understood.

Pronunciation. Word pronunciation is important to your verbal communication skill. There are often many correct pronunciations for words, but you can check your own by learning to look in the dictionary for correct and preferred pronunciations of words. There is usually a pronunciation symbols page of explanations of markings for words in the front of a dictionary.

You will find that the same letter of the alphabet may be pronounced in several ways. The letter "a" for example, may be pronounced as it is heard in: banana, map, day, cart, saw, and ahead. In addition, there are often pronunciation aids at the bottom of each page. Learn what these symbols mean in your own dictionary and use them to help you pronounce words correctly.

Often there are two or more pronunciations given. They may be of equal usage or one of them may be preferred. The explanation of the markings in the pronunication guide will explain how you can determine which one is preferred.

Photography by Terry Webb

ILLUS. 16-2 *A dictionary can help with pronunciations.*

Improvement will occur if you practice aloud when you are pronouncing a new word or one that has given you trouble in the past. Using a tape-recorder, practice pronunciation with it; and listen to the playback to check yourself.

GESTURES

As discussed in Chapter 5, the way you sit, stand, walk, and carry yourself will communicate to others messages about your poise and confidence.

As you converse with them, your physical presence, facial expressions, eye contact, hands, and body placement can be used to emphasize what you are saying. You can add interest to your presentations and responses if you learn to gesture appropriately and well.

Physical Presence. An important part of communication that is often overlooked is simply your visible presence. If you take time to visit someone personally in the hospital rather than just to place a call, your personal presence itself reassures the patient of your concern. Often in an office there is an opportunity and a need for you to walk to another person's office or desk to convey a message rather than to write or to telephone the message. Your physical presence may indicate that the message is important or that the person is important.

At work such use of physical presence should be limited to very important matters and people. If you use it indiscriminately, you will waste your time and energy scurrying around the office delivering messages when the telephone or an interoffice memo might serve as well.

Facial Gestures. The expression on your face can tell your listener more than your words do. Whether you desire it or not, your eyes and facial gestures will communicate your attitude about the conversation or communication you are experiencing. Learn to keep an open mind and to give your speaker or listener an opportunity to express his opinion before you indicate a position with your facial expression.

Beware of exhibiting a forced smile. It looks quite different from a genuine one. A strained look about the muscles in the face shows up even when you are forcing your lips to a smile position. If you cannot feel a smile, do not try to fake it. It is better to have merely a pleasant look on your face than the facade of a smile.

A genuine smile comes from feeling good about people and about yourself. If you find it hard to smile genuinely, look inside first to see if you are unhappy with yourself or with something about your surroundings. If these feelings are in good order, look at other people to see what it is about them that makes you unable to appreciate and enjoy them. The problem may lie in your perception of them rather than in what they are. A genuine smile is appreciated. Learn to feel happiness and to reflect it with your facial expression.

Eye Contact. When you are speaking to someone, try to look your listener in the eye. It is very important to hold the other person's eyes when you are conversing. This is especially effective when you are trying to make a point or to answer emphatically. It is not necessary to stare eye-to-eye during the entire conversation, but it is very important to have substantial eye contact. Learn to recognize when you are making people uncomfortable with your eye contact and when they are appreciative of the openness your eyes indicate to them.

Your eyes may show boredom, interest, pleasure, displeasure, and other feelings. You can indicate a lack of understanding with a questioning expression. Squinting or wrinkling the brow can indicate displeasure with the conversation or the speaker. Observe yourself carefully in a mirror to determine the many expressions you communicate with your eyes. You can enhance your effectiveness in communicating by controlling your feelings and letting your eyes express what you feel.

When a person refuses to look another person in the eye when they are communicating, it signals that one has something to hide or that there is fear of exposing oneself to another. A poised, self-assured person overcomes such fear and learns to express thoughts and feelings openly by using good eye contact.

Hand Gestures. Some hand gestures are useful in communication. If they are natural for you, feel free to use them. If they are not natural, do not try to cultivate them; artificial hand gestures look unnatural. They do more to detract from what you are saying than they do to add to or emphasize your points.

Generally, open hands show an open attitude. Clenched hands indicate a closed attitude. If you find that you are clenching your hands when you are listening to someone, check your attitude. You may also have a closed mind on the subject. It will be helpful to you to observe in others the position of their hands when you are explaining your message or asking for a favor.

Hands may communicate more than you want them to if you are nervous or apprehensive about the conversation or what is being said. Try to relax when you are conversing with others. Some situations will be frightening, especially the first time you experience them. Some relaxing techniques that may help are deep breathing and conscious relaxing of your arms and shoulders before you encounter such situations. During the encounter, hold your hands in such a position, either loosely clasped or cupped in your lap, so that trembling, if there is any, will not be obvious. As you gain confidence, such apprehension will disappear and so will the trembling. In the meantime, you will avoid making others uncomfortable with your own anxiety by concealing it.

Body Placement. Everyone has a personal body zone, which is a periphery of area around the body that is held inviolate. This area may vary somewhat from person to person and from situation to situation. When it is encroached upon, however, you will become uncomfortable.

Photography by Terry Webb

ILLUS. 16-3 *If you are nervous, cup your hands in front of you near your waist. Breathe deeply to relax and conceal any trembling.*

Usually the relationship of two people determines the size of the body zone that is needed for comfort. For example, two very close women friends may need only two or three feet between them to be comfortable; but a boss and secretary may need four to seven feet (the size of a desk) between them. Two men, when one is superior in the organization, may need as much as twelve feet between them for comfort (the distance of a large desk plus room for chairs on each side).

The necessity of recognizing body zones or personal territory needed for a person to be comfortable can enhance your relationships in communicating with people at various distances. If you accidentally intrude upon a person's body zone, you may irritate the person to the point that you will be denied any request or your information may not be readily accepted. If you respect body zones, your communication may have a better chance of accomplishing its purpose.

Often in a crowded elevator or subway, there is no room for body zones. During these crowded times, people often hold their bodies rigid in acknowledgment of the infringement of their body zones. To relax in these crowded circumstances may be considered uncouth and discourteous. Another way to compensate for crowded conditions in such circumstances among strangers is to avoid eye contact. Should the eyes meet, usually a faint smile of apology for the infringement takes place.

Various parts of the country dictate different amounts of body zone space for comfort. In the East where the population is dense, people may be more careful of protecting their body zones but may be able to accept less space. In the West and Southwest, where population is less dense, people may require more body zone space but may not be as irritated if it is momentarily violated. Learn to respect the needs of others for space around their bodies. Your communications and relationships will be more effective.

WRITING

Writing a message may mean cursive writing, printing, or typewriting. These forms of communicating have the advantage of providing a permanent record of the transaction. Businesses largely depend upon typewritten records of their transactions. Frequently written records of spoken messages, such as telephone conversations, are made for future reference, especially when instructions or decisions are part of the telephone conversation.

It is important to a well-trained career person to develop good writing skills, both cursive and printing. Neatness and legibility are always noticed and appreciated.

If office work is in your future, typewriting will be useful whether you aspire to clerical or management positions.

Cursive Writing. The deciphering of handwritten messages has been the subject of much speculation about the writer's personality traits. Most of the time, though, when the message is to you, you want simply to know what the message says, not what the loops and bars mean about the person writing the message. The same is true about those messages you send.

Often handwriting is poor only because you do not take time to make it better. Hurriedly scratching a message down can actually cost you time later in deciphering it for the intended reader or in recopying it before you pass it on. Taking a little time when you handwrite a message will make it neater and will save time in the long run.

Sometimes handwriting is poor because you have not had training in good cursive style. Illustration 16-4 shows a simple chart that includes cursive letters for you to practice if you have poor handwriting. Take time to practice from that chart if your handwriting is poor. You may improve your ability to get your message across and enhance your image in accomplishing it.

Prospective employers frequently require applicants to handwrite a paragraph before they are considered for employment. Care in handwriting, making it neat and legible, often is interpreted as the reflection of a person who will take similar care in other areas of work. Sometimes neat

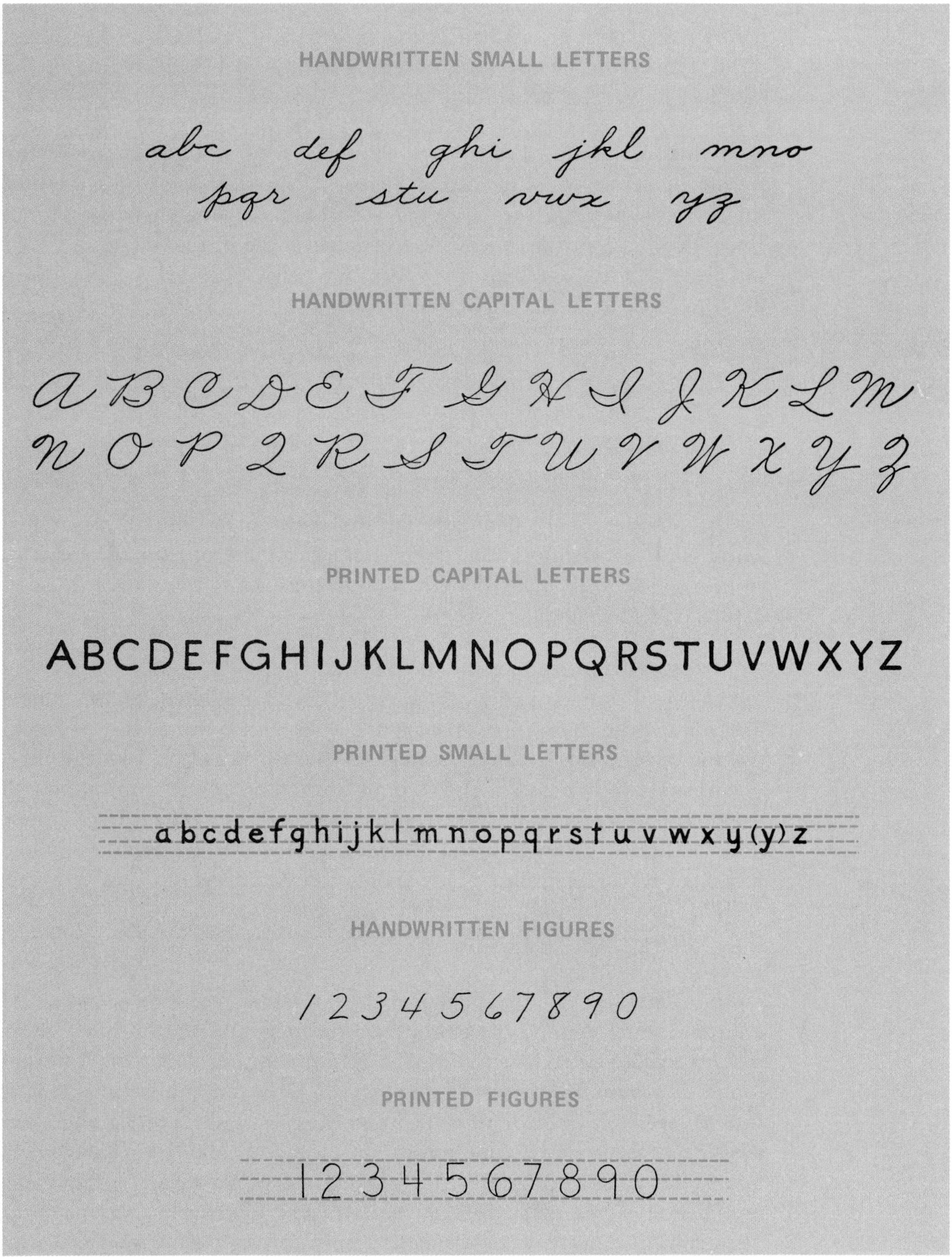

HANDWRITTEN SMALL LETTERS

abc def ghi jkl mno
pqr stu vwx yz

HANDWRITTEN CAPITAL LETTERS

A B C D E F G H I J K L M
N O P Q R S T U V W X Y Z

PRINTED CAPITAL LETTERS

ABCDEFGHIJKLMNOPQRSTUVWXYZ

PRINTED SMALL LETTERS

a b c d e f g h i j k l m n o p q r s t u v w x y (y) z

HANDWRITTEN FIGURES

1 2 3 4 5 6 7 8 9 0

PRINTED FIGURES

1 2 3 4 5 6 7 8 9 0

ILLUS. 16-4 *Good examples to practice from are important in improving your handwriting.*

handwriting is taken as a reflection of a person who has an organized mind. Since you may be judged somewhat by your handwriting, make an effort to write as neatly and legibly as you can.

Printing. Handprinting is most easily read when you follow the simple principle of using capital letters when they are necessary and small ones when they are required. That sounds altogether too simple. Take a look at a printed message sometime to see if it is followed. Often capital letters are used within words but simply printed smaller. Note the difference in the following examples:

EvEry DAY is beAutiFUL.
Every day is beautiful.

An alternate method of printing that is used by specialized professions, such as architects and engineers, is to use all capital letters for printing. Your own style, though, should conform to the standard use of capital and small letters.

Typewriting. One of the most commonly used methods of writing messages, of course, is to typewrite them. Such a skill is useful to almost everyone. Typewriting for most people is at least twice as fast as handwriting or printing. It can be as much as four times as fast. The legibility, of course, is what makes it such a popular method of communication. All important papers and most business papers require typewriting because of its legibility, neatness, and permanence. It is worthwhile to become a proficient typist regardless of the profession you decide to enter.

SELECTING AN APPROPRIATE FORM OF COMMUNICATION

Your messages and responses will get a better reception if you select an appropriate method of communicating them. When you have information to convey or when you need information, consider the different forms of communication available to you. Oral communication, if it is face-to-face, can be accompanied by gestures such as a smile and your physical presence. Oral communication on the telephone depends solely upon your voice and words. You lose the use of gestures. Written communication is the most difficult of all to use effectively. Neither your voice nor your presence is useful to you in conveying the message. You must depend upon the words and their presentation for your message.

Try to become at least as proficient with the language in its written form as you are with the spoken words accompanied by gestures.

Most of the time in the office you will use oral communication with your colleagues. Sometimes you will use written forms, such as interoffice memoranda, to communicate within the company. It is important, though, not to use oral communication accompanied by your presence if the importance of the message does not merit it. Often the recipient of the message prefers a written communication so that it may be read thoughtfully and reread before a decision or answer is formulated. Sometimes a message is so easily understood and an answer is so easily provided that physical presence is a waste of time. A written message or one by telephone would be more efficient and just as effective.

It is important to be sensitive to the importance of the message you wish to convey or the information you wish to ascertain when you select your mode of communication. The importance of accomplishing your purpose sometimes depends solely upon its presentation. Evaluate and choose carefully. You will achieve your goals more easily.

Improving Communication

In addition to improving the mechanics of the methods of communication you use, you can become a more effective communicator by polishing your listening skills, word choice, telephone techniques, and your confidence.

LISTENING

Part of effective communication is good listening. Hearing, interpreting, and responding as you listen are the vital parts of good communication. Hearing what is being said and ascertaining the implications and attitudes projected help in developing good listening. As you converse, try to fit what you hear into what you already know about the subject. Then, either confirm the information with what you already know or pose questions if you cannot integrate the new information with what you already know. When you are speaking, keep the listener in mind. Make your talk interesting and clear.

Your Listening. When someone is talking to you, try to maintain a facial expression that encourages the speaker. You are more likely to get the information or response you want if you show interest. A blank, passive expression makes the speaker think you are not hearing what is being said. Such an expression may prolong the message simply because the speaker feels the need to explain further.

If you do not understand what is being said, a puzzled look may bring more information or a clearer explanation. If the speaker pauses for some response, you may clear up questionable points at that time with pertinent questions, or you may smile in confirmation so that the speaker may continue, confident that you are understanding.

Responsive listening aids you in getting messages straight. If you are getting new information with which you have nothing to relate, try to take good notes. Follow the logic of the speaker and learn to discern a change in subject, similar to paragraphing in the written word.

Photography by Terry Webb

ILLUS. 16-5 *Learn to listen responsively.*

Responsive listening takes a conscientious listener. Developing and practicing responsive listening, though, aids both you and the speaker in communicating. The speaker knows when enough has been said, and you get the message straight the first time.

Others' Listening. When you are communicating with others, you will find that their point of view is the most interesting to them. How your words will affect your listeners is just as important as what you are trying to say. If you can phrase your messages in terms of what they do to or for others, you have a better chance of keeping their interest.

Even disappointing information can be communicated to colleagues more easily if you try to empathize with them before you communicate it. Try to feel what they will feel when you tell them. Examine the possibility of positive circumstances arising from such information, and phrase your message around such possibilities if you can.

When you are communicating information or events that relate to company policy or to items that are not personally either good or bad for others, try to think of the ways others will perceive their own place in such action, and include them and the part relevant to them in your communication.

Personalizing communications helps to make them more palatable and makes the communicator seem more in tune with the needs of the listener or reader. A statement such as "Vacations should be scheduled between June 1 and August 31," is not as personal as "Please schedule your vacation between June 1 and August 31." Frequently, though, the words used are not as important as the attitude coming through the words. Beware of choosing words that seem to make the message more palatable and more interesting to the listener when they are designed really to cover up disagreeable or unfair points in a message.

Take into consideration what your listener is doing with what you are saying. If you are giving new or difficult instructions or information, give it slowly and logically. If you are simply relating something to the listener that is of little import and easy to assimilate, do so quickly but considerately.

Refrain from boring others with drawn-out items that may be important to you but hold little interest for them. Few listeners are interested in how you feel about the date you had last night or the excitement you experienced over acquiring a new garment. Only intimate friends share such excitement with you — not acquaintances at work. Refrain from droning on and on about things you do not like about your living conditions, your car, your job, or anything else that is personal to you. Others do not wish to listen. They usually wish you would do something to improve your situation but prefer that you refrain from burdening them with the details of it.

When you are conversing, take into consideration the time you are taking from that allowed for the communication. Try not to dominate a conversation that should be a dialogue. Allow the other participants to speak. Other ideas, although they may not be as important to you as your own, are important to other members of the group. Allow others the opportunity to participate in conversations. Listen and respond when your turn comes, but do not dominate.

Refrain from being repetitive. Sometimes if you think others do not agree with you, it is tempting to repeat your position until they do. That procedure usually is not effective. Allow others to disagree if they wish. It is not necessary in communication to win points or agreement with your position. It is only necessary to be understood.

WORD CHOICE

The words you choose to use should be an accurate reflection of your thoughts. Your vocabulary and the colloquialism, slang, or profanity that have become part of your thoughts will become part of your speech. You must be on guard to increase your vocabulary so that you will have words that accurately and completely express your thoughts without resorting to unacceptable words for their expression.

In some circles, it is considered "cool" or "keen" to use slang words. Supposedly it shows that your thoughts are very current and that you fit easily into the group. In the office, such slang words and expressions are out of place and usually they label you as slightly immature. It is important to make a distinction between communicating in a recreative situation with your peers and communicating in a business situation with your colleagues.

Slang words may be appropriate for writing in a letter to a friend in college, but they are not appropriate for writing to a colleague in business. Often the use of slang substitutes for expressions of thoughts for which you have not learned appropriate words. Be careful not to neglect your vocabulary development by relying on slang to express your thoughts. To do so will hamper your progress in the adult world.

Profanity, too, usually is substituted in your vocabulary for words you do not know to express your feelings. When you have strong, disagreeable feelings you wish to express, learn to use more desirable words. You can relieve such feelings just as easily with acceptable words as you can with unacceptable ones.

One of the easiest ways to build your choice of words is to develop a repertoire of colorful verbs. Use a thesaurus or dictionary to learn several alternatives for verbs that you frequently use. For example, the word "said" has many acceptable alternatives that are not difficult to learn and to use in appropriate ways. Some of them are: *told, expressed, stated, uttered, pronounced, recited, repeated, indicated, showed, communicated,* and *spoke*.

Another important way to develop your vocabulary is to develop your range of adjectives. Very often, these words are the slang ones you use because you don't know appropriate ones. For example, the adjective "cool" has a slang meaning of "very good or excellent." There are at least seven other meanings, though, that are more acceptable. When you use the word "cool" try to use it in an appropriate situation. Some of its synonyms are: *composed, collected, unruffled, imperturbable,* and *nonchalant*. One of those might express your feelings more accurately and give your listener a break from an overused word.

Observe and listen to your own speech. Pick out times when you use slang expressions or words. Write them down and check a dictionary or thesaurus at your first opportunity. Compile a list of alternative words that accurately express your thoughts, and learn to substitute more acceptable words. You will find that you have a greater command of language and can feel some satisfaction in being able to express accurately what you feel.

There are many ways to communicate your message. You can dwell on the negatives of it or you can emphasize the positives of it. The effect you wish to evoke from your listener or reader determines the approach you will take. Most of the time it is to your benefit and makes life more pleasant for both you and your listener if you will take the opportunity to make your communications positive rather than negative. There are some negatives words that you can learn to avoid. Some that are usually offensive to people are:

> *annoyance, bad, careless, complaint, disagreeable, disgruntled, disgusted, dishonest, displeased, failure, false, ignorant, incorrect, inconvenient, inferior, misconception, misled, must, negligence, poor, terrible, unfair, unjust, untrue,* and *worthless*.

There are also some negative phrases and statements that people find offensive. Some of them are:

> *If you actually did; It is unreasonable of you to; The mistake you made; You are wrong to think that; You claim that; You failed to: You do not understand; You say; Your error; Your ignorance of the situation;* and *You neglected to*.

Sometimes it is necessary to give bad news to someone. Even in these instances, you can state it positively. For example, it is better to say, "We can ship the merchandise you ordered on April 15" than to say, "We cannot ship the merchandise you ordered before April 15." The idea is to say what you can and will do, not what you cannot and will not do. "Reservations are available in April" is more palatable than, "There are no reservations available until April.'' ''I can help you with your overload later this afternoon'' sounds better than, ''I can't help you until later this afternoon.'' The meanings are the same, but somehow the bad news is not as hard to take when it is stated positively.

TELEPHONE TECHNIQUES

Some considerations in improving your telephone techniques are simple to employ. They center around thoughtfulness for the person to whom you are speaking.

The first consideration is that of timing. Try to place your calls when the person being called is not likely to be very busy. Between 8:00 and 10:00 in the morning on Monday usually is a very busy time, because weekend mail and other matters are being attended to. Just before lunch is a hard time to get a good response from someone. If the person being called is hungry and anxious for a break from work, your call will not be very welcome. Just before quitting time is another difficult time to get a good response. If you are placing a social call from your home to someone else's, try to time your call so that you don't interfere with meals, arrivals, departures, and bedtime. You will be received better if you are considerate of others' schedules.

If you have a lengthy message to convey on the telephone, it is courteous to ask if it is convenient for the person you've called to talk at the moment or if you should call at a better time. Short messages usually need not be preceded by such a suggestion. Since you have already interrupted the person, less overall time will be taken if you complete your business quickly instead of offering to interrupt again later.

It is a good idea to outline your call before you place it. Decide what you want to accomplish and the procedure you wish to employ to pursue your business. You will be less likely to forget important points and more likely to make yourself understood if you present your business in a previously outlined, logical manner. Make a list of items for which you need answers and jot the answers down as you obtain them. You can save much time, and the person being called will appreciate your efficient manner of conducting the call. Little time will be wasted, and you are less likely to have to call back later for more information.

If you should reach a wrong number, apologize, but be sure to check the number you intended to dial before you hang up. For example, if you wanted 334-1032, but the person you asked for was not at that number,

ILLUS. 16-6 *Take time to organize your message before you place a telephone call.*

Photography by Terry Webb

tell the person who answered that you intended to call 334-1032 and ask if you have indeed reached that number. If you misdialed, apologize and redial. If you reached the number you expected to dial but it turned out to be a wrong number, apologize and find the correct number. If someone calls you on a wrong number, courteously repeat the number that has been reached, and ask the caller to recheck the number and redial.

CONFIDENCE IN SPEAKING

You can gain confidence by developing interests in local and national events. Your confidence grows as your understanding grows. Promote your understanding by concentration on the subject at hand. Confidence grows, too, as you become increasingly able to respond appropriately in all situations.

Developing Interests. It is important for a poised person to be alert for suitable subjects for all occasions. Some subjects are taboo for social conversation. To open them or to participate in them is not appropriate in some situations.

A person's personal life usually is not discussed socially. Neither are opinions about politics or religion. You can cultivate many alternate acceptable areas of conversation by keeping yourself informed.

It is important to read a good newspaper or to listen intently to at least two different newscasts, a local and a national one, every day to keep abreast of events in your community and throughout the world. You can gain deeper insight into news events by reading weekly national newsmagazines or weekly national newspapers.

ILLUS. 16-7 *One way to keep current in your conversational subjects is to read a good newspaper every day.*

Photography by Terry Webb

Travel is another excellent way to acquire areas of conversational interest. Associating yourself with people who have interesting things to talk about and who are concerned with improving themselves by enlarging their interests is a good way to acquaint yourself with wide areas of knowledge.

You can improve your knowledge and your vocabulary by reading one good nonfiction book per month. The list of nonfiction best-sellers appears in most Sunday newspapers. You can pick from that list, assured that the material represents a current view and usually that the book is interestingly written. Use the facilities of your library or purchase paperbacks if you feel you cannot invest in the hard-cover books as they are released from the press.

Suitable Responses. When you are conversing with someone, keep to the subject. It can be very disconcerting if you spring a question or statement into the conversation that is inappropriate.

During a business conversation, for example, it is usually out of place to inquire about someone's family or health. Keep your mind on the subject at hand and try to develop the ideas you are discussing.

If there are items you don't understand in the conversation, try to pose your questions so that the listener can answer them easily. Learn to anticipate the listener's feelings as you ask the question, and try to phrase it in sympathetic, unthreatening tones.

When you are asking for specific information, phrase your question so that there is no doubt about what you want to know. When you are asking a general question to learn more about a person to whom you are speaking or a product you are considering, try to phrase the question in terms that allow the response to be general and to provide for opinion and extraneous information.

When you are asked a question, try to answer it directly. If your answer requires explanation, give it as clearly and concisely as you can. If your answer is self-explanatory, do not feel compelled to explain it. You may only bore the listener.

Questions are sometimes phrased in an open-ended manner to get you to "open-up" when you answer. "What do you expect to be doing five years from now?" is an example of such a question. These kinds of questions are asked when the questioner wants to learn about you and your opinions on the subject. They occur frequently in interviews for jobs. When such a question is asked, consider your answer and the way you will phrase it before you begin. The words you speak will be more than an answer; they will be a reflection of your beliefs.

If you do not understand a question, ask for clarification by saying, "I'm not sure what information you want. Could you be a little more specific?" That kind of response is better than rambling on and on, trying to cover every possibility suggested by a vague question. If you are asked questions you feel you should not answer because the information is confidential, it is appropriate to say, "I'm sorry, that information is confidential," or to say that you do not feel free to discuss the matter. To respond in that manner is more palatable than to hedge or to lie about knowing. The questioner may appear somewhat irritated, but you will maintain the respect of those who have entrusted information to you and the respect you have for yourself in having the courage to protect confidential information.

SUMMARY

Personal relationships often depend on how well you communicate your feelings, needs, and information. Develop the mechanics of speaking, gesturing, and writing so that you have command of the method you need. Improve the techniques of listening, word usage, telephone usage, and your range and selection of subjects to enable you to relate effectively through your communication abilities.

Understanding Communication

1. What can you do to make your voice a more pleasant sound?
2. How do you determine the rapidity with which you should speak?
3. How can you avoid monotonous speech?
4. How can you determine the correct pronunciation of words?
5. Why is eye contact important in communication?
6. What are the causes of poor handwriting?
7. How can you improve your listening?
8. How can you improve others' listening?
9. How can you get better responses from your telephone calls?
10. How can you gain confidence in your ability to converse?

Chapter 17

Etiquette

There are some generally accepted modes of behavior that have come to be accepted among people in business and social situations. These rules constitute the etiquette of people in groups in our culture. These are not always hard and fast rules that are observed infallibly by everyone; but you will feel more confident and comfortable if you know what behavior is generally practiced and accepted as suitable in common, everyday situations.

Such rules usually are made to facilitate order in groups and situations. People who follow the generally accepted rules know what to expect of others and what is expected of them. They can function more efficiently and be more socially competent when some order of behavior is followed. These practices are not binding in all situations, of course; but they are helpful, especially when you are entering new situations that may hold experiences for which you have no background. It is not necessary to follow the forms of behavior religiously in every situation. It is necessary, though, to be aware of them and to have at your command the knowledge of acceptable and preferred behavioral patterns when you need it.

Etiquette Helps You Get a Job

Employers have more or less formulated some practices that enable them to learn about a prospective employee, and applicants have come to use certain forms of behavior to show their competencies, personalities, and job preferences. Learning and following these practices will help you get a job.

In observing the etiquette expected of you in interviewing for a job, learn to prepare yourself adequately and to be yourself during the interview. Some of the preparatory practices that are expected of you are to be sure that you interview only for jobs that you are interested in and that you assess and present your qualifications completely and in the best light. You can also prepare yourself by anticipating questions and formulating answers that you may be asked. You can enhance the impression you make on the interviewer if you prepare yourself by dressing appropriately and providing for your transportation and arrival at the appointed time.

ILLUS. 17-1 *Take into consideration inclement weather and make arrangements to arrive on time for appointments.*

Vogue Pattern Service

For the interviewer to make an accurate assessment of your qualifications, both professional and personal, you must be open and friendly during the interview. When you answer questions, do so with thought and consideration. Try to be objective about what you want and what you expect from the job you seek.

Following the interview, review what you have learned about the job. Remember that the interviewer is thinking, too, about what he has learned about you. Follow up the interview with a thank-you letter or telephone call by: (1) expressing interest, if you have it, in the job; or (2) expressing rejection if you feel the job is not what you want; or (3) conveying acceptance if the job has been offered and you feel it is the job you want.

PAVE THE WAY FOR THE INTERVIEW

One rarely gets a job without an interview. Frequently, it is the most critical part in the entire job-seeking process. The time you spend preparing for your interviews will be some of the most wisely used time you invest in your career. There are several ways to pave the way for a good interview.

It is a good idea to scrutinize yourself closely before you decide what kind of job of want. Survey the job market to see what kinds of jobs are available, and try to match yourself with some of the available ones.

In scrutinizing yourself, formulate a presentation of your qualifications. Gear your presentation to the kind of job you want by emphasizing those qualities you believe are desirable for that job.

Prepare yourself for the interview by trying to anticipate what questions might be asked of you in light of your background, the nature of the job, and the nature of the company. Examine your attitude carefully, and formulate tentative answers to questions that you foresee occurring in the interview. A poor attitude or poor preparation are excellent reasons for turning down an otherwise well-qualified applicant.

Before you go to your interview, check your appearance, your clothing, and grooming. Be sure that you do not schedule an interview when you are ill or when you may be late due to other commitments. Learn to present yourself at your best both physically and emotionally.

Select Jobs You Are Interested In. Interviews take a great amount of time, both yours and that of the person interviewing you. Before you ask for an interview, think about the kind of jobs you truly are interested in. It is wasteful to interview for jobs in which you are not sincerely interested.

The range of jobs available to well-qualified people is innumerable. One of the general considerations for a person looking for a job is the location of the company. Would you be willing, for example, to commute to another city, to move to another city, to commute across town perhaps for 45 minutes to one and one-half hours one way? Do you want to work in a downtown area where individual car parking can be very expensive but where public transportation usually is very good? Downtown offices offer some advantages of good noon-time shopping facilities and lovely parks. They also mean, though, that you usually will find yourself in a multi-storied building, working far away from trees and grass and perhaps in the thick of polluted air. Working in downtown offices usually gives you the feeling of being in the mainstream of the city, but it also gives you the feeling of being crowded among masses of people during arrival, noon, and departure times as you struggle for your bus, subway, train, or car.

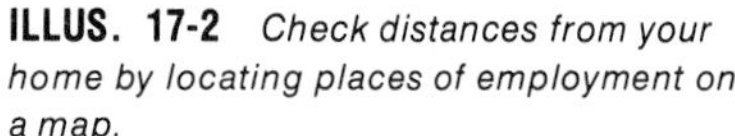

ILLUS. 17-2 *Check distances from your home by locating places of employment on a map.*

Photography by Terry Webb

Companies located away from the downtown area often are in buildings with more windows and sometimes among well-cared-for lawns that give a restful feeling as you glance out of a window. These companies, though, frequently cannot be reached by public transportation and require that you have your own car. Parking frequently is provided by the company near the building in which you work. Often these companies are not easily accessible to good eating places for lunch; and you must plan to eat from vending machines or to take your lunch from home. There is usually little opportunity to shop. People who work in outlying companies sometimes feel isolated from the main activities of the downtown scene.

Another important consideration is to affilitate yourself with a company involved in activity which you can support. If you do not believe in insurance, for example, you probably should not interview for a job with an insurance company. If you think advertising firms generally are not truthful, you will be uncomfortable trying to work for them. Select a company that promotes or produces services or products that you can support and that you have some interest in. You will be more willing to devote your loyalty, talent, and enthusiasm to building the business of the company.

Try to obtain a job in a company of a size in which you will be comfortable. Small-office situations can be challenging because you frequently have a great deal more responsibility than in large offices. However, they can be very lonely if you are a person who likes to have people working nearby. There often is little room for advancement in the very small office.

Medium-sized offices usually offer many challenging jobs and often have room for advancement. Most medium-sized offices are eyeing the opportunity to become larger and may present the biggest opportunity for hard work that produces promise of promotion should the company grow.

Large companies usually allow employees to be very specialized. They frequently have very good fringe benefits and accommodating vacation and leave policies. Sometimes, though, the competition for advancement in a large company can be very stiff. You may be lost among the masses.

Assess and Present Your Qualifications. When you know more or less the kind of job and company in which you wish to apply for work, assess your own qualifications for the job. If you have, indeed, selected an advertising firm, for example, think about what you have that will make you a desirable employee in that field. In addition to specialized skills required, can you write? Are you creative? Do you communicate well? Are you aware of new products and innovative ways of exhibiting them? Are you interested in learning what makes people buy and use products and in developing ways to appeal to that motivation?

If you have selected some other kind of job or firm, assess your interests and qualifications in the same way. Make a list of the contributions you can make. Make a list of your deficiencies and a proposal of how you can remedy them.

Informally, list all the qualifications that could contribute to your effectiveness in such a job. Include any education you have, emphasizing that which is especially suitable for the specific job. Review any previous experience you have had, paid or unpaid, that would be helpful in showing that you can do the kind of work for which you are applying and that shows your willingness to work. List any honors or achievements that show that you are recognized by your colleagues as a contributing member of the society, community, church, school, or profession. List names and addresses of people whom you have asked to give you character references.

Peruse everything you have written down and think about what an interviewer will find most appealing about your qualifications. Make up a formal data sheet listing your qualifications. Illustration 17-3 shows an example of a good data sheet or resumé.

Prepare Yourself Mentally for Questions. The person interviewing you usually has a list of questions casually prepared to learn whether you will fit into the company, whether you plan to work for a substantial period of time, whether you desire advancement, whether you plan to advance your education, and something about your personal adjustment to life. Some questions that you can think about before you are asked them are:

(1) How do you like to spend your spare time?
(2) Why do you think you would like to work for our company?
(3) Why did you choose your particular field of work?
(4) What do you know about our company?
(5) What do you expect to be doing five years from now?
(6) What kinds of books do you read?
(7) What types of people offend you?
(8) What do you believe to be special about yourself?
(9) What is your most serious weakness?
(10) Will you object to working overtime occasionally? Would transportation be a problem?
(11) What have you done that shows initiative and willingness to do a good job?
(12) Tell me a story.
(13) Do you feel you have done the best scholastic work of which you are capable? Should grades be considered by employers?
(14) Do you prefer to work alone or with other people?
(15) Do you plan to advance your education? Part-time? Full-time? When? Where?

Often an interviewer will ask an open-ended question to get you to talk. Your speech, grammar, attitudes, and ability to express yourself are on parade when you are answering. The more you prepare yourself for such expression, the better view of yourself you can present.

Prepare Yourself Physically. You indicate good manners and show that you care about whether you get a job or not by how well you prepare yourself for the interview. The fact that you are really interested in the job, have assessed and presented your qualifications, and have prepared yourself for questions that may be asked will be obvious to the

RESUMÉ

Maria Perez
4929 Arborlawn Drive
Fort Worth, Texas 76133
AC 817-926-4994

Date of Birth: May 5, 1959
Health: Excellent
Social Security: 555-66-7777
Marital Status: Single

Education:

The Business School of the Southwest, Fort Worth, Texas, 1977 - 19--
Major: Executive Secretary/ Administrative Assistant

Fort Worth High School, Fort Worth, Texas, 1974 - 1977

Business Courses:

Shorthand, 120 words per minute
Typewriting, 80 words per minute
Secretarial Procedures
Office Machines
Office Management
Administrative Decision Making
Accounting
Business Law
Economics
Personnel Management

Other Courses:

English
Personal Development
Psychology
Mathematics

Activities, Honors, and Hobbies:

Member, National Honor Society
Treasurer, Business Club
High School Cheerleader
Member, Concert Orchestra
Member, Mathematics Club
Daughters of American Revolution Citizenship Award
Rank in High School Class, 17/180
Member of church choir
Volunteer at local hospital

Experience:

Assistant to the principal's secretary in high school, 1974 - 1975, volunteer.
Library assistant, Southwest Branch, Fort Worth, Texas, 1975 - 1976, part-time.
Day-Camp Counselor, YMCA, Fort Worth, Texas, 1976, summer only.

References:

Dean Mary Smith, The Business School of the Southwest, Fort Worth, Texas 76110
Mr. Walter Jones, Minister, First United Methodist Church, Fort Worth, Texas 76101
Mr. Sam Whitsett, 2525 Hildring Drive, Fort Worth, Texas 76132

ILLUS. 17-3 Resumé

person interviewing you. The first impression the interviewer gets, though, is through a visual perception of the way you look when you arrive for the interview.

If you have watched your weight, exercised regularly, practiced good posture, kept your grooming regime, and chosen your wardrobe well, all your efforts will pay off at this time.

Consideration is shown for the person interviewing you if you dress appropriately. The interviewer expects to see the same well-groomed person two weeks after the interview as has been presented at the interview itself. Make sure that no offensive habits of garish clothing, overpowering perfume, poor posture, and unkempt hair have invaded your grooming.

Take special care of your health. A potential employee who is frequently sick usually is of no help to the company and will not be hired.

It is absolutely necessary that you arrive on time for the interview. This is a courtesy that cannot be overlooked. Arrive early enough to allow yourself to catch your breath, arrange the extra copy of your data sheet that you brought, locate the appropriate office, and rest a moment before you are shown into the interviewer's office. You will make a good impression, and you will show consideration for the person who is spending time interviewing you.

BE YOURSELF IN THE INTERVIEW

It is important to try to relax and be yourself during an interview. The person interviewing you wants to be sure that you will fit into the job that is vacant; and it is to your benefit to present yourself as you are so that an accurate assessment can be made.

If you try to answer questions according to the way you think the interviewer wants to hear them, you may be giving a false impression of yourself. Try to answer honestly so that your true characteristics will be shown. It is to your advantage as well as to the company's advantage that you be able to fit into the organization. Faking answers to questions or trying to project feelings or attitudes that are not really yours will not benefit you in the long run if they land you a job for which you are not suited.

When you are asked a question for which you have no ready answer, admit that you need some time to think about the question and that you would like to come back to it later. Be reflective and considerate. The interviewer will notice and appreciate your sincerity in trying to be honest and accurate in your answers.

Learn to be objective about questions about yourself. Try to acknowledge your strong points without being conceited about them. The interviewer has no way of knowing that you excel in certain activities if you do not say so. It is not bragging to present yourself objectively in the best light that you can. On the other hand, don't downgrade yourself for your past mistakes. If you have made them and have learned from them, try to present the positive side of the event. It certainly should not be embarrassing to have made mistakes; it should be embarrassing, though, not to have learned from them.

Be Open and Friendly. The attitude you exhibit during an interview will have a definite impact on the person interviewing you. Try to be open and friendly without being gushy. Keep in mind that you are looking at the job just as the interviewer is looking at you.

Both you and the interviewer want to get a good match for the job. You want a job that fits your needs and the interviewer wants an employee who fits the job.

Go into the interview with the attitude that both you and the company have good intentions of learning about one another. Answer and ask questions as the need arises so that your understanding and the understanding of the interviewer will be promoted.

A smile as you introduce yourself is a courtesy that tends to break the ice. A handshake frequently is in order if the interviewer is a man. Usually two women do not shake hands; however, if the interviewer is female and does offer her hand, by all means shake hands with her.

Seat yourself comfortably when you are asked to sit. Wait for the interviewer to signal the start of the interview either by asking you a question or by indicating that you are to start talking.

Be Reflective and Considerate. At some point in the interview, you will wonder if you should leave. Usually the end of the interview is signaled by the person conducting it. It is not wise to stay longer than is necessary, and you should be alert for even a subtle signal that the interview is over.

When you leave the office, be sure that you understand whether the next action is to be taken by you or by the interviewer. Sometimes you are to provide additional information. Often the interviewer indicates that other candidates are being considered and that a decision will be made later. If you are offered the job but are considering other positions and do not wish to make a decision about this one immediately, say so; but indicate a time that you expect to come to a decision.

After you leave the interview, be reflective about what you have learned. Go over in your mind the advantages and disadvantages of the

ILLUS. 17-4 *Be reflective after your interview.*

Vogue Pattern Service

job as you have discovered it. Consider your likes and dislikes about all the aspects of the work, the location, the opportunities for promotion, and any other features described to you. Make your decision one you can live with for a long time.

Be Objective. Be truthful with yourself about what you can and cannot do. If the job appears more difficult than you think you can handle, admit it to yourself. If it appears too simple and not challenging enough for you, consider the boredom that may result.

If the location of the company requires that you get up an hour earlier in the morning than you like to, consider whether the job will be worth it as compared to one that is offered closer to your home.

It is a good idea to list the advantages and disadvantages of each job you interview for that you have a chance to get. Compare as objectively as you can the interest the job holds for you, the qualifications you have for the job, and any other considerations that may influence your long-term happiness in the job.

FOLLOW UP YOUR INTERVIEW

After the interview, it is good etiquette to write a thank-you letter. If there is something additional you wish to provide the interviewer, it can be included in the letter with appropriate reference made to it. If the next action is to be taken by you in the form of an acceptance or rejection of the job as offered, you may do so in the form of a follow-up letter. Explain your reasons carefully if you decide to reject the job offer. Someday you may want to work for that company. If you are accepting the job, it probably is better to telephone your acceptance unless you have been specifically requested to respond in writing.

If the next action is up to the interviewer, who is considering other applicants along with you, a thank-you letter brings your name to the forefront again and lets the interviewer know that you are interested enough in the job to do something extra — write a thank-you letter. A typical follow-up letter following an interview would thank the interviewer for the time spent interviewing you, express interest in the job, and show a desire to hear whether or not it will be offered to you. Many people fail to write follow-up thank-you letters for interviews. If you take the time to do it, you will have a slight edge over those who don't.

Etiquette Helps Your Success

The simple courtesies of introducing people and addressing people whom you meet both professionally and personally are important in making people feel comfortable. Observing the rules regarding attendance and attention to your work takes into consideration the additional work load that others must bear if you do not do your part regularly and well.

Business behavior requires that you socialize only on your own time. The more effectively you plan your social life and the more you enjoy it outside of work, the better you will be able to concentrate on working at your job. Your life requires a balance of activities. A satisfying social life outside of work balances the concentration needed on your job.

A few considerations about visiting and entertaining at home and about dining at home and dining out can give you confidence that releases your energies for pleasures of the event rather than centering your concentration on the etiquette of the situation.

By avoiding offensive behavior with smoking, chewing gun, and liquor you can enhance your desirability as a companion and colleague. Learn the simple rules that show consideration for others regarding these potentially offensive items, and make life better for yourself and for those around you.

OBSERVE CUSTOMS REGARDING NAMES

People who are very easy-going and rational about everything else often are meticulous and adamant about their own names and about introductions to people. Even if the people with whom you are conversing are not so particular about such matters, it is good manners for you to make introductions appropriately and to address people suitably in all situations.

Introducing People. The general rules for introducing people are easy to learn. It is always courteous to introduce people with whom you may be talking if they do not know each other.

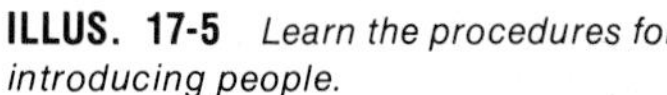

ILLUS. 17-5 *Learn the procedures for introducing people.*

Photography by Terry Webb

The generally followed procedures are:

(1) A man is presented to a woman: "Mary Adams, I would like you to know John Justin," or "Mary Adams, John Justin."

(2) A younger person is presented to an older person when the ages are obviously far apart. This means that a young girl may be presented to an older man (overriding the first rule). "Mr Jones, I'd like you to meet Mary Adams," or "Mr. Jones, Mary Adams."

(3) Two women or two men who are introduced are presented to each other when they are of equal rank. It makes no difference who is presented to whom. If one is considerably older or is more important within the group, such as the president of the group,

the younger or less important one is presented to the older or the more important one. "Sue Johnson, this is Alice Hall. Sue is President of our club."

(4) When men are introduced, they shake hands. Women usually do not shake hands. If a woman should offer her hand to you, though, it would be rude not to shake hands. Men and women who are introduced usually do not shake hands unless the woman offers her hand. If a man offers his hand, though, do not ignore it.

(5) Men always stand when they are introduced both to other men and to women. Women may remain sitting, unless they are being introduced to a woman who is somewhat older or somewhat more important than they are. Deference is shown to age, and older women are honored by standing for an introduction to them.

(6) Deference may also be shown to clergy, governors, mayors, and foreign heads of states, when they are men, by presenting women to them rather than as described in Rule 1. "Mayor Stovall, this is Linda Grimm."

When you are introduced, it is a good idea to repeat the name of the person to whom you are introduced, confirm the name, and to say something like, "Mary Adams? Nice to meet you," or, "I'm happy to meet you, Mary," or, "Hello, Mary." It is considered improper to say "Charmed" or "Delighted." Sometimes the person to whom you have been introduced does not hear your name or does not hear it correctly. It is courteous to pronounce it again very clearly if requested so that the other person understands your name correctly.

Addressing People. When you are addressing someone you've just met, either socially or in business, it is usually safer to use a title (Mrs., Ms., Miss, or Mr.) with the surname until you are asked to use a given name. An exception to this general rule is when you are introduced to someone near your own age at a social gathering. Frequently you are expected to call such a person by a given name from the beginning of the acquaintance. In the office and at formal social gatherings, follow the safer tradition of using the title and the last name until you are asked to use the given name.

You may suggest to others that they call you by your given name if you wish. Among colleagues in an office, the use of given names is usually standard procedure. An exception may be between your boss and yourself. Frequently the boss will prefer to use a title and your surname and will expect you to follow the same procedure for him or her. Other bosses will prefer to call you by your given name but have you call them by their title and surname. Follow whatever procedure seems to make the people with whom you work most comfortable.

In some professions, titles are maintained to preserve the dignity of the office rather than that of the person. The President of the United States, for example, is usually addressed as "Mr. President," never by his surname or his given name. Clergymen rarely use a given name without a title preceding it. Teachers and professors routinely use a title and surname, in respect for the position rather than for the person, who may actually prefer to be called by a given name.

More and more people are using given names. If you are in a situation where people prefer to use given names, follow the trend. If you are in charge, assess the situation, considering whether respect and dignity can be maintained with the use of given names; and make your decision about which names shall be used.

MAKE YOUR ATTENDANCE AND ATTENTION ABSOLUTE

Honoring your obligation to be at work every day on time is very much like keeping appointments and dates that you make. Etiquette and, frequently, keeping your job dictate absolute conformance with the rules of attendance at work. Often the work of other people depends upon the completion of your part. Even when your own work is caught up or is slow, you are expected to be present. Those are the times when you are able to learn more about the company or perhaps parts of a more responsible position, both of which help qualify you for advancement. To absent yourself from work for any but the most dire circumstances or most important reasons shows very poor judgment and a lack of consideration for others.

When you are at work, you are expected to devote your undivided attention to the matters at hand. To write personal letters, to place or take personal telephone calls, or simply to daydream while you are supposed to be working is an indication that you are not taking your present job seriously. Using your time more productively for the good of the company is the best way to convince others that you want to carry your share of the load and are able to advance yourself in the responsibilities of the company.

SOCIALIZE ON YOUR OWN TIME

There are some simple procedures for socializing that can make your leisure time more relaxed. The first and most important one to a career person is to socialize on your own time, never on your company's time.

There are many opportunities to balance your life with social activity. You can enjoy your friends by phone or by arranging luncheon meetings or other personal visits with them. You can plan small dinners at home, at restaurants, or "dutch treats" at restaurants. There are usually opportunities to dine with a date (or mate), a friend, and sometimes with a business associate. Observance of some generally accepted practices makes all these activities more entertaining for you.

Take time to make these forms of behavior part of your normal activity. You will make others comfortable with your confident attitude about social procedure.

Visits. A common way to enjoy your leisure time is by visiting with your friends, either by telephone or in person. Some good principles to follow in showing consideration for your friends are needed, though, to keep the relationship comfortable.

When you telephone a friend just to chat, do so with judicious timing. Try to call when the friend is likely to be free — not eating, not sleeping, not just leaving for a date or getting ready for one. When you call just to visit, ask if your friend is free to talk for a while on the telephone. If your friend is busy, offer to call later when it is more convenient, or ask your friend to return the call when it is convenient.

Telephone visits with friends should be kept reasonably short. Be very alert for any signal that the person called is ready to terminate the telephone visit. Another call could be expected, or your friend simply may be tired. Try to be sensitive to the feelings of others and do not be offended when other activities and duties interfere with a telephone visit.

When you visit a friend in person, be sure that you have actually been invited. Drop-ins are not welcome in most households even though they may have been assured that they are. It is a simple matter to call and suggest that you get together for a visit, either in your home or theirs. Be guided by the feelings of the person you want to visit in determining the time and place. If you are invited to a person's home for a visit, don't overstay your welcome. Unless you are specifically invited for a meal, it is not appropriate for you to stay through a mealtime hour.

When you invite others to your home, make clear what the visit will be: just a chat, simple refreshments, a meal, an entire day, an overnight visit, or more. If you have obligations later in the day, mention that you have a few hours to visit but that you are committed to something else later that evening. Don't allow yourself to inconvenience people you may be seeing later through a misunderstanding with someone who has been visiting earlier in the day.

ILLUS. 17-6 *Visiting friends can be a pleasant leisure-time activity.*

Photography by Terry Webb

Dining. One of the most pleasant ways to spend your social time is in dining with your friends. Dining, both in your home and out in a restaurant, can offer some of the most interesting evenings of your leisure time if you are comfortable with the etiquette of the situation.

When you plan to dine out with a friend and you intend to pay for your friend's meal, make it clear that you are treating your friend to the meal. If that is not made clear when you are asked to dine with someone else, assume that you are to pay for your own meal. Often the occasion is to be a "dutch treat" with each person paying for his or her own meal, or more commonly, dividing the total bill plus a gratuity by the number of people in the group regardless of who ate what. Many restaurants prefer to put all the meals on one check even though "dutch treats" are more convenient for the guests if each has a separate check. Try to make arrangements to have small enough bills and change in your handbag so that you can reimburse the person paying the total check if it is put on one tab, and so that you can make change, if needed, should you pay the total tab and be reimbursed by others in the group.

When you are dining out with a friend or a business associate who is paying for your meal, it is courteous, although not necessary, to ask your host what is recommended from the menu. Usually, the person makes suggestions within a particular price range. You are considerate if you adhere to that price range. Do not feel obligated, however, to order whatever has been suggested, especially if you don't like it. Do try to confine your order to the price range of the items that were suggested.

If you have been given a menu without prices (a host menu) at the request of your host, you are expected to order anything you want without regard to price. If you have been given an unrequested host menu, it is appropriate to ask the waiter for a menu with prices before you make your selection.

When you are hosting the meal for friends or business associates in a restaurant, make it clear that they are your guests. When the check is brought to the table, simply say to the waiter, "The check is mine." Should you be a woman entertaining a man, do not be intimidated by tradition. If the male guest seems somewhat squeamish about your paying the bill and you do not wish to make him uncomfortable, you can pay it quietly and unobtrusively with a credit card, gratuity and all; or you can make arrangements with many restaurants prior to the dinner to have the check waiting for you as you leave so that other diners will not observe who is paying the bill.

It is often more fun and much less expensive to invite friends into your home to eat. You can make the occasion as formal or informal as you like, and you can make the menu anything that comes to mind. You can create your own interesting atmosphere or make the food itself the center of interest for the evening. Informal dining at home may be done buffet style, as shown in Illustration 17-7.

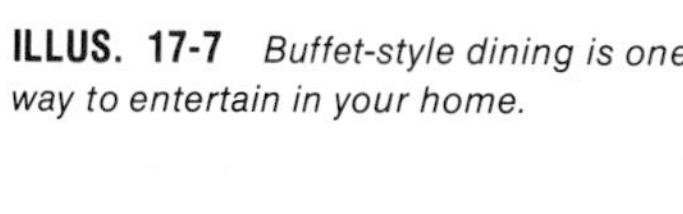

ILLUS. 17-7 *Buffet-style dining is one way to entertain in your home.*

Courtesy of Lenox China, Inc.

Card tables with bright table cloths can facilitate your entertaining eight or twelve people from such a buffet. More formal, sit-down dinners also are fun in your home. Some table settings and arrangements of table services are shown in Illustration 17-8.

Usually in a restaurant, the table service will be arranged as is shown in Illustration 17-9, page 404, for the formal table arrangement. Should you use the wrong bread plate or wrong water glass, simply quietly say to the person next to you that you think you have mistakenly used his or her plate or glass and offer your own clean, unused one. You can also ask the waiter to bring an additional plate or glass if a clean, unused one is not available to replace the one you used by mistake.

When you are invited to someone's home for a meal, it is often considerate if you ask if you can bring something, traditionally, a bottle of wine. Or, you may bring some other appropriate gift as a token of your appreciation, although, certainly it is not expected or necessary for you to do so.

At informal meals with friends in their homes it is courteous to offer to help clean the table and dishes. At a larger, formal meal, the guests are rarely expected to help with the cleanup.

After dinner, one of the most interesting ways to spend time is simply with good conversation. Organized activity, such as games or cards, is not necessary although it certainly is appropriate if you desire it.

AVOID OFFENSIVE BEHAVIOR

Rules of etiquette were devised to enable people in groups to function with more assurance because each would more-or-less know what to expect of the other in particular situations. Obviously, it is impossible to formulate policies for every situation that might occur in social encounters. Often you must make the decision yourself about what would be suitable and most comfortable for all concerned.

You will be a more welcome participant and an appreciated guest if you take into consideration the feelings and preferences of the people with whom you are associating when you must formulate a mode of behavior for yourself. Your personal poise, too, will grow as you become more confident in meeting unusual situations and in handling them with deftness.

Some of the kinds of behavior that most often seem to be offensive in groups involve smoking, chewing gum, and the use of liquor. There are some general guidelines about which you should be aware so that you can avoid being offensive should you decide to indulge in any of the three.

ILLUS. 17-8 *Tables may be set in many arrangements.*

Courtesy of Lenox China, Inc.

Courtesy of Lenox China, Inc.

ILLUS. 17-9 *Restaurant tables frequently are set in this manner.*

If You Smoke. Smoking may be very offensive to those who do not smoke. If you are in a closed room such as an office, a restaurant, a theater, an elevator, etc., be most careful. Smoke drifting from your cigarette pollutes the air of those about you, especially if the ventilation is poor. Smoke clings to other people's hair and clothing long after they have escaped your smoke. It is often an inconvenience and nuisance for nonsmokers to contend with such offensive odors on their person and clothes resulting from your inconsiderate use of smoking.

It is as inconsiderate of you to allow your smoke to permeate the hair and clothes of a nonsmoker as it would be of a nonsmoker to spray you with a fragrance you found equally unpleasant.

You should forego smoking and polluting the air of others under such circumstances. Confine your smoking to designated areas so that nonsmokers will not have to tolerate either that smoke drifting from your cigarette or that drifting from your mouth. Both may be most offensive.

If you do smoke, always remain seated or standing in one place until you finish your cigarette. To carry a lighted cigarette in either your hand or your mouth is awkward and dangerous. You may drop unnoticed hot ashes or brush them against someone's clothes as you walk. A cigarette that is hanging from your mouth looks bad and could fall, causing fire damage.

Carefully avoid smoking in a windy area since ashes frequently blow from your cigarette onto others who may be downwind. This is especially important when you are traveling in a bus, train, or car with your window open. Very often the person behind you gets hot ashes on clothing or skin if you are inconsiderate.

Before you light a cigarette, be sure that there is an ashtray available to you. If there is not, you should check with the host or hostess to see if smoking is permitted. Many people do not have ashtrays out because they prefer not to have smoking in their homes. If there are ashtrays out, be sure to use them faithfully. It is rude to drop ashes on the floor or on the furniture. Often the ashes are hot and will burn a hole in carpeting and upholstery. You should feel obligated to pay for the repair if you destroy furnishings with your ashes.

If you are permitted to smoke at your desk at work, keep your ashtray emptied regularly. An ashtray can have an offensive odor with stale cigarette butts in it. Only one or two butts should be allowed to accumulate before the ashtray is emptied. Be very careful about emptying butts in a waste can with papers because you may start a fire with live ashes. Never leave your ashtray full overnight since the stale smoke smell will permeate the entire room before the next day. Leaving your ashtray unattended with a lighted cigarette in it invites disaster. More than once a cigarette has burned down, fallen out of the tray, and burned the furniture. If you burn someone's furniture, offer to have it repaired.

If you smoke, be especially careful about stains on your teeth and fingers. You may need more frequent visits to the dental hygienist than a nonsmoker. Also, take special care to protect your breath. The odor of a smoker's breath can be as offensive as that of someone who has eaten garlic or onions. Carefully avoid speaking directly in the face of others after smoking.

Contrary to what advertisements may imply, smoking does not enhance your appeal to others. Frequently it makes you less appealing because of stained teeth; stained fingers; offensive breath; and danger to persons, clothing, and furnishings. If you do not smoke, before you start, carefully evaluate what you expect smoking to do for you and to you in light of all the facts. If you do smoke, take another look at yourself and the effect smoking has on you and on those who want to be your friends. There are no known scientific benefits from smoking; but there are many known scientific hazards. Take everything you know into consideration when you make a decision about smoking.

If You Chew Gum. The chewing gum industry would have you believe that gum chewing is a desirable and acceptable practice anywhere, anytime. It is not. Very few offices approve of chewing gum at your desk, especially if customers frequent your office.

Other offices object to chewing gum because the smacking, popping, and constant movement of your mouth are distracting to colleagues. Others disapprove because of the frequency with which the gum seems to end up on floors, and shoe soles, under chair seats, and stuck in wastebaskets.

The only proper use of chewing gum is in private, where others will not be subjected to the distractions of it. If you chew it immediately after meals to help clean your teeth or freshen your breath, do so in the restroom. Then throw it away, wrapped in paper so that it won't stick to the waste can, before you return to work.

Toothpicks and other items that are used in your mouth for cleaning food from your teeth and gums should never be used in public. Just as you would not brush your teeth in public, you should not use other methods of cleaning your teeth in public.

If You Use Liquor. Liquor is frequently accepted as part of the social scene in our culture. It is always proper for you to refuse to drink if you prefer not to. No one should ever be offended if you do not wish to drink, and you should never apologize. Most hosts and hostesses provide nonalcoholic beverages for those who do not wish to imbibe.

If you are hosting a gathering yourself, be very alert to the needs of your guests. Provide nonalcoholic beverages along with alcoholic ones, if you desire, and be unobtrusive about it. Never encourage guests to drink liquor if they have indicated a preference for a nonalcoholic beverage. People do not indulge for many reasons. Some have moral objections to its consumption. Liquor does not mix with certain commonly used medications. It cannot be used by people with heart or stomach problems. People who have a tendency to alcoholism must avoid it completely.

SUMMARY

Etiquette is merely showing consideration for others. You can enjoy your friends and your leisure time much more by knowing the common courtesies expected of you and routinely practicing them. Your employment can be facilitated and your job made more pleasant by observing the customs people have come to expect of applicants and colleagues. Since there cannot be a predetermined behavioral pattern for every situation, learn to make decisions in the best interests of the comfort of those about you. You will become a valued colleague and friend.

Understanding Etiquette

1. What are some considerations in deciding what jobs you wish to interview for?
2. Of your qualifications, what do you consider the one that would be most appealing to a prospective employer?
3. Why is it necessary to "be yourself" in the interview?
4. What is the purpose of a follow-up letter?
5. How would you introduce a girl friend and your mother? a boy friend and your mother?
6. What is a "dutch treat"? A "host menu"?
7. How do you know whether you are a "guest" or whether you are to pay for your own meal?
8. What is wrong with subjecting nonsmokers to your smoke?
9. Where is chewing gum appropriate?
10. Why must you use great care in serving and in drinking liquor?

Projects for Part 4

1. Make a close observation of several verbal exchanges you have had with people during a given time period (a day, or a half-day). Record to the best of your memory what was said, what ego state it came from, and whether or not it was appropriate to the circumstances. Rewrite parts of conversations you believed to be inappropriate.
2. Record your behavior for a day. Decide how you structured your time most of each hour. Select the one way you feel least competent with and describe a program of improvement for yourself.
3. Enumerate the ways you communicate in a day. Analyze the effect you had on your listener, and decide specifically what improvements you should make in communications. Give examples of topics, gestures, voice variations, etc., that would have improved your effectiveness in communicating.
4. Select three companies for which you think you might want to work. Make a data sheet and explain what you can expect to be asked and what the considerations for the different companies might be in terms of size, distance from home, and opportunities for advancement.

APPENDIX

NUTRITIVE VALUES OF THE EDIBLE PART OF FOODS

Source: "*Nutritive Value of Foods,*" *Home and Garden Bulletin No. 72, published by U.S. Department of Agriculture.*

[Dashes in the columns for nutrients show that no suitable value could be found although there is reason to believe that a measurable amount of the nutrient may be present.]

	FOOD, APPROXIMATE MEASURE, AND WEIGHT (IN GRAMS)			WATER	FOOD ENERGY	PROTEIN	FAT	FATTY ACIDS			CARBOHYDRATE	CALCIUM	IRON	VITAMIN A VALUE	THIAMIN	RIBOFLAVIN	NIACIN	ASCORBIC ACID
								SATURATED (TOTAL)	UNSATURATED									
									OLEIC	LINOLEIC								
			Grams	*Percent*	*Calories*	*Grams*	*Grams*	*Grams*	*Grams*	*Grams*	*Grams*	*Milligrams*	*Milligrams*	*International units*	*Milligrams*	*Milligrams*	*Milligrams*	*Milligrams*
	MILK, CHEESE, CREAM, IMITATION CREAM; RELATED PRODUCTS																	
	Milk:																	
	Fluid:																	
1	Whole, 3.5% fat	1 cup	244	87	160	9	9	5	3	Trace	12	288	.1	350	.07	.41	.2	2
2	Nonfat (skim)	1 cup	245	90	90	9	Trace				12	296	.1	10	.09	.44	.2	2
3	Partly skimmed, 2% nonfat milk solids added.	1 cup	246	87	145	10	5	3	2	Trace	15	352	.1	200	.10	.52	.2	2
	Canned, concentrated, undiluted:																	
4	Evaporated, unsweetened.	1 cup	252	74	345	18	20	11	7	1	24	635	.3	810	.10	.86	.5	3
5	Condensed, sweetened.	1 cup	306	27	980	25	27	15	9	1	166	802	.3	1,100	.24	1.16	.6	3
	Dry, nonfat instant:																	
6	Low-density (1⅓ cups needed for reconstitution to 1 qt.).	1 cup	68	4	245	24	Trace				35	879	.4	[1] 20	.24	1.21	.6	5
7	High-density (⅞ cup needed for reconstitution to 1 qt.).	1 cup	104	4	375	37	1				54	1,345	.6	[1] 30	.36	1.85	.9	7

	Buttermilk:																	
8	Fluid, cultured, made from skim milk.	1 cup	245	90	90	9	Trace	....	....	....	12	296	.1	10	.10	.44	.2	2
9	Dried, packaged	1 cup	120	3	465	41	6	3	2	Trace	60	1,498	.7	260	.31	2.06	1.1	....
	Cheese:																	
	Natural:																	
	Blue or Roquefort type:																	
10	Ounce	1 oz.	28	40	105	6	9	5	3	Trace	1	89	.1	350	.01	.17	.3	0
11	Cubic inch	1 cu. in.	17	40	65	4	5	3	2	Trace	Trace	54	.1	210	.01	.11	.2	0
12	Camembert, packaged in 4-oz. pkg. with 3 wedges per pkg.	1 wedge	38	52	115	7	9	5	3	Trace	1	40	.2	380	.02	.29	.3	0
	Cheddar:																	
13	Ounce	1 oz.	28	37	115	7	9	5	3	Trace	1	213	.3	370	.01	.13	Trace	0
14	Cubic inch	1 cu. in.	17	37	70	4	6	3	2	Trace	Trace	129	.2	230	.01	.08	Trace	0
	Cottage, large or small curd:																	
	Creamed:																	
15	Package of 12-oz., net wt.	1 pkg.	340	78	360	46	14	8	5	Trace	10	320	1.0	580	.10	.85	.3	0
16	Cup, curd pressed down.	1 cup	245	78	260	33	10	6	3	Trace	7	230	.7	420	.07	.61	.2	0
	Uncreamed:																	
17	Package of 12-oz., net wt.	1 pkg.	340	79	290	58	1	1	Trace	Trace	9	306	1.4	30	.10	.95	.3	0
18	Cup, curd pressed down.	1 cup	200	79	170	34	1	Trace	Trace	Trace	5	180	.8	20	.06	.56	.2	0
	Cream:																	
19	Package of 8-oz., net wt.	1 pkg.	227	51	850	18	86	48	28	3	5	141	.5	3,500	.05	.54	.2	0
20	Package of 3-oz., net wt.	1 pkg.	85	51	320	7	32	18	11	1	2	53	.2	1,310	.02	.20	.1	0
21	Cubic inch.	1 cu. in.	16	51	60	1	6	3	2	Trace	Trace	10	Trace	250	Trace	.04	Trace	0
	Parmesan, grated:																	
22	Cup, pressed down.	1 cup	140	17	655	60	43	24	14	1	5	1,893	.7	1,760	.03	1.22	.3	0
23	Tablespoon	1 tbsp.	5	17	25	2	2	1	Trace	Trace	Trace	68	Trace	60	Trace	.04	Trace	0
24	Ounce	1 oz.	28	17	130	12	9	5	3	Trace	1	383	.1	360	.01	.25	.1	0
	Swiss:																	
25	Ounce	1 oz.	28	39	105	8	8	4	3	Trace	1	262	.3	320	Trace	.11	Trace	0
26	Cubic inch.	1 cu. in.	15	39	55	4	4	2	1	Trace	Trace	139	.1	170	Trace	.06	Trace	0
	Pasteurized processed cheese:																	
	American:																	
27	Ounce.	1 oz.	28	40	105	7	9	5	3	Trace	1	198	.3	350	.01	.12	Trace	0
28	Cubic inch.	1 cu. in.	18	40	65	4	5	3	2	Trace	Trace	122	.2	210	Trace	.07	Trace	0
	Swiss:																	
29	Ounce.	1 oz.	28	40	100	8	8	4	3	Trace	1	251	.3	310	Trace	.11	Trace	0
30	Cubic inch.	1 cu. in.	18	40	65	5	5	3	2	Trace	Trace	159	.2	200	Trace	.07	Trace	0
	Pasteurized process cheese food, American:																	
31	Tablespoon.	1 tbsp.	14	43	45	3	3	2	1	Trace	1	80	.1	140	Trace	.08	Trace	0
32	Cubic inch.	1 cu. in.	18	43	60	4	4	2	1	Trace	1	100	.1	170	Trace	.10	Trace	0
33	Pasteurized process cheese spread, American.	1 oz.	28	49	80	5	6	3	2	Trace	2	160	.2	250	Trace	.15	Trace	0
	Cream:																	
34	Half-and-half (cream and milk).	1 cup	242	80	325	8	28	15	9	1	11	261	.1	1,160	.07	.39	.1	2
35		1 tbsp.	15	80	20	1	2	1	1	Trace	1	16	Trace	70	Trace	.02	Trace	Trace

NUTRITIVE VALUES OF THE EDIBLE PART OF FOODS — Continued

[Dashes in the columns for nutrients show that no suitable value could be found although there is reason to believe that a measurable amount of the nutrient may be present]

	FOOD, APPROXIMATE MEASURE, AND WEIGHT (IN GRAMS)			WATER	FOOD ENERGY	PRO-TEIN	FAT	FATTY ACIDS			CARBO-HY-DRATE	CAL-CIUM	IRON	VITA-MIN A VALUE	THIA-MIN	RIBO-FLAVIN	NIACIN	ASCOR-BIC ACID
								SATU-RATED (TOTAL)	UNSATURATED									
									OLEIC	LIN-OLEIC								
			Grams	*Percent*	*Calories*	*Grams*	*Grams*	*Grams*	*Grams*	*Grams*	*Grams*	*Milli-grams*	*Milli-grams*	*Inter-national units*	*Milli-grams*	*Milli-grams*	*Milli-grams*	*Milli-grams*
	MILK, CHEESE, CREAM, IMITATION CREAM; RELATED PRODUCTS — Continued:																	
	Cream, Continued:																	
36	Light, coffee or table.	1 cup	240	72	505	7	49	27	16	1	10	245	.1	2,020	.07	.36	.1	2
37		1 tbsp.	15	72	30	1	3	2	1	Trace	1	15	Trace	130	Trace	.02	Trace	Trace
38	Sour.	1 cup	230	72	485	7	47	26	16	1	10	235	.1	1,930	.07	.35	.1	2
39		1 tbsp.	12	72	25	Trace	2	1	1	Trace	1	12	Trace	100	Trace	.02	Trace	Trace
40	Whipped topping (pressurized).	1 cup	60	62	155	2	14	8	5	Trace	6	67	....	570	....	.04	....	....
41		1 tbsp.	3	62	10	Trace	1	Trace	Trace	Trace	Trace	3	....	30	....	Trace	....	....
	Whipping, unwhipped (volume about double when whipped):																	
42	Light.	1 cup	239	62	715	6	75	41	25	2	9	203	.1	3,060	.05	.29	.1	2
43		1 tbsp.	15	62	45	Trace	5	3	2	Trace	1	13	Trace	190	Trace	.02	Trace	Trace
44	Heavy.	1 cup	238	57	840	5	90	50	30	3	7	179	.1	3,670	.05	.26	.1	2
45		1 tbsp.	15	57	55	Trace	6	3	2	Trace	1	11	Trace	230	Trace	.02	Trace	Trace
	Imitation cream products (made with vegetable fat):																	
	Creamers:																	
46	Powdered.	1 cup	94	2	505	4	33	31	1	0	52	21	.6	[2] 200	....	....	Trace	....
47		1 tsp.	2	2	10	Trace	1	Trace	Trace	0	1	1	Trace	[2] Trace	....	....	....	....
48	Liquid (frozen).	1 cup	245	77	345	3	27	25	1	0	25	29	....	[2] 100	0	0	....	....
49		1 tbsp.	15	77	20	Trace	2	1	Trace	0	2	2	....	[2] 10	0	0	....	....
50	Sour dressing (imitation sour cream) made with nonfat dry milk.	1 cup	235	72	440	9	38	35	1	Trace	17	277	.1	10	.07	.38	.2	1
51		1 tbsp.	12	72	20	Trace	2	2	Trace	Trace	1	14	Trace	Trace	Trace	Trace	Trace	Trace
	Whipped topping:																	
52	Pressurized.	1 cup	70	61	190	1	17	15	1	0	9	5	....	[2] 340	....	0	....	....
53		1 tbsp.	4	61	10	Trace	1	1	Trace	0	Trace	Trace	....	[2] 20	....	0	....	....
54	Frozen.	1 cup	75	52	230	1	20	18	Trace	0	15	5	....	[2] 560	....	0	....	....
55		1 tbsp.	4	52	10	Trace	1	1	Trace	0	1	Trace	....	[2] 30	....	0	....	....
56	Powdered, made with whole milk.	1 cup	75	58	175	3	12	10	1	Trace	15	62	Trace	[2] 330	.02	.08	.1	Trace
57		1 tbsp.	4	58	10	Trace	1	1	Trace	Trace	1	3	Trace	[2] 20	Trace	Trace	Trace	Trace

	Milk beverages:																	
58	Cocoa, homemade.	1 cup	250	79	245	10	12	7	4	Trace	27	295	1.0	400	.10	.45	.5	3
59	Chocolate-flavored drink made with skim milk and 2% added butterfat.	1 cup	250	83	190	8	6	3	2	Trace	27	270	.5	210	.10	.40	.3	3
	Malted milk:																	
60	Dry powder, approximately 3 heaping teaspoons per ounce.	1 oz.	28	3	115	4	2				20	82	.6	290	.09	.15	.1	0
61	Beverage.	1 cup	235	78	245	11	10				28	317	.7	590	.14	.49	.2	2
	Milk desserts:																	
62	Custard, baked	1 cup	265	77	305	14	15	7	5	1	29	297	1.1	930	.11	.50	.3	1
	Ice cream:																	
63	Regular (approx. 10% fat).	½ gal.	1,064	63	2,055	48	113	62	37	3	221	1,553	.5	4,680	.43	2.23	1.1	11
64		1 cup	133	63	255	6	14	8	5	Trace	28	194	.1	590	.05	.28	.1	1
65		3 fl. oz. cup	50	63	95	2	5	3	2	Trace	10	73	Trace	220	.02	.11	.1	1
66	Rich (approx. 16% fat).	½ gal.	1,188	63	2,635	31	191	105	63	6	214	927	.2	7,840	.24	1.31	1.2	12
67		1 cup	148	63	330	4	24	13	8	1	27	115	Trace	980	.03	.16	.1	1
	Ice milk:																	
68	Hardened.	½ gal.	1,048	67	1,595	50	53	29	17	2	235	1,635	1.0	2,200	.52	2.31	1.0	10
69		1 cup	131	67	200	6	7	4	2	Trace	29	204	.1	280	.07	.29	.1	1
70	Soft-serve.	1 cup	175	67	265	8	9	5	3	Trace	39	273	.2	370	.09	.39	.2	2
	Yogurt:																	
71	Made from partially skimmed milk.	1 cup	245	89	125	8	4	2	1	Trace	13	294	.1	170	.10	.44	.2	2
72	Made from whole milk.	1 cup	245	88	150	7	8	5	3	Trace	12	272	.1	340	.07	.39	.2	2

EGGS

	Eggs, large, 24 ounces per dozen:																	
	Raw or cooked in shell or with nothing added:																	
73	Whole, without shell.	1 egg	50	74	80	6	6	2	3	Trace	Trace	27	1.1	590	.05	.15	Trace	0
74	White of egg.	1 white	33	88	15	4	Trace				Trace	3	Trace	0	Trace	.09	Trace	0
75	Yolk of egg.	1 yolk	17	51	60	3	5	2	2	Trace	Trace	24	.9	580	.04	.07	Trace	0
76	Scrambled with milk and fat.	1 egg	64	72	110	7	8	3	3	Trace	1	51	1.1	690	.05	.18	Trace	0

NUTRITIVE VALUES OF THE EDIBLE PART OF FOODS — Continued

[Dashes in the columns for nutrients show that no suitable value could be found although there is reason to believe that a measurable amount of the nutrient may be present]

No.	FOOD, APPROXIMATE MEASURE, AND WEIGHT (IN GRAMS)			WATER	FOOD ENERGY	PRO-TEIN	FAT	FATTY ACIDS: SATU-RATED (TOTAL)	FATTY ACIDS: UNSATURATED: OLEIC	FATTY ACIDS: UNSATURATED: LIN-OLEIC	CARBO-HY-DRATE	CAL-CIUM	IRON	VITA-MIN A VALUE	THIA-MIN	RIBO-FLAVIN	NIACIN	ASCOR-BIC ACID
			Grams	Percent	Calories	Grams	Grams	Grams	Grams	Grams	Grams	Milli-grams	Milli-grams	Inter-national units	Milli-grams	Milli-grams	Milli-grams	Milli-grams
	MEAT, POULTRY, FISH, SHELLFISH; RELATED PRODUCTS																	
77	**Bacon, (20 slices per lb. raw), broiled or fried, crisp.**	2 slices	15	8	90	5	8	3	4	1	1	2	.5	0	.08	.05	.8	....
	Beef,[3] cooked:																	
	Cuts braised, simmered, or pot-roasted:																	
78	Lean and fat.	3 ounces	85	53	245	23	16	8	7	Trace	0	10	2.9	30	.04	.18	3.5	....
79	Lean only.	2.5 ounces	72	62	140	22	5	2	2	Trace	0	10	2.7	10	.04	.16	3.3	....
	Hamburger (ground beef), broiled:																	
80	Lean.	3 ounces	85	60	185	23	10	5	4	Trace	0	10	3.0	20	.08	.20	5.1	....
81	Regular.	3 ounces	85	54	245	21	17	8	8	Trace	0	9	2.7	30	.07	.18	4.6	....
	Roast, oven-cooked, no liquid added:																	
	Relatively fat, such as rib:																	
82	Lean and fat.	3 ounces	85	40	375	17	34	16	15	1	0	8	2.2	70	.05	.13	3.1	....
83	Lean only.	1.8 ounces	51	57	125	14	7	3	3	Trace	0	6	1.8	10	.04	.11	2.6	....
	Relatively lean, such as heel of round:																	
84	Lean and fat.	3 ounces	85	62	165	25	7	3	3	Trace	0	11	3.2	10	.06	.19	4.5	....
85	Lean only.	2.7 ounces	78	65	125	24	3	1	1	Trace	0	10	3.0	Trace	.06	.18	4.3	....
	Steak, broiled:																	
	Relatively, fat, such as sirloin:																	
86	Lean and fat.	3 ounces	85	44	330	20	27	13	12	1	0	9	2.5	50	.05	.16	4.0	....
87	Lean only.	2.0 ounces	56	59	115	18	4	2	2	Trace	0	7	2.2	10	.05	.14	3.6	....
	Relatively, lean, such as round:																	
88	Lean and fat.	3 ounces	85	55	220	24	13	6	6	Trace	0	10	3.0	20	.07	.19	4.8	....
89	Lean only.	2.4 ounces	68	61	130	21	4	2	2	Trace	0	9	2.5	10	.06	.16	4.1	....

	Beef, canned:																	
90	Corned beef	3 ounces	85	59	185	22	10	5	4	Trace	0	17	3.7	20	.01	.20	2.9	...
91	Corned beef hash.	3 ounces	85	67	155	7	10	5	4	Trace	9	11	1.7	...	.01	.08	1.8	...
92	**Beef, dried or chipped.**	2 ounces	57	48	115	19	4	2	2	Trace	0	11	2.9	...	.04	.18	2.2	...
93	**Beef and vegetable stew.**	1 cup	235	82	210	15	10	5	4	Trace	15	28	2.8	2,310	.13	.17	4.4	15
94	**Beef potpie, baked, 4¼-inch diam., weight before baking about 8 ounces.**	1 pie	227	55	560	23	33	9	20	2	43	32	4.1	1,860	.25	0.27	4.5	7
	Chicken, cooked:																	
95	Flesh only, broiled.	3 ounces	85	71	115	20	3	1	1	1	0	8	1.4	80	.05	.16	7.4	...
	Breast, fried, ½ breast:																	
96	With bone	3.3 ounces	94	58	155	25	5	1	2	1	1	9	1.3	70	.04	.17	11.2	...
97	Flesh and skin only.	2.7 ounces	76	58	155	25	5	1	2	1	1	9	1.3	70	.04	.17	11.2	...
	Drumstick, fried:																	
98	With bone.	2.1 ounces	59	55	90	12	4	1	2	1	Trace	6	.9	50	.03	.15	2.7	...
99	Flesh and skin only.	1.3 ounces	38	55	90	12	4	1	2	1	Trace	6	9	50	.03	.15	2.7	...
100	**Chicken, canned, boneless.**	3 ounces	85	65	170	18	10	3	4	2	0	18	1.3	200	.03	.11	3.7	3
101	**Chicken potpie, baked, 4¼-inch diam., weight before baking about 8 ounces.**	1 pie	227	57	535	23	31	10	15	3	42	68	3.0	3,020	.25	.26	4.1	5
	Chili con carne, canned:																	
102	With beans.	1 cup	250	72	335	19	15	7	7	Trace	30	80	4.2	150	.08	.18	3.2	...
103	Without beans.	1 cup	255	67	510	26	38	18	17	1	15	97	3.6	380	.05	.31	5.6	...
104	**Heart, beef, lean, braised.**	3 ounces	85	61	160	27	5	...	...	...	1	5	5.0	20	.21	1.04	6.5	1
	Lamb,[3] cooked:																	
105	Chop, thick, with bone, broiled.	1 chop, 4.8 ounces	137	47	400	25	33	18	12	1	0	10	1.5	...	.14	.25	5.6	...
106	Lean and fat.	4.0 ounces	112	47	400	25	33	18	12	1	0	10	1.5	...	.14	.25	5.6	...
107	Lean only.	2.6 ounces	74	62	140	21	6	3	2	Trace	0	9	1.5	...	.11	.20	4.5	...
	Leg, roasted:																	
108	Lean and fat.	3 ounces	85	54	235	22	16	9	6	Trace	0	9	1.4	...	.13	.23	4.7	...
109	Lean only.	2.5 ounces	71	62	130	20	5	3	2	Trace	0	9	1.4	...	.12	.21	4.4	...
	Shoulder, roasted:																	
110	Lean and fat.	3 ounces	85	50	285	18	23	13	8	1	0	9	1.0	...	.11	.20	4.0	...
111	Lean only.	2.3 ounces	64	61	130	17	6	3	2	Trace	0	8	1.0	...	.10	.18	3.7	...
112	**Liver, beef, fried.**	2 ounces	57	57	130	15	6	...	...	...	3	6	5.0	30,280	.15	2.37	9.4	15
	Pork, cured, cooked:																	
113	Ham, light cure, lean and fat, roasted.	3 ounces	85	54	245	18	19	7	8	2	0	8	2.2	0	.40	.16	3.1	...
	Luncheon meat:																	
114	Boiled ham, sliced.	2 ounces	57	59	135	11	10	4	4	1	0	6	1.6	0	.25	.09	1.5	...
115	Canned, spiced or unspiced.	2 ounces	57	55	165	8	14	5	6	1	1	5	1.2	0	.18	.12	1.6	...
	Pork, fresh,[3] cooked:																	
116	Chop, thick, with bone.	1 chop, 3.5 ounces	98	42	260	16	21	8	9	2	0	8	2.2	0	.63	.18	3.8	...
117	Lean and fat.	2.3 ounces	66	42	260	16	21	8	9	2	0	8	2.2	0	.63	.18	3.8	...
118	Lean only.	1.7 ounces	48	53	130	15	7	2	3	1	0	7	1.9	0	.54	.16	3.3	...

NUTRITIVE VALUES OF THE EDIBLE PART OF FOODS — Continued

[Dashes in the columns for nutrients show that no suitable value could be found although there is reason to believe that a measurable amount of the nutrient may be present]

	FOOD, APPROXIMATE MEASURE, AND WEIGHT (IN GRAMS)			WATER	FOOD ENERGY	PRO-TEIN	FAT	FATTY ACIDS			CARBO-HY-DRATE	CAL-CIUM	IRON	VITA-MIN A VALUE	THIA-MIN	RIBO-FLAVIN	NIACIN	ASCOR-BIC ACID
								SATU-RATED (TOTAL)	UNSATURATED									
									OLEIC	LIN-OLEIC								
			Grams	*Percent*	*Calories*	*Grams*	*Grams*	*Grams*	*Grams*	*Grams*	*Grams*	*Milli-grams*	*Milli-grams*	*Inter-national units*	*Milli-grams*	*Milli-grams*	*Milli-grams*	*Milli-grams*
	MEAT, POULTRY, FISH, SHELLFISH; RELATED PRODUCTS — Continued:																	
	Pork, Fresh,[3] cooked — Continued:																	
	Roast, oven-cooked, no liquid added:																	
119	Lean and fat.	3 ounces	85	46	310	21	24	9	10	2	0	9	2.7	0	.78	.22	4.7	....
120	Lean only.	2.4 ounces	68	55	175	20	10	3	4	1	0	9	2.6	0	.73	.21	4.4	....
	Cuts shimmered:																	
121	Lean and fat.	3 ounces	85	46	320	20	26	9	11	2	0	8	2.5	0	.46	.21	4.1	....
122	Lean only.	2.2 ounces	63	60	135	18	6	2	3	1	0	8	2.3	0	.42	.19	3.7	....
	Sausage:																	
123	Bologna, slice, 3-in. Diam. by ⅛ inch.	2 slices	26	56	80	3	7	....	....	....	Trace	2	.5	....	.04	.06	.7	....
124	Braunschweiger, slice 2-in. diam. by ¼ inch.	2 slices	20	53	65	3	5	....	....	....	Trace	2	1.2	1,310	.03	.29	1.6	....
125	Deviled ham, canned.	1 tablespoon.	13	51	45	2	4	2	2	Trace	0	1	.3	....	.02	.01	.2	....
126	Frankfurter, heated (8 per lb. purchased package).	1 frank	56	57	170	7	15	....	....	....	1	3	.8	....	.08	.11	1.4	....
127	Pork links, cooked (16 links per lb. raw).	2 links	26	35	125	5	11	4	5	1	Trace	2	.6	0	.21	.09	1.0	....
128	Salami, dry type.	1 ounce	28	30	130	7	11	....	....	....	Trace	4	1.0	....	.10	.07	1.5	....
129	Salami, cooked.	1 ounce	28	51	90	5	7	....	....	....	Trace	3	.7	....	.07	.07	1.2	....
130	Vienna, canned (7 sausages per 5-ounce can).	1 sausage	16	63	40	2	3	....	....	....	Trace	1	.3	....	.01	.02	.4	....
	Veal, medium fat, cooked, bone removed:																	
131	Cutlet.	3 ounces	85	60	185	23	9	5	4	Trace	....	9	2.7	....	.06	.21	4.6	....
132	Roast.	3 ounces	85	55	230	23	14	7	6	Trace	0	10	2.9	....	.11	.26	6.6	....
	Fish and shellfish:																	
133	Bluefish, baked with table fat.	3 ounces	85	68	135	22	4	....	....	....	0	25	.6	40	.09	.08	1.6	....
	Clams:																	
134	Raw, meat only.	3 ounces	85	82	65	11	1	....	....	....	2	59	5.2	90	.08	.15	1.1	8
135	Canned, solids and liquid.	3 ounces	85	86	45	7	1	....	....	....	2	47	3.5	....	.01	.09	.9	....

136	Crabmeat, canned.	3 ounces	85	77	85	15	2	...	...	...	1	38	.7	...	.07	.07	1.6	...
137	Fish sticks, breaded, cooked, frozen; stick 3¾ by 1 by ½ inch.	10 sticks or 8 oz. pkg.	227	66	400	38	20	5	4	10	15	25	.9	...	.09	.16	3.6	...
138	Haddock, breaded, fried	3 ounces	85	66	140	17	5	1	3	Trace	5	34	1.0	...	.03	.06	2.7	2
139	Ocean perch, breaded, fried.	3 ounces	85	59	195	16	11	...	...	...	6	28	1.1	...	.08	.09	1.5	...
140	Oysters, raw, meat only (13–19 med. selects).	1 cup	240	85	160	20	4	...	...	...	8	226	13.2	740	.33	.43	6.0	...
141	Salmon, pink, canned.	3 ounces	85	71	120	17	5	1	1	Trace	0	[4] 167	.7	60	.03	.16	6.8	...
142	Sardines, Atlantic, canned in oil, drained solids.	3 ounces	85	62	175	20	9	...	...	...	0	372	2.5	190	.02	.17	4.6	...
143	Shad, baked with table fat and bacon.	3 ounces	85	64	170	20	10	...	...	...	0	20	.5	20	.11	.22	7.3	...
144	Shrimp, canned, meat.	3 ounces	85	70	100	21	1	...	...	...	1	98	2.6	50	.01	.03	1.5	...
145	Swordfish, broiled with butter or margarine.	3 ounces	85	65	150	24	5	...	...	...	0	23	1.1	1,750	.03	.04	9.3	...
146	Tuna, canned in oil, drained solids.	3 ounces	85	61	170	24	7	2	1	1	0	7	1.6	70	.04	.10	10.1	...

MATURE DRY BEANS AND PEAS, NUTS, PEANUTS; RELATED PRODUCTS

147	**Almonds, shelled, whole kernels.**	1 cup	142	5	850	26	77	6	52	15	28	332	6.7	0	.34	1.31	5.0	Trace
	Beans, dry: Common varieties as Great Northern, navy, and others: Cooked, drained:																	
148	Great Northern	1 cup	180	69	210	14	1	...	...	...	38	90	4.9	0	.25	.13	1.3	0
149	Navy (pea).	1 cup	190	69	225	15	1	...	...	...	40	95	5.1	0	.27	.13	1.3	0
	Canned, solids and liquid: White with —																	
150	Frankfurters (sliced).	1 cup	255	71	365	19	18	...	...	...	32	94	4.8	330	.18	.15	3.3	Trace
151	Pork and tomato sauce.	1 cup	255	71	310	16	7	2	3	1	49	138	4.6	330	.20	.08	1.5	5
152	Pork and sweet sauce.	1 cup	255	66	385	16	12	4	5	1	54	161	5.9	...	.15	.10	1.3	...
153	Red kidney.	1 cup	255	76	230	15	1	...	...	...	42	74	4.6	10	.13	.10	1.5	...
154	Lima, cooked, drained.	1 cup	190	64	260	16	1	...	...	...	49	55	5.9	...	.25	.11	1.3	...
155	**Cashew nuts, roasted.**	1 cup	140	5	785	24	64	11	45	4	41	53	5.3	140	.60	.35	2.5	...
	Coconut, fresh, meat only:																	
156	Pieces, approximately 2 by 2 by ½ inch.	1 piece	45	51	155	2	16	14	1	Trace	4	6	.8	0	.02	.01	.2	1
157	Shredded or grated, firmly packed.	1 cup	130	51	450	5	46	39	3	Trace	12	17	2.2	0	.07	.03	.7	4

NUTRITIVE VALUES OF THE EDIBLE PART OF FOODS — Continued

[Dashes in the columns for nutrients show that no suitable value could be found although there is reason to believe that a measurable amount of the nutrient may be present]

	FOOD, APPROXIMATE MEASURE, AND WEIGHT (IN GRAMS)			WATER	FOOD ENERGY	PRO-TEIN	FAT	FATTY ACIDS: SATU-RATED (TOTAL)	FATTY ACIDS: UNSATURATED: OLEIC	FATTY ACIDS: UNSATURATED: LIN-OLEIC	CARBO-HY-DRATE	CAL-CIUM	IRON	VITA-MIN A VALUE	THIA-MIN	RIBO-FLAVIN	NIACIN	ASCOR-BIC ACID
			Grams	*Percent*	*Calories*	*Grams*	*Grams*	*Grams*	*Grams*	*Grams*	*Grams*	*Milli-grams*	*Milli-grams*	*Inter-national units*	*Milli-grams*	*Milli-grams*	*Milli-grams*	*Milli-grams*
	MATURE DRY BEANS AND PEAS, NUTS, PEANUTS; RELATED PRODUCTS — Continued:																	
158	**Cowpeas or blackeye peas, dry, cooked.**	1 cup	248	80	190	13	1	....	....	....	34	42	3.2	20	.41	.11	1.1	Trace
159	**Peanuts, roasted, salted, halves.**	1 cup	144	2	840	37	72	16	31	21	27	107	3.0	....	.46	.19	24.7	0
160	**Peanut butter.**	1 tablespoon	16	2	95	4	8	2	4	2	3	9	.3	....	.02	.02	2.4	0
161	**Peas, split, dry, cooked.**	1 cup	250	70	290	20	1	....	....	....	52	28	4.2	100	.37	.22	2.2	....
162	**Pecans, halves.**	1 cup	108	3	740	10	77	5	48	15	16	79	2.6	140	.93	.14	1.0	2
163	**Walnuts, black or native, chopped.**	1 cup	126	3	790	26	75	4	26	36	19	Trace	7.6	380	.28	.14	.9	....

VEGETABLES AND VEGETABLE PRODUCTS

	FOOD, APPROXIMATE MEASURE, AND WEIGHT (IN GRAMS)			WATER	FOOD ENERGY	PRO-TEIN	FAT	SATU-RATED (TOTAL)	OLEIC	LIN-OLEIC	CARBO-HY-DRATE	CAL-CIUM	IRON	VITA-MIN A VALUE	THIA-MIN	RIBO-FLAVIN	NIACIN	ASCOR-BIC ACID
	Asparagus, green: Cooked, drained:																	
164	Spears, ½-in. diam. at base.	4 spears	60	94	10	1	Trace	....	....	....	2	13	.4	540	.10	.11	.8	16
165	Pieces, 1½ to 2-inch lengths.	1 cup	145	94	30	3	Trace	....	....	....	5	30	.9	1,310	.23	.26	2.0	38
166	Canned, solids and liquid.	1 cup	244	94	45	5	1	....	....	....	7	44	4.1	1,240	.15	.22	2.0	37

	Beans:																	
167	Lima, immature seeds, cooked, drained.	1 cup	170	71	190	13	1	...	...	...	34	80	4.3	480	.31	.17	2.2	29
	Snap:																	
	Green:																	
168	Cooked, drained.	1 cup	125	92	30	2	Trace	...	...	...	7	63	.8	680	.09	.11	.6	15
169	Canned, solids and liquid.	1 cup	239	94	45	2	Trace	...	...	...	10	81	2.9	690	.07	.10	.7	10
	Yellow or wax:																	
170	Cooked, drained.	1 cup	125	93	30	2	Trace	...	...	...	6	63	.8	290	.09	.11	.6	16
171	Canned, solids and liquid.	1 cup	239	94	45	2	1	...	...	...	10	81	2.9	140	.07	.10	.7	12
172	**Sprouted mung beans,** cooked, drained.	1 cup	125	91	35	4	Trace	...	...	...	7	21	1.1	30	.11	.13	.9	8
	Beets:																	
	Cooked, drained, peeled:																	
173	Whole beets, 2-in. diam.	2 beets	100	91	30	1	Trace	...	...	...	7	14	.5	20	.03	.04	.3	6
174	Diced or sliced.	1 cup	170	91	55	2	Trace	...	...	...	12	24	.9	30	.05	.07	.5	10
175	Canned, solids and liquid.	1 cup	246	90	85	2	Trace	...	...	...	19	34	1.5	20	.02	.05	.2	7
176	**Beet greens, leaves and stems, cooked, drained.**	1 cup	145	94	25	3	Trace	...	...	...	5	144	2.8	7,400	.10	.22	.4	22
	Blackeye peas. See Cowpeas.																	
	Broccoli, cooked, drained:																	
177	Whole stalks, medium size.	1 stalk	180	91	45	6	1	...	...	...	8	158	1.4	4,500	.16	.36	1.4	162
178	Stalks cut into ½-in. pieces.	1 cup	155	91	40	5	1	...	...	...	7	136	1.2	3,880	.14	.31	1.2	140
179	Chopped, yield from 10-oz. frozen pkg.	1⅜ cups	250	92	65	7	1	...	...	...	12	135	1.8	6,500	.15	.30	1.3	143
180	**Brussels sprouts, 7–8 sprouts (1¼ to 1½ in. diam.) per cup, cooked.**	1 cup	155	88	55	7	1	...	...	...	10	50	1.7	810	.12	.22	1.2	135
	Cabbage:																	
	Common varieties:																	
	Raw:																	
181	Coarsely shredded or sliced.	1 cup	70	92	15	1	Trace	...	...	...	4	34	.3	90	.04	.04	.2	33
182	Finely shredded or chopped.	1 cup	90	92	20	1	Trace	...	...	...	5	44	.4	120	.05	.05	.3	42
183	Cooked.	1 cup	145	94	30	2	Trace	...	...	...	6	64	.4	190	.06	.06	.4	48
184	Red, raw, coarsely shredded.	1 cup	70	90	20	1	Trace	...	...	...	5	29	.6	30	.06	.04	.3	43
185	Savoy, raw, coarsely shredded.	1 cup	70	92	15	2	Trace	...	...	...	3	47	.6	140	.04	.06	.2	39
186	**Cabbage, celery or Chinese, raw, cut in 1-in. pieces.**	1 cup	75	95	10	1	Trace	...	...	...	2	32	.5	110	.04	.03	.5	19
187	**Cabbage, spoon (or pakchoy), cooked.**	1 cup	170	95	25	2	Trace	...	...	...	4	252	1.0	5,270	.07	.14	1.2	26

NUTRITIVE VALUES OF THE EDIBLE PART OF FOODS — Continued

[Dashes in the columns for nutrients show that no suitable value could be found although there is reason to believe that a measurable amount of the nutrient may be present]

No.	FOOD, APPROXIMATE MEASURE, AND WEIGHT (IN GRAMS)			WATER	FOOD ENERGY	PRO-TEIN	FAT	FATTY ACIDS: SATU-RATED (TOTAL)	FATTY ACIDS: UNSATURATED: OLEIC	FATTY ACIDS: UNSATURATED: LIN-OLEIC	CARBO-HY-DRATE	CAL-CIUM	IRON	VITA-MIN A VALUE	THIA-MIN	RIBO-FLAVIN	NIACIN	ASCOR-BIC ACID
			Grams	Percent	Calories	Grams	Grams	Grams	Grams	Grams	Grams	Milli-grams	Milli-grams	Inter-national units	Milli-grams	Milli-grams	Milli-grams	Milli-grams
	VEGETABLES AND VEGETABLE PRODUCTS — Continued:																	
	Carrots:																	
	Raw:																	
188	Whole, 5½ by 1 inch, (25 thin strips).	1 carrot	50	88	20	1	Trace	…	…	…	5	18	.4	5,500	.03	.03	.3	4
189	Grated.	1 cup	110	88	45	1	Trace	…	…	…	11	41	.8	12,100	.06	.06	.7	9
190	Cooked, diced.	1 cup	145	91	45	1	Trace	…	…	…	10	48	.9	15,220	.08	.07	.7	9
191	Canned, strained or chopped (baby food).	1 ounce	28	92	10	Trace	Trace	…	…	…	2	7	.1	3,690	.01	.01	.1	1
192	**Cauliflower, cooked, flowerbuds.**	1 cup	120	93	25	3	Trace	…	…	…	5	25	.8	70	.11	.10	.7	66
	Celery, raw:																	
193	Stalk, large outer, 8 by about 1½ inches, at root end.	1 stalk	40	94	5	Trace	Trace	…	…	…	2	16	.1	100	.01	.01	.1	4
194	Pieces, diced.	1 cup	100	94	15	1	Trace	…	…	…	4	39	.3	240	.03	.03	.3	9
195	**Collards, cooked.**	1 cup	190	91	55	5	1	…	…	…	9	289	1.1	10,260	.27	.37	2.4	87
	Corn sweet:																	
196	Cooked, ear 5 by 1¾ inches.[5]	1 ear	140	74	70	3	1	…	…	…	16	2	.5	[6] 310	.09	.08	1.0	7
197	Canned, solids and liquid.	1 cup	256	81	170	5	2	…	…	…	40	10	1.0	[6] 690	.07	.12	2.3	13
198	**Cowpeas, cooked, immature seeds.**	1 cup	160	72	175	13	1	…	…	…	29	38	3.4	560	.49	.18	2.3	28
	Cucumbers, 10-ounce; 7½ by about 2 inches:																	
199	Raw, pared.	1 cucumber	207	96	30	1	Trace	…	…	…	7	35	.6	Trace	.07	.09	.4	23
200	Raw, pared, center slice ⅛-inch thick.	6 slices	50	96	5	Trace	Trace	…	…	…	2	8	.2	Trace	.02	.02	.1	6
201	**Dandelion greens, cooked.**	1 cup	180	90	60	4	1	…	…	…	12	252	3.2	21,060	.24	.29	…	32

202	**Endive, curly (including escarole).**	2 ounces	57	93	10	1	Trace				2	46	1.0	1,870	.04	.08	.3	6
203	**Kale, leaves including stems, cooked.**	1 cup	110	91	30	4	1				4	147	1.3	8,140				68
	Lettuce, raw:																	
204	Butterhead, as Boston types; head, 4-inch diameter.	1 head	220	95	30	3	Trace				6	77	4.4	2,130	.14	.13	.6	18
205	Crisphead, as Iceburg; head, 4¾-inch diameter.	1 head	454	96	60	4	Trace				13	91	2.3	1,500	.29	.27	1.3	29
206	Looseleaf, or bunching varieties, leaves.	2 large	50	94	10	1	Trace				2	34	.7	950	.03	.04	.2	9
207	**Mushrooms, canned, solids and liquid.**	1 cup	244	93	40	5	Trace				6	15	1.2	Trace	.04	.60	4.8	4
208	**Mustard greens, cooked.**	1 cup	140	93	35	3	1				6	193	2.5	8,120	.11	.19	.9	68
209	**Okra, cooked, pod 3 by ⅝ inch.**	8 pods	85	91	25	2	Trace				5	78	.4	420	.11	.15	.8	17
	Onions:																	
	Mature:																	
210	Raw, onion 2½-inch diameter.	1 onion	110	89	40	2	Trace				10	30	.6	40	.04	.04	.2	11
211	Cooked.	1 cup	210	92	60	3	Trace				14	50	.8	80	.06	.06	.4	14
212	Young green, small, without tops.	6 onions	50	88	20	1	Trace				5	20	.3	Trace	.02	.02	.2	12
213	**Parsley, raw, chopped.**	1 tablespoon	4	85	Trace	Trace	Trace				Trace	8	.2	340	Trace	.01	Trace	7
214	**Parsnips, cooked.**	1 cup	155	82	100	2	1				23	70	.9	50	.11	.12	.2	16
	Peas, green:																	
215	Cooked.	1 cup	160	82	115	9	1				19	37	2.9	860	.44	.17	3.7	33
216	Canned, solids and liquid.	1 cup	249	83	165	9	1				31	50	4.2	1,120	.23	.13	2.2	22
217	Canned, strained (baby food).	1 ounce	28	86	15	1	Trace				3	3	.4	140	.02	.02	.4	3
218	**Peppers, hot, red, without seeds, dried (ground chili powder, added seasonings).**	1 tablespoon	15	8	50	2	2				8	40	2.3	9,750	.03	.17	1.3	2
	Peppers, sweet:																	
	Raw, about 5 per pound:																	
219	Green pod without stem and seeds.	1 pod	74	93	15	1	Trace				4	7	.5	310	.06	.06	.4	94
220	Cooked, boiled, drained.	1 pod	73	95	15	1	Trace				3	7	.4	310	.05	.05	.4	70
	Potatoes, medium (about 3 per pound raw):																	
221	Baked, peeled after baking.	1 potato	99	75	90	3	Trace				21	9	.7	Trace	.10	.04	1.7	20
	Boiled:																	
222	Peeled after boiling.	1 potato	136	80	105	3	Trace				23	10	.8	Trace	.13	.05	2.0	22
223	Peeled before boiling.	1 potato	122	83	80	2	Trace				18	7	.6	Trace	.11	.04	1.4	20

NUTRITIVE VALUES OF THE EDIBLE PART OF FOODS — Continued

[Dashes in the columns for nutrients show that no suitable value could be found although there is reason to believe that a measurable amount of the nutrient may be present]

	FOOD, APPROXIMATE MEASURE, AND WEIGHT (IN GRAMS)			WATER	FOOD ENERGY	PRO-TEIN	FAT	FATTY ACIDS: SATU-RATED (TOTAL)	FATTY ACIDS: UNSATURATED: OLEIC	FATTY ACIDS: UNSATURATED: LIN-OLEIC	CARBO-HY-DRATE	CAL-CIUM	IRON	VITA-MIN A VALUE	THIA-MIN	RIBO-FLAVIN	NIACIN	ASCOR-BIC ACID
			Grams	Percent	Calories	Grams	Grams	Grams	Grams	Grams	Grams	Milli-grams	Milli-grams	Inter-national units	Milli-grams	Milli-grams	Milli-grams	Milli-grams
	VEGETABLES AND VEGETABLE PRODUCTS — Continued:																	
	Potatoes, Medium — Continued:																	
	French-fried, piece 2 by ½ by ½ inch:																	
224	Cooked in deep fat.	10 pieces	57	45	155	2	7	2	2	4	20	9	.7	Trace	.07	.04	1.8	12
225	Frozen, heated.	10 pieces	57	53	125	2	5	1	1	2	19	5	1.0	Trace	.08	.01	1.5	12
	Mashed:																	
226	Milk added.	1 cup	195	83	125	4	1				25	47	.8	50	.16	.10	2.0	19
227	Milk and butter added.	1 cup	195	80	185	4	8	4	3	Trace	24	47	.8	330	.16	.10	1.9	18
228	**Potato chips, medium, 2-inch diameter.**	10 chips	20	2	115	1	8	2	2	4	10	8	.4	Trace	.04	.01	1.0	3
229	**Pumpkin, canned.**	1 cup	228	90	75	2	1				18	57	.9	14,590	.07	.12	1.3	12
230	**Radishes, raw, small, without tops.**	4 radishes	40	94	5	Trace	Trace				1	12	.4	Trace	.01	.01	.1	10
231	**Sauerkraut, canned, solids and liquid.**	1 cup	235	93	45	2	Trace				9	85	1.2	120	.07	.09	.4	33
	Spinach:																	
232	Cooked.	1 cup	180	92	40	5	1				6	167	4.0	14,580	.13	.25	1.0	50
233	Canned, drained solids.	1 cup	180	91	45	5	1				6	212	4.7	14,400	.03	.21	.6	24
	Squash:																	
	Cooked:																	
234	Summer, diced.	1 cup	210	96	30	2	Trace				7	52	.8	820	.10	.16	1.6	21
235	Winter, baked, mashed.	1 cup	205	81	130	4	1				32	57	1.6	8,610	.10	.27	1.4	27
	Sweetpotatoes:																	
	Cooked, medium, 5 by 2 inches, weight raw about 6 ounces:																	
236	Baked, peeled after baking.	1 sweetpotato.	110	64	155	2	1				36	44	1.0	8,910	.10	.07	.7	24

237	Boiled, peeled after boiling.	1 sweetpotato	147	71	170	2	1	...	...	...	39	47	1.0	11,610	.13	.09	.9	25
238	Candied, 3½ by 2¼ inches.	1 sweetpotato	175	60	295	2	6	2	3	1	60	65	1.6	11,030	.10	.08	.8	17
239	Canned, vacuum or solid pack.	1 cup	218	72	235	4	Trace	...	...	...	54	54	1.7	17,000	.10	.10	1.4	30
	Tomatoes:																	
240	Raw, approx. 3-in. diam. 2⅛ in. high; wt., 7 oz.	1 tomato	200	94	40	2	Trace	...	...	...	9	24	.9	1,640	.11	.07	1.3	[7] 42
241	Canned, solids and liquid.	1 cup	241	94	50	2	1	...	...	...	10	14	1.2	2,170	.12	.07	1.7	41
	Tomato catsup:																	
242	Cup.	1 cup	273	69	290	6	1	...	...	...	69	60	2.2	3,820	.25	.19	4.4	41
243	Tablespoon.	1 tablespoon	15	69	15	Trace	Trace	...	...	...	4	3	.1	210	.01	.01	.2	2
	Tomato juice, canned:																	
244	Cup.	1 cup	243	94	45	2	Trace	...	...	...	10	17	2.2	1,940	.12	.07	1.9	39
245	Glass (6 fl. oz.).	1 glass	182	94	35	2	Trace	...	...	...	8	13	1.6	1,460	.09	.05	1.5	29
246	**Turnips, cooked, diced.**	1 cup	155	94	35	1	Trace	...	...	...	8	54	.6	Trace	.06	.08	.5	34
247	**Turnip greens, cooked.**	1 cup	145	94	30	3	Trace	...	...	...	5	252	1.5	8,270	.15	.33	.7	68

FRUITS AND FRUIT PRODUCTS

248	**Apples, raw (about 3 per lb.).**[5]	1 apple	150	85	70	Trace	Trace	...	...	...	18	8	.4	50	.04	.02	.1	3
249	**Apple juice, bottled or canned.**	1 cup	248	88	120	Trace	Trace	...	...	...	30	15	1.5	...	.02	.05	.2	2
	Applesauce, canned:																	
250	Sweetened.	1 cup	255	76	230	1	Trace	...	...	...	61	10	1.3	100	.05	.03	.1	[8] 3
251	Unsweetened or artificially sweetened.	1 cup	244	88	100	1	Trace	...	...	...	26	10	1.2	100	.05	.02	.1	[8] 2
	Apricots:																	
252	Raw (about 12 per lb.)[5]	3 apricots	114	85	55	1	Trace	...	...	...	14	18	.5	2,890	.03	.04	.7	10
253	Canned in heavy sirup.	1 cup	259	77	220	2	Trace	...	...	...	57	28	.8	4,510	.05	.06	.9	10
254	Dried, uncooked (40 halves per cup).	1 cup	150	25	390	8	1	...	...	...	100	100	8.2	16,350	.02	.23	4.9	19
255	Cooked, unsweetened, fruit and liquid.	1 cup	285	76	240	5	1	...	...	...	62	63	5.1	8,550	.01	.13	2.8	8
256	**Apricot nectar, canned.**	1 cup	251	85	140	1	Trace	...	...	...	37	23	.5	2,380	.03	.03	.5	[8] 8

NUTRITIVE VALUES OF THE EDIBLE PART OF FOODS — Continued

[Dashes in the columns for nutrients show that no suitable value could be found although there is reason to believe that a measurable amount of the nutrient may be present]

No.	FOOD, APPROXIMATE MEASURE, AND WEIGHT (IN GRAMS)			WATER	FOOD ENERGY	PROTEIN	FAT	FATTY ACIDS: SATURATED (TOTAL)	FATTY ACIDS: UNSATURATED: OLEIC	FATTY ACIDS: UNSATURATED: LINOLEIC	CARBOHYDRATE	CALCIUM	IRON	VITAMIN A VALUE	THIAMIN	RIBOFLAVIN	NIACIN	ASCORBIC ACID
			Grams	Percent	Calories	Grams	Grams	Grams	Grams	Grams	Grams	Milligrams	Milligrams	International units	Milligrams	Milligrams	Milligrams	Milligrams
	FRUITS AND FRUIT PRODUCTS — Continued:																	
	Avocados, whole fruit, raw:[5]																	
257	California (mid- and late-winter; diam. 3⅛ in.).	1 avocado	284	74	370	5	37	7	17	5	13	22	1.3	630	.24	.43	3.5	30
258	Florida (late summer, fall; diam. 3⅝ in.).	1 avocado	454	78	390	4	33	7	15	4	27	30	1.8	880	.33	.61	4.9	43
259	**Bananas, raw, medium size.**[5]	1 banana	175	76	100	1	Trace	....	....	....	26	10	.8	230	.06	.07	.8	12
260	**Banana flakes.**	1 cup	100	3	340	4	1	....	....	....	89	32	2.8	760	.18	.24	2.8	7
261	**Blackberries, raw.**	1 cup	144	84	85	2	1	....	....	....	19	46	1.3	290	.05	.06	.5	30
262	**Blueberries, raw.**	1 cup	140	83	85	1	1	....	....	....	21	21	1.4	140	.04	.08	.6	20
263	**Cantaloups, raw; medium, 5-inch diameter about 1⅔ pounds.**[5]	½ melon	385	91	60	1	Trace	....	....	....	14	27	.8	[9] 6,540	.08	.06	1.2	63
264	**Cherries, canned, red, sour, pitted, water pack.**	1 cup	244	88	105	2	Trace	....	....	....	26	37	.7	1,660	.07	.05	.5	12
265	**Cranberry juice cocktail, canned.**	1 cup	250	83	165	Trace	Trace	....	....	....	42	13	.8	Trace	.03	.03	.1	[10] 40
266	**Cranberry sauce, sweetened, canned, strained.**	1 cup	277	62	405	Trace	1	....	....	....	104	17	.6	60	.03	.03	.1	6
267	**Dates, pitted, cut.**	1 cup	178	22	490	4	1	....	....	....	130	105	5.3	90	.16	.17	3.9	0
268	**Figs, dried, large, 2 by 1 in.**	1 fig	21	23	60	1	Trace	....	....	....	15	26	.6	20	.02	.02	.1	0
269	**Fruit cocktail, canned, in heavy sirup.**	1 cup	256	80	195	1	Trace	....	....	....	50	23	1.0	360	.05	.03	1.3	5

	Grapefruit:																	
	Raw, medium, 3¾-in. diam.[5]																	
270	White.	½ grapefruit	241	89	45	1	Trace	....	....	....	12	19	.5	10	.05	.02	.2	44
271	Pink or red.	½ grapefruit	241	89	50	1	Trace	....	....	....	13	20	.5	540	.05	.02	.2	44
272	Canned, sirup pack.	1 cup	254	81	180	2	Trace	....	....	....	45	33	.8	30	.08	.05	.5	76
	Grapefruit juice:																	
273	Fresh.	1 cup	246	90	95	1	Trace	....	....	....	23	22	.5	(11)	.09	.04	.4	92
	Canned, white:																	
274	Unsweetened.	1 cup	247	89	100	1	Trace	....	....	....	24	20	1.0	20	.07	.04	.4	84
275	Sweetened.	1 cup	250	86	130	1	Trace	....	....	....	32	20	1.0	20	.07	.04	.4	78
	Frozen, concentrate, unsweetened:																	
276	Undiluted, can, 6 fluid ounces.	1 can	207	62	300	4	1	....	....	....	72	70	.8	60	.29	.12	1.4	286
277	Diluted with 3 parts water, by volume.	1 cup	247	89	100	1	Trace	....	....	....	24	25	.2	20	.10	.04	.5	96
278	Dehydrated crystals.	4 ounces	113	1	410	6	1	....	....	....	102	100	1.2	80	.40	.20	2.0	396
279	Prepared with water (1 pound yields about 1 gallon).	1 cup	247	90	100	1	Trace	....	....	....	24	22	.2	20	.10	.05	.5	91
	Grapes, raw:[5]																	
280	American type (slip skin).	1 cup	153	82	65	1	1	....	....	....	15	15	.4	100	.05	.03	.2	3
281	European type (adherent skin).	1 cup	160	81	95	1	Trace	....	....	....	25	17	.6	140	.07	.04	.4	6
	Grapejuice:																	
282	Canned or bottled.	1 cup	253	83	165	1	Trace	....	....	....	42	28	.8	....	.10	.05	.5	Trace
	Frozen concentrate, sweetened:																	
283	Undiluted, can, 6 fluid ounces.	1 can	216	53	395	1	Trace	....	....	....	100	22	.9	40	.13	.22	1.5	(12)
284	Diluted with 3 parts water, by volume.	1 cup	250	86	135	1	Trace	....	....	....	33	8	.3	10	.05	.08	.5	(12)
285	**Grapejuice drink, canned.**	1 cup	250	86	135	Trace	Trace	....	....	....	35	8	.3	....	.03	.03	.3	(12)
286	**Lemons, raw, 2⅛-in. diam., size 165.**[5] **Used for juice.**	1 lemon	110	90	20	1	Trace	....	....	....	6	19	.4	10	.03	.01	.1	39
287	**Lemon juice, raw.**	1 cup	244	91	60	1	Trace	....	....	....	20	17	.5	50	.07	.02	.2	112
	Lemonade concentrate:																	
288	Frozen, 6 fl. oz. per can.	1 can	219	48	430	Trace	Trace	....	....	....	112	9	.4	40	.04	.07	.7	66
289	Diluted with 4⅓ parts water, by volume.	1 cup	248	88	110	Trace	Trace	....	....	....	28	2	Trace	Trace	Trace	.02	.2	17
	Lime juice:																	
290	Fresh.	1 cup	246	90	65	1	Trace	....	....	....	22	22	.5	20	.05	.02	.2	79
291	Canned, unsweetened.	1 cup	246	90	65	1	Trace	....	....	....	22	22	.5	20	.05	.02	.2	52
	Limeade concentrate, frozen:																	
292	Undiluted, can, 6 fluid ounces.	1 can	218	50	410	Trace	Trace	....	....	....	108	11	.2	Trace	.02	.02	.2	26
293	Diluted with 4⅓ parts water, by volume.	1 cup	247	90	100	Trace	Trace	....	....	....	27	2	Trace	Trace	Trace	Trace	Trace	5

NUTRITIVE VALUES OF THE EDIBLE PART OF FOODS — Continued

[Dashes in the columns for nutrients show that no suitable value could be found although there is reason to believe that a measurable amount of the nutrient may be present]

	FOOD, APPROXIMATE MEASURE, AND WEIGHT (IN GRAMS)			WATER	FOOD ENERGY	PRO-TEIN	FAT	FATTY ACIDS: SATU-RATED (TOTAL)	FATTY ACIDS: UNSATURATED: OLEIC	FATTY ACIDS: UNSATURATED: LIN-OLEIC	CARBO-HY-DRATE	CAL-CIUM	IRON	VITA-MIN A VALUE	THIA-MIN	RIBO-FLAVIN	NIACIN	ASCOR-BIC ACID
			Grams	Percent	Calories	Grams	Grams	Grams	Grams	Grams	Grams	Milli-grams	Milli-grams	Inter-national units	Milli-grams	Milli-grams	Milli-grams	Milli-grams
	FRUITS AND FRUIT PRODUCTS — Continued:																	
294	**Oranges, raw, 2⅝-in. diam., all commercial, varieties.**[5]	1 orange	180	86	65	1	Trace				16	54	.5	260	.13	.05	.5	66
295	**Orange juice, fresh, all varieties.**	1 cup	248	88	110	2	1				26	27	.5	500	.22	.07	1.0	124
296	Canned, unsweetened.	1 cup	249	87	120	2	Trace				28	25	1.0	500	.17	.05	.7	100
	Frozen concentrate:																	
297	Undiluted, can, 6 fluid ounces.	1 can	213	55	360	5	Trace				87	75	.9	1,620	.68	.11	2.8	360
298	Diluted with 3 parts water, by volume.	1 cup	249	87	120	2	Trace				29	25	.2	550	.22	.02	1.0	120
299	Dehydrated crystals.	4 ounces	113	1	430	6	2				100	95	1.9	1,900	.76	.24	3.3	408
300	Prepared with water (1 pound yields about 1 gallon).	1 cup	248	88	115	2	1				27	25	.5	500	.20	.07	1.0	109
301	**Orange-apricot juice drink.**	1 cup	249	87	125	1	Trace				32	12	.2	1,440	.05	.02	.5	[10] 40
	Orange and grapefruit juice:																	
	Frozen concentrate:																	
302	Undiluted, can, 6 fluid ounces.	1 cup	210	59	330	4	1				78	61	.8	800	.48	.06	2.3	302
303	Diluted with 3 parts water, by volume.	1 cup	248	88	110	1	Trace				26	20	.2	270	.16	.02	.8	102
304	**Papayas, raw, ½-inch cubes.**	1 cup	182	89	70	1	Trace				18	36	.5	3,190	.07	.08	.5	102
	Peaches:																	
	Raw:																	
305	Whole, medium, 2-inch diameter, about 4 per pound.[5]	1 peach	114	89	35	1	Trace				10	9	.5	[31] 1,320	.02	.05	1.0	7
306	Sliced.	1 cup	168	89	65	1	Trace				16	15	.8	[32] 2,230	.03	.08	1.6	12

	Canned, yellow-fleshed, solids and liquid:																	
	Sirup pack, heavy:																	
307	Halves or slices.	1 cup	257	79	200	1	Trace	...	...	...	52	10	.8	1,100	.02	.06	1.4	7
308	Water pack.	1 cup	245	91	75	1	Trace	...	...	...	20	10	.7	1,100	.02	.06	1.4	7
309	Dried, uncooked.	1 cup	160	25	420	5	1	...	...	...	109	77	9.6	6,240	.02	.31	8.5	28
310	Cooked, unsweetened, 10–12 halves and juice.	1 cup	270	77	220	3	1	...	...	...	58	41	5.1	3,290	.01	.15	4.2	6
	Frozen:																	
311	Carton, 12 ounces, not thawed.	1 carton	340	76	300	1	Trace	...	...	...	77	14	1.7	2,210	.03	.14	2.4	[14] 135
	Pears:																	
312	Raw, 3 by 2½-inch diameter.[5]	1 pear	182	83	100	1	1	...	...	...	25	13	.5	30	.04	.07	.2	7
	Canned, solids and liquid:																	
	Sirup pack, heavy:																	
313	Halves or slices.	1 cup	255	80	195	1	1	...	...	...	50	13	.5	Trace	.03	.05	.3	4
	Pineapple:																	
314	Raw, diced.	1 cup	140	85	75	1	Trace	...	...	...	19	24	.7	100	.12	.04	.3	24
	Canned, heavy sirup pack, solids and liquid:																	
315	Crushed.	1 cup	260	80	195	1	Trace	...	...	...	50	29	.8	120	.20	.06	.5	17
316	Sliced, slices and juice.	2 small or 1 large	122	80	90	Trace	Trace	...	...	...	24	13	.4	50	.09	.03	.2	8
317	**Pineapple juice, canned.**	1 cup	249	86	135	1	Trace	...	...	...	34	37	.7	120	.12	.04	.5	[3] 22
	Plums, all except prunes:																	
318	Raw, 2-inch diameter, about 2 ounces.[5]	1 plum	60	87	25	Trace	Trace	...	...	...	7	7	.3	140	.02	.02	.3	3
	Canned, sirup pack (Italian prunes):																	
319	Plums (with pits) and juice.[5]	1 cup	256	77	205	1	Trace	...	...	...	53	22	2.2	2,970	.05	.05	.9	4
	Prunes, dried, "softenized", medium:																	
320	Uncooked.[5]	4 prunes	32	28	70	1	Trace	...	...	...	18	14	1.1	440	.02	.04	.4	1
321	Cooked, unsweetened, 17–18 prunes and ⅓ cup liquid.[5]	1 cup	270	66	295	2	1	...	...	...	78	60	4.5	1,860	.08	.18	1.7	2
322	**Prune juice, canned or bottled.**	1 cup	256	80	200	1	Trace	...	...	...	49	36	10.5	...	.03	.03	1.0	[3] 5
	Raisins, seedless:																	
323	Packaged, ½ oz. or 1½ tbsp. per pkg.	1 pkg.	14	18	40	Trace	Trace	...	...	...	11	9	.5	Trace	.02	.01	1	Trace
324	Cup, pressed down.	1 cup	165	18	480	4	Trace	...	...	...	128	102	5.8	30	.18	.13	.8	2
	Raspberries, red:																	
325	Raw	1 cup	123	84	70	1	1	...	...	...	17	27	1.1	160	.04	.11	1.1	31
326	Frozen, 10-ounce carton, not thawed.	1 carton	284	74	275	2	1	...	...	...	70	37	1.7	200	.06	.17	1.7	59
327	**Rhubarb, cooked, sugar added.**	1 cup	272	63	385	1	Trace	...	...	...	98	212	1.6	220	.06	.15	.7	17
	Strawberries:																	
328	Raw, capped.	1 cup	149	90	55	1	1	...	...	...	13	31	1.5	90	.04	.10	1.0	88
329	Frozen, 10-ounce carton, not thawed.	1 carton	284	71	310	1	1	...	...	...	79	40	2.0	90	.06	.17	1.5	150

NUTRITIVE VALUES OF THE EDIBLE PART OF FOODS — Continued

[Dashes in the columns for nutrients show that no suitable value could be found although there is reason to believe that a measurable amount of the nutrient may be present]

	FOOD, APPROXIMATE MEASURE, AND WEIGHT (IN GRAMS)			WATER	FOOD ENERGY	PROTEIN	FAT	FATTY ACIDS: SATURATED (TOTAL)	FATTY ACIDS: UNSATURATED: OLEIC	FATTY ACIDS: UNSATURATED: LINOLEIC	CARBOHYDRATE	CALCIUM	IRON	VITAMIN A VALUE	THIAMIN	RIBOFLAVIN	NIACIN	ASCORBIC ACID
			Grams	*Percent*	*Calories*	*Grams*	*Grams*	*Grams*	*Grams*	*Grams*	*Grams*	*Milligrams*	*Milligrams*	*International units*	*Milligrams*	*Milligrams*	*Milligrams*	*Milligrams*
	FRUITS AND FRUIT PRODUCTS — Continued:																	
330	**Tangerines, raw, medium, 2⅜-in. diam., size 176.**[5]	1 tangerine	116	87	40	1	Trace	....	....	....	10	34	.3	360	.05	.02	.1	27
331	**Tangerine juice, canned, sweetened.**	1 cup	249	87	125	1	1	....	....	....	30	45	.5	1,050	.15	.05	.2	55
332	**Watermelon, raw, wedge, 4 by 8 inches (1/16 of 10 by 16-inch melon, about 2 pounds with rind).**[5]	1 wedge	925	93	115	2	1	....	....	....	27	30	2.1	2,510	.13	.13	.7	30

GRAIN PRODUCTS

	FOOD, APPROXIMATE MEASURE, AND WEIGHT (IN GRAMS)			WATER	FOOD ENERGY	PROTEIN	FAT	SATURATED (TOTAL)	OLEIC	LINOLEIC	CARBOHYDRATE	CALCIUM	IRON	VITAMIN A VALUE	THIAMIN	RIBOFLAVIN	NIACIN	ASCORBIC ACID
	Bagel, 3-in. diam.:																	
333	Egg.	1 bagel	55	32	165	6	2	....	....	....	28	9	1.2	30	.14	.10	1.2	0
334	Water.	1 bagel	55	29	165	6	2	....	....	....	30	8	1.2	0	.15	.11	1.4	0
335	**Barley, pearled, light, uncooked.**	1 cup	200	11	700	16	2	Trace	1	1	158	32	4.0	0	.24	.10	6.2	0
336	**Biscuits, baking powder from home recipe with enriched flour, 2-in. diam.**	1 biscuit	28	27	105	2	5	1	2	1	13	34	.4	Trace	.06	.06	.1	Trace
337	**Biscuits, baking powder from mix, 2-in. diam.**	1 biscuit	28	28	90	2	3	1	1	1	15	19	.6	Trace	.08	.07	.6	Trace

338	**Bran flakes (40% bran), added thiamin and iron.**	1 cup	35	3	105	4	1				28	25	12.3	0	.14	.06	2.2	0
339	**Bran flakes with raisins, added thiamin and iron.**	1 cup	50	7	145	4	1				40	28	13.5	Trace	.16	.07	2.7	0
	Breads:																	
340	Boston brown bread, slice 3 by ¾ in.	1 slice	48	45	100	3	1				22	43	.9	0	.05	.03	.6	0
	Cracked-wheat bread:																	
341	Loaf, 1 lb.	1 loaf	454	35	1,190	40	10	2	5	2	236	399	5.0	Trace	.53	.41	5.9	Trace
342	Slice, 18 slices per loaf.	1 slice	25	35	65	2	1				13	22	.3	Trace	.03	.02	.3	Trace
	French or vienna bread:																	
343	Enriched, 1 lb. loaf.	1 loaf	454	31	1,315	41	14	3	8	2	251	195	10.0	Trace	1.27	1.00	11.3	Trace
344	Unenriched, 1 lb. loaf.	1 loaf	454	31	1,315	41	14	3	8	2	251	195	3.2	Trace	.36	.36	3.6	Trace
	Italian bread:																	
345	Enriched 1 lb. loaf.	1 loaf	454	32	1,250	41	4	Trace	1	2	256	77	10.0	0	1.32	.91	11.8	0
346	Unenriched, 1 lb. loaf.	1 loaf	454	32	1,250	41	4	Trace	1	2	256	77	3.2	0	.41	.27	3.6	0
	Raisin bread:																	
347	Loaf, 1 lb.	1 loaf	454	35	1,190	30	13	3	8	2	243	322	5.9	Trace	.23	.41	3.2	Trace
348	Slice, 18 slices per loaf.	1 slice	25	35	65	2	1				13	18	.3	Trace	.01	.02	.2	Trace
	Rye bread:																	
	American, light (⅓ rye, ⅔ wheat):																	
349	Loaf, 1 lb.	1 loaf	454	36	1,100	41	5				236	340	7.3	0	.82	.32	6.4	0
350	Slice, 18 slices per loaf.	1 slice	25	36	60	2	Trace				13	19	.4	0	.05	.02	.4	0
351	Pumpernickel, loaf, 1 lb.	1 loaf	454	34	1,115	41	5				241	381	10.9	0	1.04	.64	5.4	0
	White bread, enriched:[15]																	
	Soft-crumb type:																	
352	Loaf, 1 lb.	1 loaf	454	36	1,225	39	15	3	8	2	229	381	11.3	Trace	1.13	.95	10.9	Trace
353	Slice, 18 slices per loaf.	1 slice	25	36	70	2	1				13	21	.6	Trace	.06	.05	.6	Trace
354	Slice, toasted.	1 slice	22	25	70	2	1				13	21	.6	Trace	.06	.05	.6	Trace
355	Slice, 22 slices per loaf.	1 slice	20	36	55	2	1				10	17	.5	Trace	.05	.04	.5	Trace
356	Slice, toasted.	1 slice	17	25	55	2	1				10	17	.5	Trace	.05	.04	.5	Trace
357	Loaf, 1½ lbs.	1 loaf	680	36	1,835	59	22	5	12	3	343	571	17.0	Trace	1.70	1.43	16.3	Trace
358	Slice, 24 slices per loaf.	1 slice	28	36	75	2	1				14	24	.7	Trace	.07	.06	.7	Trace
359	Slice, toasted.	1 slice	24	25	75	2	1				14	24	.7	Trace	.07	.06	.7	Trace
360	Slice, 28 slices per loaf.	1 slice	24	36	65	2	1				12	20	.6	Trace	.06	.05	.6	Trace
361	Slice, toasted.	1 slice	21	25	65	2	1				12	20	.6	Trace	.06	.05	.6	Trace
	Firm-crumb type:																	
362	Loaf, 1 lb.	1 loaf	454	35	1,245	41	17	4	10	2	228	435	11.3	Trace	1.22	.91	10.9	Trace
363	Slice, 20 slices per loaf.	1 slice	23	35	65	2	1				12	22	.6	Trace	.06	.05	.6	Trace
364	Slice, toasted.	1 slice	20	24	65	2	1				12	22	.6	Trace	.06	.05	.6	Trace
365	Loaf, 2 lbs.	1 loaf	907	35	2,495	82	34	8	20	4	455	871	22.7	Trace	2.45	1.81	21.8	Trace
366	Slice, 34 slices per loaf.	1 slice	27	35	75	2	1				14	26	.7	Trace	.07	.05	.6	Trace
367	Slice, toasted.	1 slice	23	35	75	2	1				14	26	.7	Trace	.07	.05	.6	Trace
	Whole-wheat bread, soft-crumb type:																	
368	Loaf, 1 lb.	1 loaf	454	36	1,095	41	12	2	6	2	224	381	13.6	Trace	1.36	.45	12.7	Trace

NUTRITIVE VALUES OF THE EDIBLE PART OF FOODS — Continued

[Dashes in the columns for nutrients show that no suitable value could be found although there is reason to believe that a measurable amount of the nutrient may be present]

	FOOD, APPROXIMATE MEASURE, AND WEIGHT (IN GRAMS)			WATER	FOOD ENERGY	PRO-TEIN	FAT	FATTY ACIDS: SATU-RATED (TOTAL)	FATTY ACIDS: UNSATURATED: OLEIC	FATTY ACIDS: UNSATURATED: LIN-OLEIC	CARBO-HY-DRATE	CAL-CIUM	IRON	VITA-MIN A VALUE	THIA-MIN	RIBO-FLAVIN	NIACIN	ASCOR-BIC ACID
			Grams	Percent	Calories	Grams	Grams	Grams	Grams	Grams	Grams	Milli-grams	Milli-grams	Inter-national units	Milli-grams	Milli-grams	Milli-grams	Milli-grams
	GRAIN PRODUCTS — Continued:																	
	Breads — Continued:																	
369	Slice, 16 slices per loaf.	1 slice	28	36	65	3	1				14	24	.8	Trace	.09	.03	.8	Trace
370	Slice, toasted.	1 slice	24	24	65	3	1				14	24	.8	Trace	.09	.03	.8	Trace
	Whole-wheat bread, firm-crumb type:																	
371	Loaf, 1 lb.	1 loaf	454	36	1,100	48	14	3	6	3	216	449	13.6	Trace	1.18	.54	12.7	Trace
372	Slice, 18 slices per loaf.	1 slice	25	36	60	3	1				12	25	.8	Trace	.06	.03	.7	Trace
373	Slice, toasted.	1 slice	21	24	60	3	1				12	25	.8	Trace	.06	.03	.7	Trace
374	**Breadcrumbs, dry, grated.**	1 cup	100	6	390	13	5	1	2	1	73	122	3.6	Trace	.22	.30	3.5	Trace
375	**Buckwheat flour, light, sifted.**	1 cup	98	12	340	6	1				78	11	1.0	0	.08	.04	.4	0
376	**Bulgur, canned, seasoned.**	1 cup	135	56	245	8	4				44	27	1.9	0	.08	.05	4.1	0
	Cakes made from cake mixes:																	
	Angelfood:																	
377	Whole cake.	1 cake	635	34	1,645	36	1				377	603	1.9	0	.03	.70	.6	0
378	Piece, 1/12 of 10-in. diam. cake.	1 piece	53	34	135	3	Trace				32	50	.2	0	Trace	.06	.1	0
	Cupcakes, small, 2½ in. diam.:																	
379	Without icing.	1 cupcake	25	26	90	1	3	1	1	1	14	40	.1	40	.01	.03	.1	Trace
380	With chocolate icing.	1 cupcake	36	22	130	2	5	2	2	1	21	47	.3	60	.01	.04	.1	Trace
	Devil's food, 2-layer, with chocolate icing:																	
381	Whole cake.	cake	1,107	24	3,755	49	136	54	58	16	645	653	8.9	1,660	.33	.89	3.3	1
382	Piece, 1/16 of 9-in. diam. cake.	1 piece	69	24	235	3	9	3	4	1	40	41	.6	100	.02	.06	.2	Trace
383	Cupcake, small, 2½ in. diam.	1 cupcake	35	24	120	2	4	1	2	Trace	20	21	.3	50	.01	.03	.1	Trace
	Gingerbread:																	
384	Whole cake.	1 cake	570	37	1,575	18	39	10	19	9	291	513	9.1	Trace	.17	.51	4.6	2
385	Piece, 1/9 of 8-in. square cake.	1 piece	63	37	175	2	4	1	2	1	32	57	1.0	Trace	.02	.06	.5	Trace

	White, 2-layer, with chocolate icing:																		
386	Whole cake.	1 cake	1,140	21	4,000	45	122	45	54	17	716	1,129	5.7	680	.23	.91	2.3	2
387	Piece, 1/16 of 9-in. diam. cake.	1 piece	71	21	250	3	8	3	3	1	45	70	.4	40	.01	.06	.1	Trace
	Cakes made from home recipes:[16]																		
388	Boston cream pie; piece 1/12 of 8-in. diam.	1 piece	69	35	210	4	6	2	3	1	34	46	.3	140	.02	.08	.1	Trace
	Fruitcake, dark, made with enriched flour:																		
389	Loaf, 1 lb.	1 loaf	454	18	1,720	22	69	15	37	13	271	327	11.8	540	.59	.64	3.6	2
390	Slice, 1/30 of 8-in. loaf.	1 slice	15	18	55	1	2	Trace	1	Trace	9	11	.4	20	.02	.02	.1	Trace
	Plain sheet cake:																		
	Without icing:																		
391	Whole cake.	1 cake	777	25	2,830	35	108	30	52	21	434	497	3.1	1,320	.16	.70	1.6	2
392	Piece, 1/9 of 9-in. square cake.	1 piece	86	25	315	4	12	3	6	2	48	55	.3	150	.02	.08	.2	Trace
393	With boiled white icing, piece, 1/9 of 9-in. square cake.	1 piece	114	23	400	4	12	3	6	2	71	56	.3	150	.02	.08	.2	Trace
	Pound:																		
394	Loaf, 8½ by 3½ by 3 in.	1 loaf	514	17	2,430	29	152	34	68	17	242	108	4.1	1,440	.15	.46	1.0	0
395	Slice, ½-in. thick.	1 slice	30	17	140	2	9	2	4	1	14	6	.2	80	.01	.03	.1	0
	Sponge:																		
396	Whole cake.	1 cake	790	32	2,345	60	45	14	20	4	427	237	9.5	3,560	.40	1.11	1.6	Trace
397	Piece, 1/12 of 10-in. diam. cake.	1 piece	66	32	195	5	4	1	2	Trace	36	20	.8	300	.03	.09	.1	Trace
	Yellow, 2-layer, without icing:																		
398	Whole cake.	1 cake	870	24	3,160	39	111	31	53	22	506	618	3.5	1,310	.17	.70	1.7	2
399	Piece, 1/16 of 9-in. diam. cake.	1 piece	54	24	200	2	7	2	3	1	32	39	.2	80	.01	.04	.1	Trace
	Yellow, 2-layer, with chocolate icing:																		
400	Whole cake.	1 cake	1,203	21	4,390	51	156	55	69	23	727	818	7.2	1,920	.24	.96	2.4	Trace
401	Piece, 1/16 of 9-in. diam. cake.	1 piece	75	21	275	3	10	3	4	1	45	51	.5	120	.02	.06	.2	Trace
	Cake icings. See Sugars, Sweets.																		
	Cookies:																		
	Brownies with nuts:																		
402	Made from home recipe with enriched flour.	1 brownie	20	10	95	1	6	1	3	1	10	8	.4	40	.04	.02	.1	Trace
403	Made from mix.	1 brownie	20	11	85	1	4	1	2	1	13	9	.4	20	.03	.02	.1	Trace
	Chocolate chip:																		
404	Made from home recipe with enriched flour.	1 cookie	10	3	50	1	3	1	1	1	6	4	.2	10	.01	.01	.1	Trace
405	Commercial.	1 cookie	10	3	50	1	2	1	1	Trace	7	4	.2	10	Trace	Trace	Trace	Trace
406	Fig bars, commercial.	1 cookie	14	14	50	1	1				11	11	.2	20	Trace	.01	.1	Trace
407	Sandwich, chocolate or vanilla, commercial.	1 cookie	10	2	50	1	2	1	1	Trace	7	2	.1	0	Trace	Trace	.1	0
	Corn flakes, added nutrients:																		
408	Plain.	1 cup	25	4	100	2	Trace				21	4	.4	0	.11	.02	.5	0
409	Sugar-covered.	1 cup	40	2	155	2	Trace				36	5	.4	0	.16	.02	.8	0
	Corn (hominy) grits, degermed, cooked:																		
410	Enriched.	1 cup	245	87	125	3	Trace				27	2	.7	[17] 150	.10	.07	1.0	0
411	Unenriched.	1 cup	245	87	125	3	Trace				27	2	.2	[17] 150	.05	.02	.5	0

NUTRITIVE VALUES OF THE EDIBLE PART OF FOODS — Continued

[Dashes in the columns for nutrients show that no suitable value could be found although there is reason to believe that a measurable amount of the nutrient may be present]

	FOOD, APPROXIMATE MEASURE, AND WEIGHT (IN GRAMS)			WATER	FOOD ENERGY	PRO-TEIN	FAT	FATTY ACIDS: SATU-RATED (TOTAL)	FATTY ACIDS: UNSATURATED: OLEIC	FATTY ACIDS: UNSATURATED: LIN-OLEIC	CARBO-HY-DRATE	CAL-CIUM	IRON	VITA-MIN A VALUE	THIA-MIN	RIBO-FLAVIN	NIACIN	ASCOR-BIC ACID
			Grams	Percent	Calories	Grams	Grams	Grams	Grams	Grams	Grams	Milli-grams	Milli-grams	Inter-national units	Milli-grams	Milli-grams	Milli-grams	Milli-grams
	GRAIN PRODUCTS — Continued:																	
	Cornmeal:																	
412	Whole-ground, unbolted, dry.	1 cup	122	12	435	11	5	1	2	2	90	24	2.9	[17] 620	.46	.13	2.4	0
413	Bolted (nearly wholegrain) dry.	1 cup	122	12	440	11	4	Trace	1	2	91	21	2.2	[17] 590	.37	.10	2.3	0
	Degermed, enriched:																	
414	Dry form.	1 cup	138	12	500	11	2	...	...	...	108	8	4.0	[17] 610	.61	.36	4.8	0
415	Cooked.	1 cup	240	88	120	3	1	...	...	...	26	2	1.0	[17] 140	.14	.10	1.2	0
	Degermed, unenriched:																	
416	Dry form.	1 cup	138	12	500	11	2	...	...	...	108	8	1.5	[17] 610	.19	.07	1.4	0
417	Cooked.	1 cup	240	88	120	3	1	...	...	...	26	2	.5	[17] 140	.05	.02	.2	0
418	**Corn muffins, made with enriched degermed cornmeal and enriched flour; muffin 2⅜-in. diam.**	1 muffin	40	33	125	3	4	2	2	Trace	19	42	.7	[17] 120	.08	.09	.6	Trace
419	**Corn muffins, made with mix, egg, and milk; muffin 2⅜-in. diam.**	1 muffin	40	30	130	3	4	1	2	1	20	96	.6	100	.07	.08	.6	Trace
420	**Corn, puffed, presweetened, added nutrients.**	1 cup	30	2	115	1	Trace	...	...	...	27	3	.5	0	.13	.05	.6	0
421	**Corn, shredded, added nutrients.**	1 cup	25	3	100	2	Trace	...	...	...	22	1	.6	0	.11	.05	.5	0
	Crackers:																	
422	Graham, 2½-in. square.	4 crackers	28	6	110	2	3	...	...	...	21	11	.4	0	.01	.06	.4	0
423	Saltines.	4 crackers	11	4	50	1	1	...	1	...	8	2	.1	0	Trace	Trace	.1	0
	Danish pastry, plain (without fruit or nuts):																	
424	Packaged ring, 12 ounces.	1 ring	340	22	1,435	25	80	24	37	15	155	170	3.1	1,050	.24	.51	2.7	Trace

425	Round piece, approx. 4¼-in. diam. by 1 in.	1 pastry	65	22	275	5	15	5	7	3	30	33	.6	200	.05	.10	.5	Trace
426	Ounce.	1 ounce	28	22	120	2	7	2	3	1	13	14	.3	90	.02	.04	.2	Trace
427	**Doughnuts, cake type.**	1 doughnut	32	24	125	1	6	1	4	Trace	16	13	[18].4	30	[18].05	[18].05	[18].4	Trace
428	**Farina, quick-cooking, enriched, cooked.**	1 cup	245	89	105	3	Trace				22	147	[19].7	0	[19].12	[19].07	[19] 1.0	0
	Macaroni, cooked:																	
	Enriched:																	
429	Cooked, firm stage (undergoes additional cooking in a food mixture).	1 cup	130	64	190	6	1				39	14	[19] 1.4	0	[19].23	[19].14	[19] 1.8	0
430	Cooked until tender.	1 cup	140	72	155	5	1				32	8	[19] 1.3	0	[19].20	[19].11	[19] 1.5	0
	Unenriched:																	
431	Cooked, firm stage (undergoes additional cooking in a food mixture).	1 cup	130	64	190	6	1				39	14	.7	0	.03	.03	.5	0
432	Cooked until tender.	1 cup	140	72	155	5	1				32	11	.6	0	.01	.01	.4	0
433	**Macaroni (enriched) and cheese, baked.**	1 cup	200	58	430	17	22	10	9	2	40	362	1.8	860	.20	.40	1.8	Trace
434	Canned.	1 cup	240	80	230	9	10	4	3	1	26	199	1.0	260	.12	.24	1.0	Trace
435	**Muffins, with enriched white flour; muffin, 3-inch diameter.**	1 muffin	40	38	120	3	4	1	2	1	17	42	.6	40	.07	.09	.6	Trace
	Noodles (egg noodles), cooked:																	
436	Enriched.	1 cup	160	70	200	7	2	1	1	Trace	37	16	[19] 1.4	110	[19].22	[19].13	[19] 1.9	0
437	Unenriched.	1 cup	160	70	200	7	2	1	1	Trace	37	16	1.0	110	.05	.03	.6	0
438	**Oats (with or without corn) puffed, added nutrients.**	1 cup	25	3	100	3	1				19	44	1.2	0	.24	.04	.5	0
439	**Oatmeal or rolled oats, cooked.**	1 cup	240	87	130	5	2			1	23	22	1.4	0	.19	.05	.2	0
	Pancakes, 4-inch diameter:																	
440	Wheat, enriched flour (home recipe).	1 cake	27	50	60	2	2	Trace	1	Trace	9	27	.4	30	.05	.06	.4	Trace
441	Buckwheat (made from mix with egg and milk).	1 cake	27	58	55	2	2	1	1	Trace	6	59	.4	60	.03	.04	.2	Trace
442	Plain or buttermilk (made from mix with egg and milk).	1 cake	27	51	60	2	2	1	1	Trace	9	58	.3	70	.04	.06	.2	Trace
	Pie (piecrust made with unenriched flour):																	
	Sector, 4-in., 1/7 of 9-in. diam. pie:																	
443	Apple (2-crust).	1 sector	135	48	350	3	15	4	7	3	51	11	.4	40	.03	.03	.5	1
444	Butterscotch (1-crust).	1 sector	130	45	350	6	14	5	6	2	50	98	1.2	340	.04	.13	.3	Trace
445	Cherry (2-crust).	1 sector	135	47	350	4	15	4	7	3	52	19	.4	590	.03	.03	.7	Trace
446	Custard (1-crust).	1 sector	130	58	285	8	14	5	6	2	30	125	.8	300	.07	.21	.4	0
447	Lemon meringue (1-crust).	1 sector	120	47	305	4	12	4	6	2	45	17	.6	200	.04	.10	.2	4

NUTRITIVE VALUES OF THE EDIBLE PART OF FOODS — Continued

[Dashes in the columns for nutrients show that no suitable value could be found although there is reason to believe that a measurable amount of the nutrient may be present]

	FOOD, APPROXIMATE MEASURE, AND WEIGHT (IN GRAMS)			WATER	FOOD ENERGY	PRO-TEIN	FAT	FATTY ACIDS			CARBO-HY-DRATE	CAL-CIUM	IRON	VITA-MIN A VALUE	THIA-MIN	RIBO-FLAVIN	NIACIN	ASCOR-BIC ACID
								SATU-RATED (TOTAL)	UNSATURATED OLEIC	UNSATURATED LIN-OLEIC								
			Grams	Percent	Calories	Grams	Grams	Grams	Grams	Grams	Grams	Milli-grams	Milli-grams	Inter-national units	Milli-grams	Milli-grams	Milli-grams	Milli-grams
	GRAIN PRODUCTS — Continued:																	
	Pie (Piecrust made with unenriched flour) — Continued:																	
	Sector, 4-in., 1/7 of 9-in. diam. pie:																	
448	Mince (2-crust).	1 sector	135	43	365	3	16	4	8	3	56	38	1.4	Trace	.09	.05	.5	1
449	Pecan (1-crust).	1 sector	118	20	490	6	27	4	16	5	60	55	3.3	190	.19	.08	.4	Trace
450	Pineapple chiffon (1-crust).	1 sector	93	41	265	6	11	3	5	2	36	22	.8	320	.04	.08	.4	1
451	Pumpkin (1-crust).	1 sector	130	59	275	5	15	5	6	2	32	66	.7	3,210	.04	.13	.7	Trace
	Piecrust, baked shell for pie made with:																	
452	Enriched flour.	1 shell	180	15	900	11	60	16	28	12	79	25	3.1	0	.36	.25	3.2	0
453	Unenriched flour.	1 shell	180	15	900	11	60	16	28	12	79	25	.9	0	.05	.05	.9	0
	Piecrust mix including stick form:																	
454	Package, 10-oz., for double crust.	1 package	284	9	1,480	20	93	23	46	21	141	131	1.4	0	.11	.11	2.0	0
455	**Pizza (cheese) 5½-in. sector; ⅛ of 14-in. diam. pie.**	1 sector	75	45	185	7	6	2	3	Trace	27	107	.7	290	.04	.12	.7	4
	Popcorn, popped:																	
456	Plain, large kernel.	1 cup	6	4	25	1	Trace	...	...	...	5	1	.2	...	...	.01	.1	0
457	With oil and salt.	1 cup	9	3	40	1	2	1	Trace	Trace	5	1	.2	...	...	.01	.2	0
458	Sugar coated.	1 cup	35	4	135	2	1	...	...	...	30	2	.5	...	...	.02	.4	0
	Pretzels:																	
459	Dutch, twisted.	1 pretzel	16	5	60	2	1	...	...	...	12	4	.2	0	Trace	Trace	.1	0
460	Thin, twisted.	1 pretzel	6	5	25	1	Trace	...	...	...	5	1	.1	0	Trace	Trace	Trace	0
461	Stick, small, 2¼ inches.	10 sticks	3	5	10	Trace	Trace	...	...	...	2	1	Trace	0	Trace	Trace	Trace	0
462	Stick, regular, 3⅛ inches.	5 sticks	3	5	10	Trace	Trace	...	...	...	2	1	Trace	0	Trace	Trace	Trace	0
	Rice, white:																	
	Enriched:																	
463	Raw.	1 cup	185	12	670	12	1	...	...	...	149	44	[20] 5.4	0	[20] .81	[20] .06	[20] 6.5	0

464	Cooked.	1 cup	205	73	225	4	Trace				50	21	[20] 1.8	0	[20] .23	[20] .02	[20] 2.1	0
465	Instant, ready-to-serve.	1 cup	165	73	180	4	Trace				40	5	[20] 1.3	0	[20] .21	[20] ...	[20] 1.7	0
466	Unenriched, cooked.	1 cup	205	73	225	4	Trace				50	21	.4	0	.04	.02	.8	0
467	Parboiled, cooked.	1 cup	175	73	185	4	Trace				41	33	[20] 1.4	0	[20] .19	[20] ...	[20] 2.1	0
468	**Rice, puffed, added nutrients.**	1 cup	15	4	60	1	Trace				13	3	.3	0	.07	.01	.7	0
	Rolls, enriched:																	
	Cloverleaf or pan:																	
469	Home recipe.	1 roll	35	26	120	3	3	1	1	1	20	16	.7	30	.09	.09	.8	Trace
470	Commercial.	1 roll	28	31	85	2	2	Trace	1	Trace	15	21	.5	Trace	.08	.05	.6	Trace
471	Frankfurter or hamburger.	1 roll	40	31	120	3	2	1	1	1	21	30	.8	Trace	.11	.07	.9	Trace
472	Hard, round or rectangular.	1 roll	50	25	155	5	2	Trace	1	Trace	30	24	1.2	Trace	.13	.12	1.4	Trace
473	**Rye wafers, whole-grain, 1⅞ by 3½ inches.**	2 wafers	13	6	45	2	Trace				10	7	.5	0	.04	.03	.2	0
474	**Spaghetti, cooked, tender stage, enriched.**	1 cup	140	72	155	5	1				32	11	[19] 1.3	0	[19] .20	[19] .11	[19] 1.5	0
	Spaghetti with meat balls, and tomato sauce:																	
475	Home recipe.	1 cup	248	70	330	19	12	4	6	1	39	124	3.7	1,590	.25	.30	4.0	22
476	Canned.	1 cup	250	78	260	12	10	2	3	4	28	53	3.3	1,000	.15	.18	2.3	5
	Spaghetti in tomato sauce with cheese:																	
477	Home recipe.	1 cup	250	77	260	9	9	2	5	1	37	80	2.3	1,080	.25	.18	2.3	13
478	Canned.	1 cup	250	80	190	6	2	1	1	1	38	40	2.8	930	.35	.28	4.5	10
479	**Waffles, with enriched flour, 7-in. diam.**	1 waffle	75	41	210	7	7	2	4	1	28	85	1.3	250	.13	.19	1.0	Trace
480	**Waffles, made from mix, enriched, egg and milk added, 7-in. diam.**	1 waffle	75	42	205	7	8	3	3	1	27	179	1.0	170	.11	.17	.7	Trace
481	**Wheat, puffed, added nutrients.**	1 cup	15	3	55	2	Trace				12	4	.6	0	.08	.03	1.2	0
482	**Wheat, shredded, plain.**	1 biscuit	25	7	90	2	1				20	11	.9	0	.06	.03	1.1	0
483	**Wheat flakes, added nutrients.**	1 cup	30	4	105	3	Trace				24	12	1.3	0	.19	.04	1.5	0
	Wheat flours:																	
484	Whole-wheat, from hard wheats, stirred.	1 cup	120	12	400	16	2	Trace	1	1	85	49	4.0	0	.66	.14	5.2	0
	All purpose or family flour, enriched:																	
485	Sifted.	1 cup	115	12	420	12	1				88	18	[19] 3.3	0	[19] .51	[19] .30	[19] 4.0	0
486	Unsifted.	1 cup	125	12	455	13	1				95	20	[19] 3.6	0	[19] .55	[19] .33	[19] 4.4	0
487	Self-rising, enriched.	1 cup	125	12	440	12	1				93	331	[19] 3.6	0	[19] .55	[19] .33	[19] 4.4	0
488	Caked or pastry flour, sifted.	1 cup	96	12	350	7	1				76	16	.5	0	.03	.03	.7	0

NUTRITIVE VALUES OF THE EDIBLE PART OF FOODS — Continued

[Dashes in the columns for nutrients show that no suitable value could be found although there is reason to believe that a measurable amount of the nutrient may be present]

	FOOD, APPROXIMATE MEASURE, AND WEIGHT (IN GRAMS)			WATER	FOOD ENERGY	PROTEIN	FAT	FATTY ACIDS: SATURATED (TOTAL)	FATTY ACIDS: UNSATURATED: OLEIC	FATTY ACIDS: UNSATURATED: LINOLEIC	CARBOHYDRATE	CALCIUM	IRON	VITAMIN A VALUE	THIAMIN	RIBOFLAVIN	NIACIN	ASCORBIC ACID
			Grams	Percent	Calories	Grams	Grams	Grams	Grams	Grams	Grams	Milligrams	Milligrams	International units	Milligrams	Milligrams	Milligrams	Milligrams
	FATS, OILS																	
	Butter:																	
	Regular, 4 sticks per pound:																	
489	Stick	½ cup	113	16	810	1	92	51	30	3	1	23	0	[21]3,750				0
490	Tablespoon (approx. ⅛ stick).	1 tablespoon	14	16	100	Trace	12	6	4	Trace	Trace	3	0	[21]470				0
491	Pat (1-in. sq. ⅓-in. high; 90 per lb.).	1 pat	5	16	35	Trace	4	2	1	Trace	Trace	1	0	[21]170				0
	Whipped, 6 sticks, or 2, 8-oz. containers per pound:																	
492	Stick.	½ cup	76	16	540	1	61	34	20	2	Trace	15	0	[21]2,500				0
493	Tablespoon (approx. ⅛ stick).	1 tablespoon	9	16	65	Trace	8	4	3	Trace	Trace	2	0	[21]310				0
494	Pat (1¼-in. sq. ⅓-in. high; 120 per lb.).	1 pat	4	16	25	Trace	3	2	1	Trace	Trace	1	0	[21]130				0
	Fats, cooking:																	
495	Lard.	1 cup	205	0	1,850	0	205	78	94	20	0	0	0	0	0	0	0	0
496		1 tablespoon	13	0	115	0	13	5	6	1	0	0	0	0	0	0	0	0
497	Vegetable fats.	1 cup	200	0	1,770	0	200	50	100	44	0	0	0		0	0	0	0
		1 tablespoon	13	0	110	0	13	3	6	3	0	0	0		0	0	0	0
	Margarine:																	
	Regular, 4 sticks per pound:																	
499	Stick.	½ cup	113	16	815	1	92	17	46	25	1	23	0	[22]3,750				0
500	Tablespoon (approx. ⅛ stick).	1 tablespoon	14	16	100	Trace	12	2	6	3	Trace	3	0	[22]470				0
501	Pat (1-in. sq. ⅓-in. high; 90 per lb.).	1 pat	5	16	35	Trace	4	1	2	1	Trace	1	0	[22]170				0

	Whipped, 6 sticks per pound:																		
502	Stick.	½ cup	76	16	545	1	61	11	31	17	Trace	15	0	[22]2,500	...	...	...	0
	Soft, 2 8-oz. tubs per pound:																		
503	Tub.	1 tub	227	16	1,635	1	184	34	68	68	1	45	0	[22]7,500	...	...	...	0
504	Tablespoon.	1 tablespoon	14	16	100	Trace	11	2	4	4	Trace	3	0	[22]470	...	...	...	0
	Oils, salad or cooking:																		
505	Corn.	1 cup	220	0	1,945	0	220	22	62	117	0	0	0	...	0	0	0	0
506		1 tablespoon	14	0	125	0	14	1	4	7	0	0	0	...	0	0	0	0
507	Cottonseed.	1 cup	220	0	1,945	0	220	55	46	110	0	0	0	...	0	0	0	0
508		1 tablespoon	14	0	125	0	14	4	3	7	0	0	0	...	0	0	0	0
509	Olive.	1 cup	220	0	1,945	0	220	24	167	15	0	0	0	...	0	0	0	0
510		1 tablespoon	14	0	125	0	14	2	11	1	0	0	0	...	0	0	0	0
511	Peanut.	1 cup	220	0	1,945	0	220	40	103	64	0	0	0	...	0	0	0	0
512		1 tablespoon	14	0	125	0	14	3	7	4	0	0	0	...	0	0	0	0
513	Safflower	1 cup	220	0	1,945	0	220	18	37	165	0	0	0	...	0	0	0	0
514		1 tablespoon	14	0	125	0	14	1	2	10	0	0	0	...	0	0	0	0
515	Soybean.	1 cup	220	0	1,945	0	220	33	44	114	0	0	0	...	0	0	0	0
516		1 tablespoon	14	0	125	0	14	2	3	7	0	0	0	...	0	0	0	0
	Salad dressings:																		
517	Blue cheese.	1 tablespoon	15	32	75	1	8	2	2	4	1	12	Trace	30	Trace	0.02	Trace	Trace
	Commercial, mayonnaise type:																		
518	Regular.	1 tablespoon	15	41	65	Trace	6	1	1	3	2	2	Trace	30	Trace	Trace	Trace	...
519	Special dietary, low-calorie.	1 tablespoon	16	81	20	Trace	2	Trace	Trace	1	1	3	Trace	40	Trace	Trace	Trace	...
	French:																		
520	Regular.	1 tablespoon	16	39	65	Trace	6	1	1	3	3	2	.1	...	...	...	...	...
521	Special dietary, low-fat with artificial sweeteners.	1 tablespoon	15	95	Trace	Trace	Trace	...	...	...	Trace	2	.1	...	...	...	...	...
522	Home cooked, boiled.	1 tablespoon	16	68	25	1	2	1	1	Trace	2	14	.1	80	.01	.03	Trace	Trace
523	Mayonnaise.	1 tablespoon	14	15	100	Trace	11	2	2	6	Trace	3	.1	40	Trace	.01	Trace	...
524	Thousand island.	1 tablespoon	16	32	80	Trace	8	1	2	4	3	2	.1	50	Trace	Trace	Trace	Trace

SUGARS, SWEETS

	Cake icings:																	
525	Cocolate made with milk and table fat.	1 cup	275	14	1,035	9	38	21	14	1	185	165	3.3	580	.06	.28	.6	1
526	Coconut (with boiled icing).	1 cup	166	15	605	3	13	11	1	Trace	124	10	.8	0	.02	.07	.3	0
527	Creamy fudge from mix with water only.	1 cup	245	15	830	7	16	5	8	3	183	96	2.7	Trace	.05	.20	.7	Trace
528	White, boiled.	1 cup	94	18	300	1	0	...	...	...	76	2	Trace	0	Trace	.03	Trace	0
	Candy:																	
529	Caramels, plain or chocolate.	1 ounce	28	8	115	1	3	2	1	Trace	22	42	.4	Trace	.01	.05	.1	Trace

NUTRITIVE VALUES OF THE EDIBLE PART OF FOODS — Continued

[Dashes in the columns for nutrients show that no suitable value could be found although there is reason to believe that a measurable amount of the nutrient may be present]

	FOOD, APPROXIMATE MEASURE, AND WEIGHT (IN GRAMS)			WATER	FOOD ENERGY	PRO-TEIN	FAT	FATTY ACIDS: SATU-RATED (TOTAL)	FATTY ACIDS: UNSATURATED: OLEIC	FATTY ACIDS: UNSATURATED: LIN-OLEIC	CARBO-HY-DRATE	CAL-CIUM	IRON	VITA-MIN A VALUE	THIA-MIN	RIBO-FLAVIN	NIACIN	ASCOR-BIC ACID
			Grams	Percent	Calories	Grams	Grams	Grams	Grams	Grams	Grams	Milli-grams	Milli-grams	Inter-national units	Milli-grams	Milli-grams	Milli-grams	Milli-grams
	SUGARS, SWEETS — Continued:																	
	Candy — Continued:																	
530	Chocolate, milk, plain.	1 ounce	28	1	145	2	9	5	3	Trace	16	65	.3	80	.02	.10	.1	Trace
531	Chocolate-coated peanuts.	1 ounce	28	1	160	5	12	3	6	2	11	33	.4	Trace	.10	.05	2.1	Trace
532	Fondant; mints, uncoated; candy corn.	1 ounce	28	8	105	Trace	1	...	...	...	25	4	.3	0	Trace	Trace	Trace	0
533	Fudge, plain.	1 ounce	28	8	115	1	4	2	1	Trace	21	22	.3	Trace	.01	.03	.1	Trace
534	Gum drops.	1 ounce	28	12	100	Trace	Trace	...	...	...	25	2	.1	0	0	Trace	Trace	0
535	Hard.	1 ounce	28	1	110	0	Trace	...	...	...	28	6	.5	0	0	0	0	0
536	Marshmallows.	1 ounce	28	17	90	1	Trace	...	...	...	23	5	.5	0	0	Trace	Trace	0
	Chocolate-flavored sirup or topping:																	
537	Thin type.	1 fluid ounce	38	32	90	1	1	Trace	Trace	Trace	24	6	.6	Trace	.01	.03	.2	0
538	Fudge type.	1 fluid ounce	38	25	2	5	3	2	Trace	20	48	.5	60	.02	.08	.2	Trace	
	Chocolate-flavored beverage powder (approx. 4 heaping teaspoons per oz.):																	
539	With nonfat dry milk.	1 ounce	28	2	100	5	1	Trace	Trace	Trace	20	167	.5	10	.04	.21	.2	1
540	Without nonfat dry milk.	1 ounce	28	1	100	1	1	Trace	Trace	Trace	25	9	.6	...	.01	.03	.1	0
541	**Honey, strained or extracted.**	1 tablespoon	21	17	65	Trace	0	...	...	...	17	1	.1	0	Trace	.01	.1	Trace
542	**Jams and preserves.**	1 tablespoon	20	29	55	Trace	Trace	...	...	...	14	4	.2	Trace	Trace	.01	Trace	Trace
543	**Jellies.**	1 tablespoon	18	29	50	Trace	Trace	...	...	...	13	4	.3	Trace	Trace	.01	Trace	1
	Molasses, cane:																	
544	Light (first extraction).	1 tablespoon	20	24	50	...	...	...	...	...	13	33	.9	...	.01	.01	Trace	...
545	Blackstrap (third extraction).	1 tablespoon	20	24	25	...	...	...	...	...	11	137	3.2	...	.02	.04	.4	...
	Sirups:																	
546	Sorghum.	1 tablespoon	21	23	55	...	...	...	...	...	14	35	2.6	...	...	.02	Trace	...
547	Table blends, chiefly corn, light and dark.	1 tablespoon	21	24	60	0	0	...	...	...	15	9	.8	0	0	0	0	0

	Sugars:																	
548	Brown, firm packed.	1 cup	220	2	820	0	0	...	...	...	212	187	7.5	0	.02	.07	.4	0
	White:																	
549	Granulated.	1 cup	200	Trace	770	0	0	...	...	...	199	0	.2	0	0	0	0	0
550		1 tablespoon	11	Trace	40	0	0	...	...	...	11	0	Trace	0	0	0	0	0
551	Powdered, stirred before measuring.	1 cup	120	Trace	460	0	0	...	...	...	119	0	.1	0	0	0	0	0

MISCELLANEOUS ITEMS

552	**Barbecue sauce.**	1 cup	250	81	230	4	17	2	5	9	20	53	2.0	900	.03	.03	.8	13
	Beverages, alcoholic:																	
553	Beer.	12 fl. oz.	360	92	150	1	0	...	...	...	14	18	Trace	...	.01	.11	2.2	...
	Gin, rum, vodka, whiskey:																	
554	80-proof.	1½ fl. oz. jigger	42	67	100	...	...	...	...	...	Trace	...	...	...	...	...	...	...
555	86-proof.	1½ fl. oz. jigger	42	64	105	...	...	...	...	...	Trace	...	...	...	...	...	...	...
556	90-proof.	1½ fl. oz. jigger	42	62	110	...	...	...	...	...	Trace	...	...	...	...	...	...	...
557	94-proof.	1½ fl. oz. jigger	42	60	115	...	...	...	...	...	Trace	...	...	...	...	...	...	...
558	100-proof.	1½ fl. oz. jigger	42	58	125	...	...	...	...	...	Trace	...	...	...	...	...	...	...
	Wines:																	
559	Dessert.	3½ fl. oz. glass	103	77	140	Trace	0	...	...	...	8	8	...	...	.01	.02	.2	...
560	Table.	3½ fl. oz. glass	102	86	85	Trace	0	...	...	...	4	9	.4	...	Trace	.01	.1	...
	Beverages, carbonated, sweetened, nonalcoholic:																	
561	Carbonated water.	12 fl. oz.	366	92	115	0	0	...	...	...	29	...	...	0	0	0	0	0
562	Cola type.	12 fl. oz.	369	90	145	0	0	...	...	...	37	...	...	0	0	0	0	0
563	Fruit-flavored sodas and Tom Collins mixes.	12 fl. oz.	372	88	170	0	0	...	...	...	45	...	...	0	0	0	0	0
564	Ginger ale.	12 fl. oz.	366	92	115	0	0	...	...	...	29	...	...	0	0	0	0	0
565	Root beer.	12 fl. oz.	370	90	150	0	0	...	...	...	39	...	...	0	0	0	0	0
566	**Bouillon cubes, approx. ½ in.**	1 cube	4	4	5	1	Trace	...	...	...	Trace	...	...	...	...	...	...	...
	Chocolate:																	
567	Bitter or baking.	1 oz.	28	2	145	3	15	8	6	Trace	8	22	1.9	20	.01	.07	.4	0
568	Semi-sweet, small pieces.	1 cup	170	1	860	7	61	34	22	1	97	51	4.4	30	.02	.14	.9	0

NUTRITIVE VALUES OF THE EDIBLE PART OF FOODS — Continued

[Dashes in the columns for nutrients show that no suitable value could be found although there is reason to believe that a measurable amount of the nutrient may be present]

	FOOD, APPROXIMATE MEASURE, AND WEIGHT (IN GRAMS)			WATER	FOOD ENERGY	PRO-TEIN	FAT	FATTY ACIDS: SATU-RATED (TOTAL)	FATTY ACIDS: UNSATURATED: OLEIC	FATTY ACIDS: UNSATURATED: LIN-OLEIC	CARBO-HY-DRATE	CAL-CIUM	IRON	VITA-MIN A VALUE	THIA-MIN	RIBO-FLAVIN	NIACIN	ASCOR-BIC ACID
			Grams	Percent	Calories	Grams	Grams	Grams	Grams	Grams	Grams	Milli-grams	Milli-grams	Inter-national units	Milli-grams	Milli-grams	Milli-grams	Milli-grams
	MISCELLANEOUS ITEMS — Continued:																	
	Gelatin:																	
569	Plain, dry powder in envelope.	1 envelope	7	13	25	6	Trace	…	…	…	0	…	…	…	…	…	…	…
570	Dessert powder, 3-oz. package.	1 package	85	2	315	8	0	…	…	…	75	…	…	…	…	…	…	…
571	**Gelatin dessert, prepared with water.**	1 cup	240	84	140	4	0	…	…	…	34	…	…	…	…	…	…	…
	Olives, pickled:																	
572	Green.	4 medium or 3 extra large or 2 giant.	16	78	15	Trace	2	Trace	2	Trace	Trace	8	.2	40	…	…	…	…
573	Ripe: Mission.	3 small or 2 large	10	73	15	Trace	2	Trace	2	Trace	Trace	9	.1	10	Trace	Trace	…	…
	Pickles, cucumber:																	
574	Dill, medium, whole, 3¾ in. long, 1¼ in. diam.	1 pickle	65	93	10	1	Trace	…	…	…	1	17	.7	70	Trace	.01	Trace	4
575	Fresh, sliced, 1½ in. diam., ¼ in. thick.	2 slices	15	79	10	Trace	Trace	…	…	…	3	5	.3	20	Trace	Trace	Trace	1
576	Sweet, gherkin, small, whole, approx. 2½ in. long, ¾ in. diam.	1 pickle	15	61	20	Trace	Trace	…	…	…	6	2	.2	10	Trace	Trace	Trace	1
577	Relish, finely chopped, sweet.	1 tablespoon	15	63	20	Trace	Trace	…	…	…	5	3	.1	…	…	…	…	…
	Popcorn. See Grain Products.																	
578	**Popsicle, 3 fl. oz. size.**	1 popsicle	95	80	70	0	0	0	0	0	18	.0	Trace	0	0	0	0	0
	Pudding, home recipe with starch base:																	
579	Chocolate.	1 cup	260	66	385	8	12	7	4	Trace	67	250	1.3	390	.05	.36	.3	1
580	Vanilla (blanc mange).	1 cup	255	76	285	9	10	5	3	Trace	41	298	Trace	410	.08	.41	.3	2
581	**Pudding mix, dry form, 4-oz. package.**	1 package	113	2	410	3	2	1	1	Trace	103	23	1.8	Trace	.02	.08	.5	0

582	**Sherbet.**	1 cup	193	67	260	2	2	…	…	…	59	31	Trace	120	.02	.06	Trace	4
	Soups:																	
	Canned, condensed, ready-to-serve:																	
	Prepared with an equal volume of milk:																	
583	Cream of chicken.	1 cup	245	85	180	7	10	3	3	3	15	172	.5	610	.05	.27	.7	2
584	Cream of mushroom.	1 cup	245	83	215	7	14	4	4	5	16	191	.5	250	.05	.34	.7	1
585	Tomato.	1 cup	250	84	175	7	7	3	2	1	23	168	.8	1,200	.10	.25	1.3	15
	Prepared with an equal volume of water:																	
586	Bean with pork.	1 cup	250	84	170	8	6	1	2	2	22	63	2.3	650	.13	.08	1.0	3
587	Beef broth, bouillon consomme.	1 cup	240	96	30	5	0	…	…	…	3	Trace	.5	Trace	Trace	.02	1.2	…
588	Beef noodle.	1 cup	240	93	70	4	3	1	1	1	7	7	1.0	50	.05	.07	1.0	Trace
589	Clam chowder, Manhattan type (with tomatoes, without milk).	1 cup	245	92	80	2	3	…	…	…	12	34	1.0	880	.02	.02	1.0	…
590	Cream of chicken.	1 cup	240	92	95	3	6	1	2	3	8	24	.5	410	.02	.05	.5	Trace
591	Cream of mushroom.	1 cup	240	90	135	2	10	1	3	5	10	41	.5	70	.02	.12	.7	Trace
592	Minestrone.	1 cup	245	90	105	5	3	…	…	…	14	37	1.0	2,350	.07	.05	1.0	…
593	Split pea.	1 cup	245	85	145	9	3	1	2	Trace	21	29	1.5	440	.25	.15	1.5	1
594	Tomato.	1 cup	245	90	90	2	3	Trace	1	1	16	15	.7	1,000	.05	.05	1.2	12
595	Vegetable beef.	1 cup	245	92	80	5	2	…	…	…	10	12	.7	2,700	.05	.05	1.0	…
596	Vegeterian.	1 cup	245	92	80	2	2	…	…	…	13	20	1.0	2,940	.05	.05	1.0	…
	Dehydrated, dry form:																	
597	Chicken noodle (2 oz. package).	1 package	57	6	220	8	6	2	3	1	33	34	1.4	190	.30	.15	2.4	3
598	Onion mix (1½-oz. package).	1 package	43	3	150	6	5	1	2	1	23	42	.6	30	.05	.03	.3	6
599	Tomato vegetable with noodles (2½-oz. pkg.).	1 package	71	4	245	6	6	2	3	1	45	33	1.4	1,700	.21	.13	1.8	18
	Frozen, condensed:																	
	Clam chowder, New England type (with milk, without tomatoes):																	
600	Prepared with equal volume of milk.	1 cup	245	83	210	9	12	…	…	…	16	240	1.0	250	.07	.29	.5	Trace
601	Prepared with equal volume of water.	1 cup	240	89	130	4	8	…	…	…	11	91	1.0	50	.05	.10	.5	…
	Cream of potato:																	
602	Prepared with equal volume of milk.	1 cup	245	83	185	8	10	5	3	Trace	18	208	1.0	590	.10	.27	.5	Trace
603	Prepared with equal volume of water.	1 cup	240	90	105	3	5	3	2	Trace	12	58	1.0	410	.05	.05	.5	…
	Cream of shrimp:																	
604	Prepared with equal volume of milk.	1 cup	245	82	245	9	16	…	…	…	15	189	.5	290	.07	.27	.5	Trace
605	Prepared with equal volume of water.	1 cup	240	88	160	5	12	…	…	…	8	38	.5	120	.05	.05	.5	…

NUTRITIVE VALUES OF THE EDIBLE PART OF FOODS — Continued

[Dashes in the columns for nutrients show that no suitable value could be found although there is reason to believe that a measurable amount of the nutrient may be present]

	FOOD, APPROXIMATE MEASURE, AND WEIGHT (IN GRAMS)			WATER	FOOD ENERGY	PRO-TEIN	FAT	FATTY ACIDS			CARBO-HY-DRATE	CAL-CIUM	IRON	VITA-MIN A VALUE	THIA-MIN	RIBO-FLAVIN	NIACIN	ASCOR-BIC ACID
								SATU-RATED (TOTAL)	UNSATURATED									
									OLEIC	LIN-OLEIC								
			Grams	Percent	Calories	Grams	Grams	Grams	Grams	Grams	Grams	Milli-grams	Milli-grams	Inter-national units	Milli-grams	Milli-grams	Milli-grams	Milli-grams
	MISCELLANEOUS ITEMS — Continued:																	
	Soups — Continued:																	
	Oyster stew:																	
606	Prepared with equal volume of milk.	1 cup	240	83	200	10	12	......	......	......	14	305	1.4	410	.12	.41	.5	Trace
607	Prepared with equal volume of water.	1 cup	240	90	120	6	8	......	......	......	8	158	1.4	240	.07	.19	.5	......
608	**Tapioca, dry, quickcooking.**	1 cup	152	13	535	1	Trace	......	......	......	131	15	.6	0	0	0	0	0
	Tapioca desserts:																	
609	Apple.	1 cup	250	70	295	1	Trace	......	......	......	74	8	.5	30	Trace	Trace	Trace	Trace
610	Cream pudding.	1 cup	165	72	220	8	8	4	3	Trace	28	173	.7	480	.07	.30	.2	2
611	**Tartar sauce.**	1 tablespoon	14	34	75	Trace	8	1	1	4	1	3	.1	30	Trace	Trace	Trace	Trace
612	**Vinegar.**	1 tablespoon.	15	94	Trace	Trace	0	......	......	......	1	1	.1	......	......	......	......	......
613	**White sauce, medium.**	1 cup	250	73	405	10	31	16	10	1	22	288	.5	1,150	.10	.43	.5	2
	Yeast:																	
614	Baker's, dry, active.	1 package	7	5	20	3	Trace	......	......	......	3	3	1.1	Trace	.16	.38	2.6	Trace
615	Brewer's, dry.	1 tablespoon	8	5	25	3	Trace	......	......	......	3	17	1.4	Trace	1.25	.34	3.0	Trace
	Yogurt. See Milk, Cheese, Cream, Imitation Cream.																	

Footnotes:

[1]*Value applies to unfortified product: value for fortified low-density product would be 1500 I.U. and the fortified high-density product would be 2290 I.U.*

[2]*Contributed largely from beta-carotene used for coloring.*

[3]*Outer layer of fat on the cut was removed to within approximately ½ inch of the lean. Deposits of fat within the cut were not removed.*

[4]*If bones are discarded, value will be greatly reduced.*

[5]*Measure and weight apply to entire vegetable or fruit including parts not usually eaten.*

[6]*Based on yellow varieties. White varieties contain only a trace of cryptoxanthin and carotenes, the pigments in corn that have biologic activity.*

[7]*Year-round average. Samples marketed from November through May, average 20 milligrams per 200-gram tomato; from June through October, around 52 milligrams.*

[8]*This is the amount from the fruit. Additional ascorbic acid may be added by the manufacturer. Refer to the label for this information.*

[9]*Value for varieties with orange-colored flesh; value for varieties with green flesh would be about 540 I.U.*

[10]*Value listed is based on products with label stating 30 mg per 6-fl.-oz. serving.*

[11]*For white fleshed varieties, value is about 20 I.U. per cup, for red-fleshed varieties, 1,080 I.U. per cup.*

[12]*Present only if added by the manufacturer. Refer to the label for this information.*

[13]*Based on yellow-fleshed varieties; for white-fleshed varieties value is about 50 I.U. per 114-gm peach and 80 I.U. per cup of sliced peaches.*

[14]*This value includes ascorbic acid added by manufacturer.*

[15]*Values for iron, thiamine, riboflavin, and niacin per pound of unenriched white bread would be as follows:*

	Iron	*Thiamin*	*Riboflavin*	*Niacin*
Soft crumb	*3.2*	*.31*	*.39*	*5.0*
Firm c	*3.2*	*.32*	*.59*	*4.1*

[16]*Unenriched cake flour used unless otherwise specified.*

[17]*This value is based on product made from yellow varieties of corn; white varieties contain only a trace.*

[18]*Based on product made with enriched flour. With unenriched flour, approximate values per doughnut are: iron, 0.2 mg; thiamin, 0.01 mg, riboflavin, 0.03 mg, niacin, 0.2 mg.*

[19]*Iron, thiamine, riboflavin, and niacin are based on the minimum levels of enrichment specified in standards of identity promulgated under the Federal Food, Drug, and Cosmetic Act.*

[20]*Iron, thiamine, and niacin are based on the minimum levels of enrichment specified in standards of identity promulgated under the Federal Food, Drug, and Cosmetic Act. Riboflavin is based on unenriched rice. When the minimum level of enrichment specified in the standards of identity becomes effective the value will be 0.12 mg per cup of parboiled rich and of white rice.*

[21]*Year-round average.*

[22]*Based on the average vitamin A content of fortified margarine. Federal specifications for fortified margarine require a minimum of 15,000 I.U. of vitamin A per pound.*

Index

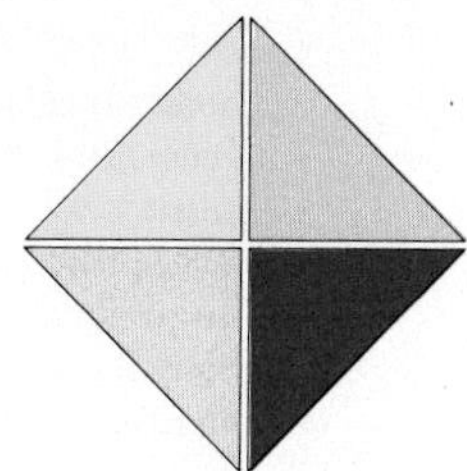

C

D

E

F

G

Q

R

S

T